Waubonsee Community College

Books by Robert Cantwell

ALEXANDER WILSON: NATURALIST AND PIONEER

NATHANIEL HAWTHORNE: THE AMERICAN YEARS

THE LAND OF PLENTY

LAUGH AND LIE DOWN

ALEXANDER WILSON

Naturalist and Pioneer

ALEXANDER WILSON

NATURALIST AND PIONEER

A BIOGRAPHY BY

Robert Cantwell

WITH DECORATIONS BY ROBERT BALL

J. B. LIPPINCOTT COMPANY
PHILADELPHIA AND NEW YORK

First Edition

PRINTED IN THE UNITED STATES OF AMERICA

Library of Congress Catalog Card Number 61-12246

To

Richard W. Johnston

CONTENTS

APPENDICES

✻✻✻ ILLUSTRATIONS ✻✻✻

Color Plates

Black and White Illustrations

In this sequence following page 96

ILLUSTRATIONS

I

Boyhood in Paisley

While he remained with us he knew not what he was, nor wherefore he was born. . . . At home his adventurous spirit had no means left to satisfy its boundless longing. It sickened in the little world that narrowed its movements and, like a chilling spell, froze its aspirations.

—William Motherwell, "Alexander Wilson," in *The Harp of Renfrewshire* (1819)

CHAPTER ONE

Smuggler's Son

※》※》※》》 ● 《※《※《※《

ALEXANDER WILSON was born on July 6, 1766, at Paisley, Scotland, then the third largest city in the country. His birthplace was in remarkably beautiful grounds. The White Cart River, flowing northwest through Paisley to the Clyde, foamed over a considerable falls about a quarter of a mile upstream from the city of Paisley itself, and a level, parklike field, and the ruins of the famous Paisley Abbey, lay between the falls and the city. A row of gray stone dwellings had been built at the Falls, the last house in the row actually jutting out over the water. Wilson was born in the third house from the river.

His father, also named Alexander Wilson and commonly called Saunders Wilson, was at that time a weaver in comfortable circumstances, owning his own looms, and hiring journeymen weavers to work for him. The boy's mother was Mary M'Nab, born in the village of Row, across the Clyde some twenty miles from Paisley. She was comely, winning and graceful, with good sense, good taste, and qualities that led to her being remembered, in this austere Presbyterian community, as a thoroughly good woman. There were two older girls in the Wilson household, Mary and Jean. A third daughter, Margaret, born three years before, died in infancy.

When the boy was four days old, he was baptized at the New Church in Paisley, where the Wilson family worshiped. They crossed to Paisley by the Abbey Bridge and turned down Causeyside, until they came to the mellow, dark stone church, with the pleasant manse set in shaded grounds behind it, where a thousand or twelve hundred Paisley dwellers gathered each Sabbath. They gathered to listen to the Reverend John Witherspoon, the foremost minister in Scotland at the time, who was to become a leader of the American Revolution.

Alexander Wilson was baptized by the famous preacher, who recorded the event in the parish register. Witherspoon kept his register with exemplary neatness—he could remember every man, woman and child in his flock all his life—and wrote among the entries in July: *Wilson, Alesan'd, S. L.* [son lawful] *to Alesan'd Wilson and Mary M'Nab, born 6th, bap't 10th.* The boy was born into an affectionate and prospering family at a moment when its fortunes were rising. He was called Sandy or Sannie, not from his coloring, for his hair was dark, but as the diminutive of Alexander. His father called him Sandy.

The older Alexander Wilson was a paradoxical character, a former smuggler and law-breaker who was now a respected citizen, honest and intelligent, known as a shrewd, up-right and independent man. He was tall and well built, and had been a soldier in his early life. He gave up smuggling, not from a taste for silk gauze weaving, but to please his wife. Mary M'Nab was "pious after the ancient type of fervid godliness, and in every way (in a good sense) a superior person." Her native village of Row, on the southern extremity of the Highlands, was the most famous smuggling center in Scotland. Mary M'Nab's family was not identified with the Row smugglers, but she knew these clannish and secretive people, had grown up among them, and, like most of the girls of Row (who greatly outnumbered the men, since smuggling scattered the men on secret voyages), was characterized by neat-ness and care of her person and dress, and by the desire to get away from a smuggler's existence.

When Saunders Wilson gave up smuggling for her sake, he profited beyond what could have been expected. Paisley was the fastest-growing city in Scotland, and one of the first manufacturing centers of Britain. The town had a monoply of the thread-making industry. Silk gauze had become fashionable, and the silk gauze trade brought into Paisley some £450,000 a year; twenty large silk firms, with payrolls reaching £500 a week, oper-ated their own Paisley mills and their own fashionable retail shops in London, Paris and Dublin.

The town took pride in being the best dressed in the kingdom. The weavers dressed like gentlemen, wearing cashmere or nankeen breeches, white waistcoats, boots, and long blue or dark green greatcoats. The girls wore printed gowns, with long gloves on their bare arms, and broadcloth cloaks of scarlet or brown. There was no difference in their dress and that of the women of the wealthy class, except that in winter the wealthy girls carried muffs.

A good weaver, turning out 40 ells of cloth a week, around 130 feet, earned as much as a skilled mason earned in three weeks. He could count on averaging a pound a week, in a period when domestic servants might be paid two pounds a year. The weavers of Paisley were organized into societies, not trade unions but associations of workmen with common interests. There were weavers' golf clubs, fishing clubs, hunting clubs, curling clubs, debating and literary societies, political discussion groups, clubs for the study of mechanics or natural history, some owning their own buildings and accumulating libraries and property. They were under "the management of able and active men, men of the great-est acquirements, who, although mostly belonging to the working class, had profited by the enlightened circumstances in which the town was placed."

Such was the community into which Alexander Wilson was born. If, anywhere in Scotland, an attempt was being made to fuse the industrial revolution with the best of an older order, it was in Paisley. And his early boyhood was idyllic. He grew into a tall, well-formed and muscular child, though not stoutly built, fond of the outdoors, and in appearance much like his father. He was recognized as precocious, and sent to the Paisley Grammar School. A short distance up High Street, just over the Abbey Bridge, a narrow side street led steeply to School Wynd and the squarish solid structure of the Grammar School. This venerable institution, with very high standards, was established as a royal foundation by James VI of Scotland who became King James I of England. James had always had a fondness for Paisley, where Sir James Semple, one of his favorites, lived.

Sandy was a promising student. His parents were encouraged to train him for the ministry. The boy was accordingly placed under the care of a divinity student named Barlas, of whom nothing is known, except that his instruction in doctrine was excessively dull and dry, and that he eventually became a preacher in a Secession church. In any event, young Wilson found training for the ministry to be intolerable.

In the last house of the row of Seed Hills houses where he lived, the one that jutted over the falls, lived two boys, Thomas and William Witherspoon, who became Wilson's boyhood companions and lifelong friends. They were part of the Witherspoon family scattered throughout the region around Glasgow, including merchants, weavers, customs officials, and the Reverend Mr. Witherspoon himself. Thomas Witherspoon, the younger of the two boys, was to become a weaver; William Witherspoon was being trained for the ministry. With the Witherspoon boys Wilson fished in the Cart, and learned to swim in its waters. The land upstream beyond the Seed Hills was flat or gently waving, and covered with fields of wild clover, but was thinly settled, and the farms were few because the roads were bad. The boys angled for trout and perch, then still plentiful. When they tired of fishing they dove for mussels. The medieval chronicles said that the Cart was famous for pearls, gems being found there which equaled those of the Orient. The legend still lived, and diving for pearls was a favorite sport of Paisley boys. They climbed to the highest places on the riverbank, dove to the bottom, groped in the green water to pull the mussel from the rocks, and spouted to the surface as they tore open the shellfish and held it up to the sun to see if it contained a gem.

CHAPTER TWO

The Scandal of Paisley

ABOUT THE TIME of Alexander Wilson's birth, Paisley was overwhelmed by the strangest scandal in its long history. As one result of it, Dr. Witherspoon (the University of Aberdeen made him Doctor of Divinity at the height of the scandal) went to the colonies to head the college that became Princeton. What happened is discreetly set forth in the official *Revolutionary Diplomatic Correspondence of the United States,* published under the direction of Congress, in describing Dr. Witherspoon's background before he became a signer of the Declaration of Independence. "Having heard that certain young men of fashion of the town [Paisley]," says the *Correspondence,*

> had indulged in certain irreligious orgies not unlike those by which John Wilkes and Lord Sandwich at about the same time dishonored themselves, [Dr. Witherspoon] preached and published a sermon exhibiting them by name to public scorn. They, however, denied the reports, and a suit was brought against the doctor for defamation of character, which went against him, the proof [of his defense] having been considered by the judges as defective; and he was subjected to a fine or expenses which brought him into pecuniary difficulties which caused his friends to come under engagements.

The circumstances were somewhat more sinister than the dry language of an American official document suggests. The Paisley scandal was a grotesque small-town imitation of vice in high places that had been uncovered in London. During a famous conflict between John Montagu, the Earl of Sandwich, and John Wilkes, later mayor of London, it was disclosed that both men had been members of the Hellfire Club, or the Medmenham Monks, a secret anti-Catholic and antireligious order. It was founded by the rich and eccentric Sir Francis Dashwood. The members, besides Lord Sandwich and Wilkes, included Lord Orford, the Earl of March, who lived near Paisley, Sir Thomas Stapelton, Bubb Dodington, and others as highly placed. They restored the ancient and ruined Medmenham Abbey on the Thames near Windsor for their rites. The revelations of the Lord Sandwich–John Wilkes dispute made it clear that these were blasphemous and obscene. The doorways were phallic symbols, the pictures were of such nature that it was impossible to describe them, and "all the statues and trappings were as grossly improper as perverted ingenuity could invent." In later periods the Medmenham Monks came to be dismissed as tragicomic—a graceless set of hardened old sinners who plainly lacked humor, and whose appetites evidently needed artificial stimulation, is one characteristic description—and their historic significance as slight.

But at the time, descriptions of orgies, kidnapings, assaults, and even ritual murder in the dark depths of Medmenham Abbey were widely circulated and believed. These stories filtered into Paisley (for the doings of the Medmenham Monks became a favorite subject with London hack writers), and a number of foolish young men put on an outrageous parody of the Lord's Supper in a Paisley hotel room. The following morning was Sunday, and Dr. Witherspoon conducted a communion service in the New Church. Word reached him of the blasphemous ceremony the preceding night, and he called the young men to account. Some were members of his church. He was told that it had been a stupid, drunken joke whose importance he exaggerated.

However, Dr. Witherspoon discovered that an attempt had been made to trick a Paisley girl of good family into being present. Even communities less strict than Paisley might wonder about any young woman who found herself in the company of men with such tastes—in Paisley it was a social death sentence. The leader of the group was a headstrong young lawyer, John Snodgrass. Witherspoon called Snodgrass to explain, and Snodgrass defied him. The minister then called upon the blasphemers to repent, warning them that he would call them by name from his pulpit unless they did so.

Dr. Witherspoon's standing was high, not only in Paisley and Scotland, but throughout Britain. He was the leader of the democratic minority in the Church of Scotland, in a long-drawn-out dispute having to do with the rights of congregations to approve the ministers placed over them, and his writings on this subject had made him the most widely read religious author of the time. At forty-four he was the foremost minister in Scotland, apart from the learned divines in Edinburgh who were almost his sole antagonists, and with Paisley, rich and enterprising, solidly supporting him, he had brought the weak and ineffectual democratic movement within the Church of Scotland to the point where the ancient leadership of Edinburgh was really challenged.

Dr. Witherspoon accordingly interpreted the defiance of John Snodgrass and his companions in the Paisley scandal as a blow at his authority in the community where it was strongest. He solemnly delivered his sermon, which he called "Seasonable Advice to Young Persons," and the uproar was terrific. The young men who had been named by him were regarded with loathing; they were threatened and insulted in the streets; some went into hiding and some left Paisley. Snodgrass, however, with a set pallor and a will as powerful as Witherspoon's own, defied him and went his way contemptuous of the hostility around him.

Dr. Witherspoon declared that he would publish his sermon if the blasphemers remained unrepentant. One confessed, apologized, and was brought back to the fold. The others, with Snodgrass leading them, continued to defy him. The minister did not circulate the published sermon widely. He published a few copies in a small, blue-covered pamphlet, placing them on sale in three or four bookstores in Glasgow and Paisley. Snodgrass immediately brought suit for libel. Each of those named in the published sermon asked heavy damages on the grounds that their lives had been placed in danger and their names made odious by Witherspoon's publication. The courts held that Witherspoon had been guilty of libel in publishing his sermon, though within his rights in preaching it.

However, the damages, which would have destroyed him, were scaled down, and on appeal were further reduced to £238, still far beyond his means. His congregation, which was largely made up of people in the position of Wilson's parents, raised the money by subscription. Dr. Witherspoon won a moral victory—"He did not suffer in public respect or estimation by his misfortune," says the official *Revolutionary Diplomatic Correspondence of the United States,* previously referred to, "however much his reputation for prudence might have been impaired."

Dr. Witherspoon was at the point of victory in his long-standing struggle with the church authorities in Edinburgh. But he had wearied of the whole conflict. Witherspoon had always been notoriously fond of the company of pretty women; amid the lurid charges of the Snodgrass affair, he now found himself accused of love affairs with his parishioners. In the year that the Snodgrass scandal began three of Dr. Witherspoon's children died. Unnerved, the clergyman came to believe that the blasphemers were really in league with the devil. Some time later, word reached him that Snodgrass was consorting with a lewd woman of Paisley. Dr. Witherspoon promptly denounced him from the pulpit. But this time he had been misled. There was a roar of laughter at the clergyman's expense as Snodgrass easily and good-naturedly proved his innocence to the Presbytery.

The president of Princeton College died in New Jersey in the year of Alexander Wilson's birth, and in the summer of 1667 Dr. Witherspoon was asked to take over the failing institution. Richard Stockton, a wealthy Princeton resident then in England, was sent to Paisley to appeal personally to the clergyman. He found Witherspoon, smarting from his defeat, eager to make the change. But on Stockton's second visit to the manse, Mrs. Witherspoon refused to receive him. Born Elizabeth Montgomery, she was a niece of the Earl of Eglinton, who had given Dr. Witherspoon his first church at Beith, and their marriage was a happy one. No other case was known in which she opposed her husband's wishes, but he now told Stockton that she had taken to her bed and would not get up until he dropped all thought of going to America. It was, he said, a time of great perplexity and trouble for him. He advised the trustees of Princeton College to chose as president young Charles Nisbet, an exceedingly brilliant clergyman who was making a reputation in Glasgow and at Montrose, and who at the age of thirty was already a powerful supporter of Witherspoon's followers in the General Assembly. Nisbet was from Witherspoon's own native town of Haddington, and one of the ironies of the Snodgrass case was that, whenever after it Witherspoon tried to assist any young man, rumors immediately started that that young man was his own natural son.

CHAPTER THREE

Witherspoon's Treason

IT WAS the ultimate ambition among the common people of Scotland that any gifted child born into their ranks should be destined for the ministry, but in Paisley this goal had a special meaning: the future minister was to be a minister like Dr. Witherspoon. From his earliest years it was drummed into Alexander Wilson that this great future lay before him. The ex-smuggler, who loved to argue about religion in any event, sometimes changed his mind a little and decided the boy should become a doctor, but his mother, whose health was failing, became more insistent on his place in the pulpit as her own life drew to a close. As Wilson remembered his parents, they were devoted to each other, blinded by affection when they believed they saw promise in him, and held before him, as the goal of life, the day when he should be clad in a sable gown, and the walls of a church would echo with his solemn prayers.

The trouble was that the boy had no comprehension of the meaning of the theological discussions that formed the substance of much Scottish education, and a good deal of the talk of ordinary people. During the long hours when Barlas expounded doctrine he was completely bored and bewildered, with no understanding whatever of what the divinity student was talking about. His own belief was that he was too fanciful and imaginative as a child to concentrate on such matters, and he regretted the pain of disappointment he caused his mother.

What he liked and understood was fishing in the White Cart. The purple sweep of wide moors under the golden sun, the green hills and deep dark hazel glens, the wild storms of winter that filled the farmers with dismay, all absorbed him. William Witherspoon, also destined for the ministry, was even less a student than Sandy Wilson. He had grown into a big, guileless, ruddy-cheeked boy, and these two future preachers spent as much time as they could poaching rabbits in the fields beside the river. On the hot summer days they ducked into the willows along the bank, stripped, and swam; in the winter, when the Cart was frozen solid, Sandy hunted for rabbits in the snowy fields while William, a great skater, kept him company skating over the stream.

In summer the working day of the weavers began at six, and ended in the early evening, after half an hour for lunch. The long twilights gave them their vacation: they could be seen while the sun was still up going to the golf course or the fishing grounds. In winter the weavers worked until ten, eleven, or midnight. All weaving was piecework, and theoretically each weaver was his own master, who could come and go as he pleased, choose his own hours, and make up time he lost. In practice they wove an average length of cloth each week, but the hours were shortened to take advantage of the summer daylight, and made up in winter.

When Sandy watched his father work, he saw him sitting before his loom on a kind of saddle, pressing treadles alternately on one side and the other with his feet. The web, consisting of anywhere from a hundred to a thousand threads, depending on the width of the cloth being woven, was stretched the length of the loom. When Saunders Wilson pressed the treadle, it depressed half the threads in the web, and left an opening, called the shed, through which the shuttle passed. The weaver threw the shuttle through this opening or shed, and caught it on the other side. Then he pressed the opposite treadle, depressing other threads to form another shed, and passed the shuttle to the opposite side again. It was not difficult with a narrow web, but, as one of Saunders Wilson's contemporaries wrote, with a wide piece of cloth "it was pretty hard work."

It was also occasionally nerve-wracking, especially to weavers who, like Wilson's father, had spent their lives outdoors. In particular, silk gauze weaving was a constant strain. Sometimes, as Saunders Wilson wove, he held in his free hand a light fan, and this he passed back and forth gently over the web. There were moments of crisis when the fabric threatened to twist and pleat and ruin the work of days. In silk gauze weaving the threads were crossed in such a way as to hold them apart, and permit the space between the warp (the longitudinal threads) and the woof (the cross threads) to be open at regular divisions and form a light, transparent cloth. The fabric was diaphanous, gossamer, and, when woven with craftsmanship—or even with art, for the Paisley weavers created their own designs —could be remarkably beautiful.

But silk gauze weaving could easily go wrong, and the weavers' pride in their craft was accompanied by a kind of hysteria that the transition to factory labor created in outdoor people. A weaver whose organdie had twisted and pulled from the tension or the humidity might bow his head on the breastbeam of his loom and weep like a child. More often he beat his apprentice. Weavers stormed out of dark cobwebby huts to forget in prolonged drinking bouts the misery of rotten threads, twisted webs, and the huge ungainly looms to which they seemed bound. There was a tavern, or more than one, near every group of looms, and the *Statistical History of Scotland* noted gravely that, while even a moderately industrious weaver could prosper in Paisley, there were, to that character, far too many exceptions.

Saunders Wilson was increasingly restless and dissatisfied despite his prosperity. He was hospitable, and it was said callers were sure to be offered some of his fine whisky, though with plenty of water offered with it. He was proud of his friendship with the educated class in Paisley, with its first bookseller and publisher, but he also missed the freedom and excitement of his smuggling days. His standing as a businessman was good, though he was said to be too reckless, and too willing to take chances.

His dissatisfaction, as a member of the New Church, was deepened by the departure of Dr. Witherspoon for America. When Stockton came back to America from Paisley to report the failure of his mission, the trustees of Princeton sent Dr. Benjamin Rush, the famous Philadelphia physician, to try to win Mrs. Witherspoon over. Rush, who had studied medicine in Edinburgh and had many Scottish friends, was prepared to remain indefinitely in Paisley. He was a magnetic, compelling personality, and, within a few weeks, Mrs. Witherspoon consented. The departure of Dr. Witherspoon and his family left his old congregation in an awkward position in the town. Some part of the moral leadership of the community departed with him; in addition, members of his church had been his fierce partisans, and were now left to face old enemies emboldened by his absence.

But even more disturbing were the reports of Witherspoon's disloyalty to the Throne which began to come back from the New World. The clergyman declared that he became an American the instant he set foot on American soil. His success in rebuilding Princeton was phenomenal. Within a few years it was flourishing, and its brilliant graduates, like James Madison, who studied under Witherspoon personally, were becoming well known, though touched with dangerous notions regarding liberty. Witherspoon's students included 114 ministers, 6 signers of the Declaration of Independence, 20 future Senators, 23 future members of the House of Representatives, and 1 President and 1 Vice-President of the United States. On his part, Dr. Witherspoon was inspired by his association with America's gifted youth. He begged the British government to be conciliatory with the colonies. The relations of Britain and America, he said, were a key to human history: "The state of the human race through a great part of the globe, for ages to come, depends upon it," he wrote.

Dr. Witherspoon denied that the American rebels were a handful of malcontents. He said they expressed the general feeling of the American people. Still proclaiming his personal loyalty to the Throne, he advanced the fanciful notion that the whole trouble between England and the American colonies came from a breakdown of British intelligence. Dr. Witherspoon said that British intelligence had grown corrupt. He did not mean that British brains had suddenly failed to function. He meant that British intelligence officers, the actual personnel of the different intelligence services, were corrupted.

Doubtless his own prejudices shaped his views, for such corrupt people as Lord Sandwich, the most celebrated of the Medmenham Monks, who was now first lord of the Admiralty and headed much of British intelligence, also headed the most corrupt administration in the history of the British navy. And they were adamant in demanding stern measures to bring the American colonists to terms. Witherspoon's argument was that the American people were still loyal to the Crown, but that the King's ministers relied only on the official intelligence services for information in forming policy. And that policy was driving the colonists to revolt. The information, Witherspoon said, came from British agents who were dominated by self-interest. Their personal financial ventures, their aristocratic prejudices, and their ignorance shaped the information they sent to London. And they mistook the sentiments existing in their own circles for the judgment of the American people.

Yet the King and his ministers got their information only from them. "That is to say," Witherspoon wrote, "from obsequious, interested tools of the government; many of them know little of the true state of things themselves, and when they did would not tell it, lest it should be disagreeable."

When the crisis came, Dr. Witherspoon took his stand with the American patriots, the only clergyman to sign the Declaration of Independence. "Daughter America has run away with a Presbyterian parson!" exclaimed Horace Walpole, when he heard the news. It was a fair indication of Dr. Witherspoon's standing in Britain. Among his innumerable committee activities, Dr. Witherspoon was in personal charge of American intelligence agents in foreign countries. He was a remarkably efficient director of intelligence. After Burgoyne's defeat, and especially after John Paul Jones's successful raid on the English Channel, the British ministry came to believe that American spies were everywhere in the British Isles. One of Lord Sandwich's old associates wrote to him furiously: "Good intelligence is the mainspring of war. How we are so deficient, when so many Americans are permitted to transverse France, I cannot conceive."

Witherspoon's treason was a catastrophe for Paisley in particular. The name all but disappeared from the town. Everywhere the alternative spelling—Wotherspoon—was adopted, and, for the most part, remained standard thereafter throughout Scotland. In Paisley only the family of Wilson's friends Tom and William Witherspoon retained the name of the clergyman.

Some measure of the moral collapse of Witherspoon's followers was exemplified in the lives of Wilson's parents. As the American war brought economic distress to the region and to the weaving trade, Saunders Wilson returned to smuggling. Wilson's mother had contracted tuberculosis, and died shortly before his tenth birthday. On the day that Wilson was ten years old, July 6, 1776, a proclamation of marriage was entered in the register of Dr. Witherspoon's former church: *Alex'd Wilson and Catherine Brown.*

She was Mrs. Catherine Brown Urie, the widow of a Paisley weaver. She had two sons by her first marriage, and her first child by her marriage to Saunders Wilson, a girl named Janet, was baptized in February of the following year.

II

The Tower of Auchinbathie

Lone, on the side of a high towering hill,
From whose mist-shrouded top pours many a rill;
Near where fierce Calder, down the craggy steep,
Brawls to the Loch, with wild impetuous sweep;
There, safe sheltered from the howling storm,
Stood a neat cottage of inviting form;
Where lived a soldier, home from war's alarms,
With his fair daughter, rich in beauty's charms.

The Lord of Semple loved this blooming flower,
And oft had wished he had her in his power
Safe in the Peel, his stronghold on the lake,
Where he would her his wife by force soon make—
Although he knew she said she'd share the board
Of Fulton, Auchinbathie's noble lord. . . .

—Alexander Wilson, fragment (Philadelphia, 1802)

CHAPTER ONE

The Apprentice

WILSON never attended school after his mother's death. Times had grown hard, and the Seed Hills house was overcrowded. The second Mrs. Wilson was a blunt, forthright woman, not unkind, but with a practical common sense and an earthy humor in place of the religious feeling and the intellectual interests of Wilson's mother; nothing more was heard of the boy's being trained for the ministry. He was sent out as a herd boy—a herd callan—to a farm near Beith, a dozen miles from Paisley. His duty was to keep the cows from the cultivated fields, fences then being rare.

He was doubtless a figure of pathos. His grief was deep, and he once wrote in a poem in his middle years that tears still came to his eyes when he thought on those he had loved and would see no more. But he exulted in the country. To the west, beyond Castle Semple Loch and the town of Lochwinnoch, the land was uninhabited to the coast, though the gently sloped hills were cleared, and sheep grazed up their green flanks to the summits. Misty Law, the highest of the hills, four miles west of Lochwinnoch, rose 1,200 feet. Twelve counties of Scotland were visible from Misty Law, blue rivers rolling, dark woods, glowing fields, and towns like Lochwinnoch and Beith stretched on rising ground. The River Calder, sometimes called the most beautiful and romantic stream in Scotland, rose in the wild isolation of the hills to the west, plunging in cataracts and through deep ravines as it circled the base of Misty Law and curved eastward around Lochwinnoch to fall into the lake. Wilson's midsummer memories of his childhood were fresh and untroubled—green-waving groves, meadows so deep that the cattle seemed to be drowning in them, flocks of sheep grazing on the hills, the lark's shrill song and the blackbird's wilder airs.

He was remembered as a lazy and inattentive herd boy, always reading, and letting the cows into the corn. Two characteristics that were found in him throughout his life were evident in these years: his love of nature, and his ability to content himself in solitude. In the summer of 1779, when he was thirteen, he was brought back from the farm to the over-crowded house in the Seed Hills, and did not like it. His older sisters, Mary and Jean, were at odds with their stepmother. When the two girls by his first marriage quarreled with his second wife, Saunders Wilson, as a contemporary recalled, sided with his wife, and put all the wyte—all the blame—on the two lasses. While little more than a girl herself, Mary Wilson married William Duncan, a smart, aggressive and ambitious young weaver. And her first child, a boy also named William Duncan, was a newborn infant when Alexander Wilson was brought back from the farm.

He was apprenticed to his brother-in-law. The signing of the indenture of apprenticeship was a fairly solemn occasion. Wilson himself signed the document, binding himself for three years to become his brother-in-law's apprentice and servant in his calling as a weaver, to attend his duties, obey his commands, and "do everything in his power for his benefit." His father signed with him to guarantee that the boy would keep the agreement. One witness for Wilson was Alexander Wier, the first bookseller in Paisley. James Gibson, the other, a writer by profession (a lawyer, that is), was the brother of the town clerk, and an enthusiast for native Scottish poetry.

John Finlayson, a Paisley weaver, signed for Duncan, agreeing to take over Duncan's obligations in the event of his death. Duncan promised to provide Sandy Wilson with bed, board, lodging, clothes, and all necessary instruments of the trade, to keep him in daily work, and to teach, instruct, and do everything in his power to make the boy a skilled weaver.

In their free time, if any, the weavers' apprentices clustered in the shade of the sheds and argued about which had the worst master. They were required to be at the looms at five-thirty each morning, to clean, dust and oil them, a complicated operation because of the danger of getting oil on the cloth. They dressed in rough corduroy work clothes, wore caps, and in summer went barefoot. Saturdays were theoretically free days, but they usually had to help the wife of the master with housework.

When work went well, a weaver might say to his apprentice, "Take a jink for five minutes." But these occasions were rare. When the looms were silent, the apprentices had one favorite game. Every weaver developed personal quirks and habits, little mannerisms and gestures as he threw the shuttle, and these the apprentices parodied, rolling their eyes wildly, flailing about as they threw imaginary shuttles, talking and muttering to themselves, and cursing and beating imaginary apprentices. This was a never-failing solace to weavers' apprentices, and the most popular boy among them was the one who could give the best performance.

Things were going badly for Saunders Wilson. He was still in attendance at the New Church—the birth of another daughter, Margaret, was recorded in the registry there in August, 1780—but Paisley had grown unfriendly, "and he was persuaded to leave," in the words of a contemporary, in order to pursue his smuggling trade more readily. There was a factor in his decision which, while of no immediate bearing in the life of Alexander Wilson, was later an important element in saving him from the gallows. Paisley had a new law-enforcement officer—or, more accurately, the county of Renfrewshire, of which Paisley was the principal city, had a new sheriff-substitute, the man who did the actual work of the courts. The circumstances of his installation in the post were most remarkable.

James Orr was a new member of the Masonic lodge of Paisley, and was drinking with a group of his brothers in the Saracen's Head bar when it was decided that they should beat up a penniless printer of the town. The printer's offense was that he was paying attention to a Miss Stewart, who was betrothed to Brother Archibald Paisley. The drunken young men started to search for the printer, but could not find him, staggered about the dark streets for a time, and dispersed. Orr and one other man then came unexpectedly upon the printer. They led him to the bowling green on the crest of the hill, where there were no houses nearby. There they warned him to promise to cease his attentions to Miss Stewart, or take a beating at their hands. Furious, the printer not only refused to accede to their demand; he beat them both up. They were forced to run down the hill to escape from the incensed typesetter. But as the printer went on his way, he was struck by a stone and killed. He managed to reach his own home, dying there. Orr was arrested and charged with his murder. The whole town was convinced that Orr had not thrown the fatal stone. His trial had the effect of letting the man suspected of the crime go scot-free. Orr himself bore his ordeal well, and emerged with a good public standing. He was acquitted, and as he stepped from the dock, he was appointed sheriff-substitute.

This episode had no relation to the move of Wilson's father from Paisley, except that it indicated the opening of a new period in the political organization of the city, with smuggling more difficult than under the old administration. Saunders Wilson went first to a farm near Beith, almost on the border of the town of Lochwinnoch. There he emerged as a man of substance by local standards, with fine household furniture and three cows for his farm. Almost at once he was arrested for smuggling. He was found guilty and fined. As he could not pay his fine, his property, including a clock, a fine desk, and his farm animals, was seized by the authorities.

A neighbor from Lochwinnoch, a farmer named Spruelston, paid his fine and "relieved him from the claws of the Beigles." Saunders Wilson next settled in Lochwinnoch itself, but soon made another move, the most extraordinary in his career. On a hill three miles east of Lochwinnoch there stood the Tower of Auchinbathie, one of the oldest castles in Scotland. It was partially in ruins, but still habitable, and Saunders Wilson rented this gloomy landmark, moved his family and his good furniture into its grim interior, cleared the stones that had fallen from the walls to make room for a garden, and set up his still in a deep, dark ravine nearby.

Each summer Saturday young Wilson left his loom in Paisley and walked to his father's castle. The walk took three hours or so. It was ten miles from the Cross of Paisley, which was near the Abbey Bridge, to the Cross of Lochwinnoch. Each cross was set up in ancient times for the benefit of wayfarers, and distances came to be measured from one cross to that in the next town. The Great Road, after leaving Paisley, struck the Black Cart

[29]

River, following it through the hills to its source in Castle Semple Loch, which lay at the base of the hills crowned by the Tower of Auchinbathie. Wagonloads of goods bound to and from Glasgow and the ports of Ayrshire lumbered over the Great Road—the Clyde had not then been dredged, and most shipments came overland from Port Patrick. This was the classic trade route of the smugglers, who hoisted their illicit goods up the cliffs to the high tableland over the Firth of Clyde, and mingled them with legal shipments moving over the Great Road. Near the northern end of Castle Semple Loch, the Great Road curved eastward around the lake on the way to Beith, which lay midway between Glasgow and the port towns, and was an inland capital of the smugglers.

All this land had been cleared. There were only about 30 acres of woodland left in the 20,000 acres of Lochwinnoch parish. From the height of the Tower of Auchinbathie, a solitary figure on the moor, or a wagon moving over the Great Road, or a signal from another ruined tower, was visible so long as light remained. Except for a cluster of stone buildings a hundred yards away, known as the Tower Cottages, the countryside around Auchinbathie was bare, a desolate expanse of high, windy fields on which cattle grazed, and across which no traveler could approach without being seen.

The Tower was not imposing, except as the wild and haunting relic of a violent age. It was a rectangular gray stone structure, flat-roofed, four stories high, with only one room on each floor, and with slits for arrows still visible in its immensely thick walls. Barr Castle, another partially ruined tower of the same type, and built about the same time, dominated the southern end of Castle Semple Loch a few miles away. Auchinbathie was so old that it was in existence before records began to be kept. It was first mentioned in the songs of the minstrel Blind Harry as belonging to the father of Sir William Wallace, Scotland's greatest hero. Wallace unquestionably lived there. He first defeated the English on a ridge behind the Tower of Auchinbathie, and went on to win the great victory at Castle Stirling in 1297 that lit the fires of Scottish independence.

The kitchen of the smuggler's household was now the ground floor of the Tower. There were apple trees growing by a back fence, and the ragged and dirty children played in the tower courtyard outside the kitchen door. Down a slight slope, in the Tower Cottages, lived six weavers who were busily weaving smuggled silk. They were morose men, unable to get honest work, or in some trouble, and lived almost like prisoners. A covered walkway led from the shed where they toiled at their looms to a larger house that served as the farmhouse. They could thus go to their meals without stepping outside, in case any inquisitive snooper happened to be watching the cottages.

Young Alexander Wilson had grown into a gangling, loose-jointed boy, and could now play the flute and dance, accomplishments that were highly valued among the Paisley apprentices. But it was his talent for mimicry that they admired: "His enviable faculty of seizing upon the strong and bearing points of any subject," ran a Paisley account, "and the sallies of boyish wit and ridicule . . . gained for him a superiority far beyond what was due to his years." He learned to operate a still. He had also acquired a gun, and poached in the moorlands at the base of Misty Law.

No consciousness of wrongdoing entered his mind for a moment. No one hunted there, and few people even wandered there. There was an exhilaration in the light, western air, with its curious illusive scent of the Atlantic carried across miles of scented prairie. Clusters of rowanberry, which the Scots called rown, grew thickly above the rocks beside the Calder, and he helped himself to them as he did to the hazelnuts in the groves and to the game he shot. The game he brought home was welcome. "To these poaching expeditions, perhaps," said an early writer of Wilson, "may be ascribed his first lessons in discriminating various game . . . and which showed him at once, when in a new country, the difference of its birds from those to which he had been accustomed."

The land was owned by Colonel William M'Dowell, who, however, was indifferent to hunting, and had no interest in strictly enforcing the feudal rights of the landowner. His home, Castle Semple, seemed to Sandy Wilson in his boyhood to be one of the wonders of the world. The old Colonel's wealth came from sugar plantations in the West Indies and the southern colonies of America. One of his sons was a governor of Ceylon, and he had brightened the Scottish countryside with exotic plants from both the Caribbean and the Orient. Fine gardens and orchards now surrounded the mansion, the trimmed lawn spread over the hill to the shore of the lake, tame deer browsed and bounded under the firs beyond the lawn.

Wilson wrote a song about Castle Semple. The herd boy at Castle Semple was a lad called Paul Jock, and Wilson came to know him. He taught Jock the song, and Jock happened to be singing it when Colonel M'Dowell came riding along. The Colonel asked Jock where he had learned the song.

Jock answered, "The Auchinbathie smuggler's callan made it."

M'Dowell sent for Wilson, made him sing the verses, and, highly pleased, gave him a guinea. The Colonel was a rural Peter the Great. He was modernizing farms, draining swamps, planting trees, introducing rotation of crops, putting his tenants on fixed rentals instead of the hard feudal arrangement that had existed before, and fathering large numbers of children by the village lasses. The Colonel had a reason for being interested in a song about Castle Semple. His family had systematically bought up the lands of the Semple family, which had dominated this region for centuries. And the Semples, in addition to being great lords, castle builders, warriors, and the friends and advisors of kings, were also poets and ballad writers—three generations of Semples in a row left permanent contributions to early Scottish literature.

The M'Dowells were relative newcomers. Their ancestral home was near the port of Stranaer in the south, where they had been owners from time immemorial. A younger son adventuring in the West Indies married a widow who owned sugar plantations, returned to Scotland and bought Castle Semple from the dissolute and bankrupt Lord Hew Semple for £5,000. The lands brought in £20,000 a year. That was in 1727, and in the intervening years the M'Dowells became one of the richest families in the area. Colonel M'Dowell put up the money to pay the ransom of the leading citizens of Paisley when they were captured by Prince Charles in the invasion of 1745. The Colonel was the head of Dunlop and Houston in Glasgow, the firm that owned the Ship Bank, the biggest in the country. His distilleries on Stockwell Street in Glasgow were famous because he had put in pleasant public gardens decorated with West Indian shrubs around the sugar houses and boiling houses. He was the senior partner of Alexander Houston and Company, West Indian merchants, a firm so powerful that when, long after his death, it eventually went out of business, an Act of Parliament was passed to administer its affairs and prevent a nation-wide panic.

The Colonel belonged to the new generation of liberal capitalists, modern in outlook, and benevolent. He was certainly not disposed to discipline a boy for poaching on his lands. If Wilson had any uncomfortable moments when the Colonel summoned him, they soon disappeared: like most of the people of Lochwinnoch, he had nothing but praise for the whole M'Dowell family.

The lives of the people in that region had run into new patterns that were now not easy to discern, largely because of the changes worked by the American war. Trade had fallen off, which was the main thing, and silk never again regained its importance; but then too ideas were in the air that were new to them and to everyone. In the beginning there had been widespread sympathy for the American colonists in the west of Scotland, aided by the old resentment against England. But as the war dragged on, with its losses and its confusion and incoherence, people turned against a common enemy, and their bitterness was intensified with the loss of Scottish lives in America. Recruiting for the armies was heavy, and it was noted as an exceptional fact that most of the soldiers remained in America, either because they were killed there, or, more commonly, because they became settlers in America after their discharge from the army. In either case they were lost to Scotland, and the new nation that was emerging across the water was regarded with hatred and fear.

Yet the ideals of democracy, of government with the consent of the governed, were old articles of faith in Scotland; they lay deep in the struggle against English tyranny and domestic war lords; they were forged in the conflict over church government and the resistance of the people to preachers of an alien faith placed over them against their will. In the past, in Scotland, no common grievance united the people: each segment of the population fought for its own without regard to the other classes. And in the past, also, political disputes were generally fought out in religious terms. But now the concept of political freedom, of universal suffrage, and above all of independence embraced everyone—the weavers, the liberal aristocracy, the clergy, and the intellectuals, of whom the clergy were the dominant element.

In the decades before the American Revolution the ties that linked the colonies and the west coast of Scotland were close and intimate. Every town had its citizens connected with the New World, and many communities were linked directly by trade to specific places in America. Stranaer, for instance, the original home of the M'Dowells, had a monopoly on the trade of Scottish woolen goods with Virginia, a business that was worth £2,000 a year to the inhabitants of the tiny village. Hugh Orr, who was the greatest gunmaker in the American colonies—he built most of the cannon used by Washington's army—was a native of Lochwinnoch. Orr kept in touch with Lochwinnoch all his life. He imported promising Scottish workmen to work in his shops and to keep him informed about technological changes in the old country. Among the upper classes there were ties of marriage and property: Colonel M'Dowell's daughter was married to the son of one of New York's richest merchants.

And the ties formed by ideas and character were still more influential. As the war dragged on, the wisdom of Dr. Witherspoon's warnings became plainer: the fate of mankind really hinged on the relations of America and Britain, for on them depended the nature of the society that was to come into being in the New World. Witherspoon's follower, Rev. Charles Nisbet, openly supported the colonists, an all but incredible act of courage in Britain in that time. A Glasgow merchant and friend of Witherspoon's, Richard Oswald, who had lived long in America, where he had large properties, was down in the reports of the British agents to the Home Office as a spy. Oswald had purchased and restored a fine estate in Ayrshire, the next county to Renfrewshire—an obscure farmer named Robert Burns lived on the adjoining farm—and his nephew and heir was a partner of Colonel M'Dowell in the Ship Bank of Glasgow.

Finally there was smuggling, which had forged deeper links than history could ever uncover. For more than a century before the American Revolution, the British government had been protesting to the colonial authorities about the activities of Scottish smugglers in Pennsylvania. The classic route of smuggled goods ran from Chesapeake Bay to the Great Road to Glasgow. Produce, such as sugar and tobacco, on which the duty was high, or which was monopolized by English merchants (who forced all trade to pass through their hands for resale in Europe) was smuggled out of America. Such produce was moved overland or by small boats to the eastern shore of the Delaware River, and to the hidden creeks and inlets around Great Egg and Little Egg Harbors in New Jersey. There it could be loaded without attracting the notice of customs patrols. In one year, shortly before the Revolution, the collector in Philadelphia was paid £17,000 in bribes.

Intercolonial trade being legal, sugar was shipped from the British islands in the West Indies to Boston and hidden in shipments of fish (which could be sent directly to Europe) or transshipped to Scotland to evade the customs. On the other side, the smuggled goods were unloaded at night on the beaches beneath the sheer cliffs over the Firth of Clyde, in the waterways almost due west of Misty Law. If a customs patrol was nearby, the barrels were often submerged, to be hauled up on shore again by the smugglers when the coast was clear. "In England there existed a great system of illicit trade," ran a contemporary account, "with which were believed to be connected gentlemen of rank and character in London." So widespread was smuggling that one-third of all tea from the Orient was smuggled into Europe and Britain and America; but in Britain the rings were so organized that fully half the tea consumed there was smuggled in.

So vast a network could not be broken up by the outbreak of hostilities. The trade with America in smuggled goods increased during the war years. And in the later years of the conflict, gunpowder began to move in large quantities over the traditional smuggler trade routes, moving the other way, from England to America. The Commissioners of Excise reported that "Armies of Smugglers are every day riding with Impunity through the Counties upon the Sea Coast." The leader in this business around Paisley and Lochwinnoch was Alexander Spiers. In his youth Spiers had been a tailor's apprentice in Glasgow. He was banished from the city for some offense not recorded, and in Virginia he became a leader in the colonial end of the smuggling rings, returning to Glasgow a wealthy and powerful merchant.

During the Revolution Spiers began buying up estates in the west of Scotland on a grand scale. His most famous purchase was Elderslie, the original home of Sir William Wallace, near Paisley, where he built a magnificent mansion, Inch. He moved inland, buying an estate from one of the M'Dowells, which brought him into the vicinity of Lochwinnoch, shocking the townspeople. A Lochwinnoch chronicler wrote of him: "Alexander Spiers . . . became a smuggler or an exporter from Britain to America *arms* and warlike munitions (contraband) in the rebellious war in America. . . . He was also a merchant of Virginia tobacco. He stored tobacco in the auld castle of Newark. He had so much business as to buy up all the estates in the neighborhood for many years."

The rumors of his smuggling did not affect his social standing. His son married a daughter of Lord Dundas, the power of Scottish politics, who was, of course, adamant in demanding that the war with America be pushed to the bitter end. The arrogance and the contempt for authority that was shown by the smugglers in Britain startled the old English aristocracy. "Will Washington take America?" asked the Earl of Pembroke, "or will the smugglers take England first? The bett would be a fair, even one."

When young Wilson hunted in the moorlands beneath Misty Law, he was treading into an area where a long-tolerated illegality had become a lethal crime. The old-fashioned smuggling of his family, with the general air of indulgence that surrounded it, was no more, and the boy who was illicitly poaching grouse was also wandering directly into areas of high politics and treason.

CHAPTER TWO

A Crisis in a Tower

❧❧❧❧ ◉ ❧❧❧❧

WILSON'S apprenticeship was completed in August, 1782, and he at once left Paisley for the Tower. He scribbled four lines of verse on the lower left-hand corner of his indenture of apprenticeship, the earliest scrap of his writing to survive.

Be't kent to a' the world in rhyme

or, in other words, Be It Known to All the World, in parody of the ponderous legal phrasing of the document that made him Duncan's apprentice,

That wi' right mickle work and toil,
For three lang years I've ser't my time,
Whiles feasted wi' the hazel oil.

His contract survived, and was eventually deposited in the Paisley Museum, along with some of his youthful sketches; the sketches, however, have disappeared.

The note was hardly necessary to prove his elation at being free of his brother-in-law, though his ties with the Duncan family were close. As the relationship of Duncan and Wilson's sister Mary grew cold, Mary's children had turned for affection to the apprentice. Young Sandy Wilson found himself caring for the children, a responsibility that was to last all his life. He played with them, read to them, and taught them. William Duncan, the older child, was a square-jawed, engaging boy, solemnly good-natured, and by the time Sandy Wilson was sixteen years old, the child had chosen him to be his friend, brother, and father.

Leaving Paisley also meant leaving his friends the Witherspoon brothers. Tom Witherspoon had also finished his apprenticeship and become a journeyman weaver. William Witherspoon was still studying for the ministry; he had won some local renown as an athlete, and become a big, hearty youth who blushed easily; and, said Wilson, the truth dwelt in him.

For some time after his apprenticeship ended Wilson loafed, living at the Tower of Auchinbathie, hunting, tending the still, and sometimes weaving with his father. His first real work as a journeyman weaver was in Matthew Barr's shop in Lochwinnoch, a three-loom shop called The Dovecote from its squashed-in appearance—"The Doucat" in the

Scottish pronunciation. The house was of two stories, but exceedingly narrow, with the shop on the ground floor and the owner's living quarters above. Each morning Wilson circled Castle Semple Loch, carrying his books with him, and took his place at his loom. His two fellow weavers, John Allen and John Orr, were sober, hard-working young men who found nothing exceptional in Wilson's studying in the slack times of work. And he was relieved at being free of Duncan's interruptions when he did so.

Almost the whole population of Lochwinnoch parish, twenty-five hundred persons in all, lived in the town itself, in two-story slate-roofed houses built along the half-mile street paralleling the lake shore. There were fourteen taverns on this street—far above the average for a town that size—or on the eleven short crooked alleys that branched off to the lake. Wilson was considered to be a little exceptional by the villagers, who were reputed to be the most stubborn in Scotland, because he read so much, and because he did not drink. Also, his pirn winder, the helper who kept the bobbin wound with thread, was not a young girl but a mature woman, Peggy Orr. Almost every young weaver had a young girl as his pirn winder. The shop was near the Pumpwell, where the tavern girls gathered to fill their pails of water. But Wilson did not frequent these girls either, and it was said of him that he did not like the lasses. This was not quite the case.

The summer workday ended early, and Wilson walked back to the Tower in daylight. In winter Castle Semple Loch froze solid, a glassy pavement, Wilson wrote of it, and skaters raced over a regular course that was laid out on the ice, circling the pentagon-shaped ruins of the Tower of Peel, which Robert, the Great Lord Semple, had built for protection from his neighbors in Queen Mary's time. As the winter deepened the weather grew too cold for Wilson's walk to the Tower, and he boarded in Lochwinnoch with Robert Orr, of the family of his fellow weaver. The sun barely appeared over the southern hills before its light faded; the air never warmed. Storms swept up from the Atlantic with unearthly fury, clouds spiraling over Misty Law almost instantaneously in volcanic masses.

A fourteen-year-old Paisley girl, Meg Duncan, had become a servant in Saunders Wilson's household in the Tower of Auchinbathie. She had many of the characteristics of William Duncan: great ambition, a hard, clear intelligence, and an alert provincial knowingness. Like William Duncan, she became an unsettling influence in the smuggler's family life. Saunders Wilson had established himself among the people of the neighborhood, with many visitors because callers were sure to be given a drink of the grand whisky which he had distilled himself. He was popular also because he stood up to John Craig, the landlord who owned the Tower Cottages where the weavers worked smuggled silk. Craig had been a man of some standing in his early years, a road builder, but he became a miser and a tyrant as he grew old, ruthless with his poorer tenants, and domineering with his two sons, now elderly men in their own right, who for years had been waiting for his death so they could come into their fortunes and live their own lives.

The addition of Meg Duncan to the small community around the Tower of Auchin-bathie proved to be the explosive element that ended this rural stalemate. To begin with, she fell in love with Alexander Wilson. He was writing a poem about his dog: he marveled that the animal obeyed him, learned tricks, followed him everywhere, slept with him, studied his every gesture and responded to every change in the intonations of his voice. Meg Duncan was soon doing likewise, and at sixteen Wilson soon tired of her. A poem he later wrote suggested that he did not disapprove of her conduct, but preferred to hunt grouse. But he found that misfortunes accumulated after he rebuffed her. When he re-turned to the Tower from work one night he found his dog poisoned, a warning of more serious troubles to come. He buried the dog under the apple tree that grew behind the Tower, and wrote a poem, "On the Death of a Favorite Spaniel Maliciously Poisoned." The idea of this work was that dog would rise again in apple blossoms in the spring. Wilson seemed to suspect that it was not a very successful poem.

In the summer of 1784, Dr. Witherspoon unexpectedly returned to Paisley and Beith, and something of a religious revival swept the countryside, which made Meg Duncan's un-chastity out of fashion. Witherspoon was the first American rebel to visit England after the American war. The stated reason for his visit was to raise money for Princeton College—perhaps the most forlorn expedition of its sort, in view of the feeling in England after Corn-wallis' surrender, ever undertaken by a college president. In any event, Dr. Witherspoon was unable to secure contributions in England for the college; but he moved quietly about, keeping out of public attention, and refusing to speak in places like Edinburgh for fear of violence. He spent some time with his friend the Reverend Mr. Nisbet, and Nisbet followed Witherspoon to America to become the president of Dickinson College in Carlisle, Pennsyl-vania.

When Dr. Witherspoon's many missions were concluded, and he was on the point of returning to the New World, he resumed preaching, and for several weeks mounted the pulpit he had formerly occupied at the New Church in Paisley. His old flock, disgraced and demoralized as it was, returned to be thrilled again by his matchless eloquence and his absolute integrity and courage. The crowds grew until at each appearance the church was filled to overflowing. The final triumph of Witherspoon's life then came when he went back to his first church at Beith to deliver his farewell sermon in Scotland.

Saunders Wilson, living only a short distance away, became pious again: he regretted that his son had not become a clergyman after all. Sandy Wilson had become a deist, and the dogmas of Presbyterianism bored and irritated him as much as they had when Barlas had tried to teach him years before. The subject was always an unsettling one with him; the walls of the Tower of Auchinbathie resounded with the quarrels over doctrine between the smuggler and his son. A Lochwinnoch chronicler, a contemporary, wrote of them: "Old Saunders Wilson was a great talker and greatly amused the folk about Auchinbathie with his crocks. Young Sandie regularly visited his father's family every Saturday. He [was a] fond man with a gun. His step-mother, Kate, was an independent in Religion. The poet differed with his father on Religion. Kate always said, 'Now you are beginnan on the dam thing. . . .' "

At this stage in the conflict, Meg Duncan's conduct had reached the point where Wilson's stepmother turned her out of the house. But Meg was not one to be turned out. She married old John Craig. She was then fifteen years old. He was seventy-five. He was also the richest man in the neighborhood, a feared and hated figure. He returned to the Tower Cottages with his bride, grinning his toothless smile as he clasped her to him and called her "my bonnie Peggy."

His two elderly sons were crushed. The whole area was bemused: fifty years later, the story was still a favorite item of Lochwinnoch gossip. Now safely married, Meg began large-scale scandal-making with the weavers of smuggled silk in their hidden shed. She spent Craig's money wildly, buying quantities of junk which she sent home, and turning on him savagely when he reproached her. After she had worn the old man out, and he was asleep at night, she crept out on the heather with her lovers, or searched for the money that Craig had hidden in his house.

Craig was losing his mind trying to watch her and to guard his treasure. His clothing became infested with vermin. His sons damned him for an old fool, in rebellion after a lifetime of tyranny. The old man found himself trapped, after having had his way for decades. He tried to run away. Meg went after him, scratched his face, brought him home, and threatened to set the dogs after him if he ran away again.

She found part of his hidden money—a considerable sum, according to Wilson, equal to a year's income. But old Craig was not helpless. He swore out a warrant charging Meg with trying to poison him. The authorities examined her, and, while there was no prosecution, the examination quieted her down and stopped her persecution of Craig.

Wilson wrote a poem about her and her elderly husband. One of the most brutal that he ever wrote, it could hardly have been printed, except in the candid times of George III, and even then, two stanzas were so indecent that Wilson omitted them when he brought out a second edition of his work. The poem is in effect the story of a murder, of a violent old man driven to madness and then to some sort of stroke that carries him off. It could not have been written except by someone familiar with Meg beyond the bounds of admittable experience. In fact, Craig lived several years after Wilson published his poem, and he did not publish it until eight years after the events described.

Meg "had a son Andrew Craig about nine months after the marriage," ran the account in *The Cairn of Lochwinnoch,* a collection of local history and folklore kept by a Lochwinnoch antiquarian, "and a separation ensued in the course of about two years after marriage; on which the wife pursued for and obtained a Maintenance from her husband. He was old and she was young; and he accused her of unchastity and impoverishing him, and on one occasion of attempting to poison him. . . ." The register of births in Lochwinnoch confirms the account in *The Cairn of Lochwinnoch,* noting the baptism on February 9, 1785, of Andrew, son lawful to John Craig and Marg. Duncan.

Six months later another child, Allan, was born to Saunders Wilson and his second wife, their last child, and the registry of baptism carries this entry under the date of July 10, 1785: "Allan, son lawful to Alex. Wilson, weaver in the Tower of Auchinbathie, and Katherine Brown, spouse...."

Wilson's stepmother sent him away from the Tower of Auchinbathie before Meg Duncan's child was born. George Ord, Wilson's literary executor, knowing nothing of the situation in the Tower, sternly criticized her, and pictured Wilson as a conventional un-wanted stepson, thrown out into the cold world. Thomas Crichton, who wrote the first memoir of Wilson in Scotland, angrily denied that the second Mrs. Wilson was harsh with Wilson. Both were right: Wilson's stepmother sent him away from home, and he was always grateful to her for having done so. He was plainly not innocent in the midst of the rural depravity he described, but he wrote as a satirist who pictured a rural underworld, not as a participant who employed its stratagems. He greatly admired the poetry of Pope, and to him as to Pope vice was a monster. He described old John Craig as a monster, but he failed to proceed through the steps by which vice was accepted: first endured, then pitied, then embraced. Unlike Meg, he had not embraced the monster, but it was plain that he had embraced Meg.

III

Trial in Scotland

All this week I have done nothing but read Wilson's poems. . . . They have inspired me with surprise and a very considerable admiration of their author, who . . . is now actually an operative weaver in the little village of Lochwinnoch. . . . This is the production of a manly mind, not degraded by a wholly illiterate education. . . .

—Mrs. Frances Dunlop to Robert Burns, January 25,

1792

CHAPTER ONE

Poet and Peddler

⋙⋙ ● ⋘⋘

WHEN he left the Tower of Auchinbathie Wilson worked first in a two-loom shop in Paisley. At the other loom was an owlish twenty-one-year-old weaver named David Brodie who was also busily educating himself in an effort to escape the loom. He and Wilson were both so diffident that three weeks passed before they spoke to each other, aside from formal greeting when they came to work. Brodie was planning to become a teacher. He carried Sallust, Virgil and other classics to his loom, bowing his head over Latin conjugations in the intervals of work on his web. Wilson was then deep in the study of Milton, Pope and Goldsmith. He memorized rhymed couplets, keeping the meter in time with the rhythm of the loom, until he reached the point where he thought in rhymed couplets. Wilson knew much of Pope by heart. However, he sometimes mixed up Pope's lines with his own various additions and amplifications, and in his later years gave quotations from Pope which scholars were never able to locate in the works of that poet.

As soon as Wilson and Brodie managed to speak a few words, their thoughts poured forth in torrents: history, philosophy, poetry, religion, education, and the happenings of the day, which Wilson was in the habit of putting into rhyme. Brodie was himself an author, though he published only one book. It was a textbook on double-entry bookkeeping, and was probably the funniest textbook ever written. In order to make bookkeeping interesting to his students, Brodie conceived the idea of writing a sort of mathematical novel or continued story, in which each day's mathematical problems carried the narrative a little further along.

The melodrama began when Simon Sober, a scrupulous and God-fearing man who kept his books carefully, put up £80 to form a partnership with a sly opportunist named George Greedy, who invested £60, and a junior partner, willing to put up £40, by the name of Tom Tippler. Sober, Greedy & Tippler, with £180 in capital, began business in a flush of capitalist enthusiasm, renting a fine store (£3 10/ monthly), from Charles Careful. They stocked it with a considerable variety of goods, herrings, potatoes (£47), looking glasses, and Highland whisky (which they secured at a bargain, £7 10/, through Tippler's influence), and paid themselves salaries of £4 a month each. The first entries therefore showed the firm to be flourishing, but the student had barely turned the page when a crisis began to develop; it turned out that Tippler did not have £40. He tried to make good by putting up some money owed to him by Pete Penniless, a hundred pints of whisky, a lame horse, which he valued at £17, and all sorts of unwanted goods, in lieu of cash. Now Sober and Greedy counted the stock, and found many pints of whisky already drunk (£1 8/). They discovered that, as partners, they were liable for Tippler's salary under the contract, when they decided to buy Tippler out. Lawrence Lookabout, the excise officer, arrived and they discovered also that the whisky they had been selling was smuggled. And Peter Penniless was in the almshouse.

The partners sold Tippler's horse and the whisky at a loss of £8 3/, and discovered the looking glasses were cracked. Arrested, Tippler sued for his rights under the contract, the judge finally disallowing the claim (£1). The mathematics of the firm of Sober, Greedy & Tippler were now Proustian in their complexity: everybody owed everybody else, losses came to £31, Tippler was fleeing to the coast in an effort to escape to America (under Costs for that month went the amount he took with him), Sober and Greedy were on their way to debtors' prison, and the textbook ended with a rousing climax of bankruptcy (the roof of the store fell in, £20) and an official notice of a meeting of creditors to be held the next day.

Brodie was a humorist: when he eventually became the master of a good school in Paisley, he put up a sign: *A, B, C, etc. Taught Here.* Wilson amused him, especially Wilson's habit of thinking out loud when he worked. He said that Wilson was a dreamer—"and such was his pleasure in following his fancies while asleep," said Brodie, "that he would frequently go to bed during the day, or at any hour in the evening, with the hope of following up the impression left on his mind which he imperfectly recollected in the morning." For all his raillery, however, Brodie believed Wilson to be gifted, and encouraged him to write poetry, the first person to do so.

The working friendship of these two singular Scottish youths was interrupted when Wilson again became a weaver with his brother-in-law. Duncan had started a business at Queen's Ferry, near Edinburgh. It was not doing much better than the firm of Sober, Greedy & Tippler, and Wilson unquestionably joined Duncan in order to help his sister rather than from any inclination of his own. He wove with Duncan, but was more often a peddler, selling the goods that he and Duncan produced. For nearly four years after leaving the Tower of Auchinbathie he was largely on the road, selling printed muslin, silk, handkerchiefs, ribbons, flags, and other products of his own and Duncan's looms.

On occasional trips, he visited almost all parts of Scotland, but in the main he followed a regular selling course within a circle whose outer rim was about twenty miles from Edinburgh. Between trips he worked as a weaver, either in Duncan's shop, or in Paisley or Lochwinnoch. At intervals he lived in the Tower of Auchinbathie, which was as much of a home as he ever had in Scotland, hunting over the moors and tramping along the Calder, through countryside that became the most familiar and best-loved part of the world for him. But usually he was on the road, walking from one farmhouse to the next, carrying his pack. He approached each house from the back and walked in the door. The first thing a peddler learned was never to knock. He spread out his goods on the table, and talked while it was inspected. When he was lucky he met a friendly household. He might sell some cloth, take orders for more, be invited to eat with the family, or merely visit in a friendly fashion and come back again on a later trip. When he was unlucky he met a housewife who considered all peddlers to be thieves, or he encountered the growls of a mastiff trained to go after peddlers.

Wilson slept by the roadside in good weather, and took refuge in barns during storms. When business was good he slept in inns, or paid for his lodging in a fisherman's hut. It revealed his distrust of Duncan that he told Duncan he was going in one direction and, after he set out, went the opposite way. Sometimes he loafed for long periods, leaving his pack beside the road, dozing in the shade, thinking of nothing except his own enjoyment with the hazel glen, the heather and the hawthorn.

When he prospered, and was staying in a good inn in St. Andrews or Haddington, and had an address he was proud of, he wrote to David Brodie, or to William Witherspoon, or to William Mitchell, a Paisley musician whose great store of Scottish popular tunes he admired. The times he slept in barns he kept to himself, or noted in his journal.

Intensely inquisitive, Wilson turned aside from his selling trips to investigate all curiosities, ruins, fossils, forts, castles, battlefields, birthplaces of eminent men, the homes of poets, and the many places where disaster had overtaken Scottish monarchs. At Musselburgh, where the game of golf originated, he studied the old course beside the Forth, recording his belief that golf—he spelled it "golph"—was more of a healthy exercise than an amusement.

He also turned aside in his travels to visit obscure graveyards, and copied any strange tombstone inscription he found until he had a collection of 300 of them. He looked up rural philosophers, self-taught botanists, primitive poets, and country fiddlers, interviewing them with sober respect for their unlettered accomplishments.

Most of his pilgrimages were literary. He hunted up the little-known town of Athelstaneford, east of Edinburgh, the home of James Blair, author of "The Grave," a poem much esteemed at that time. Wilson made at least one trip far to the north of Scotland. He visited the home of the Reverend Dr. Ogilvie, who had written a poem called "The Day of Judgement" that also aroused great enthusiasm at the moment. The reverend bard was working in his garden when Wilson finally located his house. Wilson did not have the courage to address him, and "after looking at him for some time, he left the spot well satisfied to have seen the man, whose work he admired, amid a scene of such rural simplicity." Dr. Ogilvie peered after him in perplexity as he made his way down the road with his pack.

Wilson himself wrote poetry that was about as cheerful as "The Grave," or "The Day of

Judgement." When he described how he waked up in a barn beside the road, shivering from the wind blowing through the cracks around the door, he began:

And see! sweet Morning comes, far in the East.

There was something wrong with this sort of poetry, some gap between the language and the experience, but he did not know what it was. He read Pope and Milton, and wrote about skylarks, deer, dawn, flowers, all in a sonorous poetic English entirely different from the spoken language of his time. From the Tower of Auchinbathie to the roads of Scotland, and from the roads to still another loom, to weave another burden of cloth—such was his life, followed with a puzzled stolidity that made him, at times, seem a legendary figure, a man under a curse, "beneath a load of silks and sorrows bent," as he wrote of a peddler like himself. He did not think he had anything to write about. There was scarcely an image in his poetry that was not derivative and forced, echoing something from the great English poets. The burden he carried consisted of more than the cloth he wove with his own hands. It was weighted with the somber lines of Milton and the bright, curt images of Pope that flashed like mirrors in his mind, and still more he bore a burden of guilt and sadness, the curious diffusion and incoherence that the English cast over all history and literature except their own.

He wrote about the time he lost his pack, or the exact slope of some long hill, or the precise tone of someone ordering him away, or the degree of chill in a winter rain, apparently unaware that no one except himself could be expected to be interested. He remembered the time he ploughed through the mud during a storm, until he fell exhausted, willing to die, and was roused when the stagecoach thundered upon him, nearly running over him, and the near-reality of the death he had accepted jolted him to awareness. There was in this, of course, no comprehension whatever of the purpose of poetry, and no inkling of a major contribution to be made: it was all personal, ingrown, the isolated experiences of a rather brash and insensitive peddler trying to make heroic some misadventure of his pitiful progress. So Wilson might write a poem about seeking shelter during a night of rain and terror, and staring in bewilderment at the genial and kindly people in their snug farmhouse who had taken him in. But he had no ability to fuse experience and image into an harmonious whole.

It sometimes seemed he would never have noticed a morning, if he had not read about one. Once having read a description, he could not get enough of it. He wrote of the dewy landscape opening to the sky, the hermit owl fretting and grudging at the approach of day, the crimson daisies and shepherd's-club bright in the immense silent landscape, birds instant awake and sporting through the groves. An uneducated, ragged, cold and miserable Scottish boy rising from a bed of straw in a barn beside a road and apostrophizing the morning light in a succession of banal metaphors made one aware of the gap between the lofty sentiments and the bedraggled experiences that inspired them. Yet Wilson seemed half to sense that the boy praising the morning was in himself a poetic image, and startling surges of emotion really communicated their intense feeling and gave a quality of grandeur to their discordant realities:

> How still is all around! far on yon height
> The new-wak'd hind has struck a glimm'ring light;
> Hushed is the breeze, while high the clouds among
> The early lark pours out her thrilling song;
> Springs from the grassy lea, or rustling corn
> Towers thro' dull night and wakes the coming morn.
>
> O thou dread Pow'r! Thou Architect divine!
> Who bids these seasons roll, these myriads shine;
> Whose smile decks Nature in her loveliest robe,
> Whose frown shakes terror o'er the astonished globe
>
> To Thee I kneel; still deign to be a friend,
> Accept my praise, and pardon when I've sinned;
> Inspire my thoughts, make them unsullied flow,
> To see Thy goodness in Thy works below. . . .

CHAPTER TWO

The Poetry of Paisley

IN THE SUMMER of 1786, when Wilson was twenty, all Scottish intellectuals were thrilled by the greatest event in the literary history of their country, the publication of Robert Burns's first book of poetry. Wilson belonged to a little circle of Paisley people with literary interests—David Brodie, who was teaching school in nearby Quarreltown; William Witherspoon, his closest friend; Ebenezer Picken, the son of a prosperous merchant; and, a little later, Gavin Turnbull, a really gifted lyric poet and an intimate friend of Burns. The effect of Burns's poetry was incalculable, the great step toward the cultural unification of Scotland, a native poetry of simple people, their lives, loves, sports and circling seasons, laid against the familiar scenes of the farmhouse and the blossomed heather, and written in their own words.

Burns's influence was pervasive throughout Scotland, but in Paisley it was magnetic. He lived only about thirty miles southeast of Lochwinnoch. His fame produced a thousand village imitators. They drank hard, published poetic jokes in dialect, and waited for recognition, preferably accompanied by a countess interested in a love affair with a poet. They produced innumerable small volumes of verse, hasty, woebegone, pamphletlike booklets, all self-consciously Scottish, and so alike that Burns himself looked with dismay on the fashion he had created. Literary groups appeared in every provincial town, filled with their own internal warfare, as always, yet with this great difference: the myth of a genial, humorous, unself-conscious country people took hold of the Scottish imagination after Burns's poetry appeared, and in their isolation these village poets felt themselves to be surrounded, just beyond the borders of their own unsympathetic households, by a warm and responsive country folk that spoke a natural poetry of its own.

Poets were found everywhere in Scotland in those years, but they particularly flourished in Paisley. The pioneer manufacturing town became known as the city of poets. In time the reputation became comical, a favorite vaudeville joke, but in the early years there was a native poetry coming into being there of great interest and considerable distinction. It sprang from the literate tradition of the community, the conditions of the weavers' trade, and the tremendous impetus that Burns gave to native poetry of all kinds. The finest poet in Paisley was Robert Tannahill, a few years younger than Wilson, a weaver all his life, the best Scottish song writer after Burns; but almost all the Paisley poets were weavers—Gavin Turnbull, who later became an actor in America, was a carpet weaver in the factory of Gregory and Thomas; James Scadlock, a close friend of Wilson and Tannahill, was a weaver with artistic ability who became an engraver; Scadlock's half-brother William M'Laren was a hand-loom weaver whose poetry and pamphlets later involved him in trouble with the authorities; James Paterson was a weaver and poet, a friend of Wilson's, who, like Wilson, was prosecuted for arousing unrest among the weavers.

These poets wrote on conventional poetic subjects. Their work as weavers had nothing to do with their writing. Gavin Turnbull, who had a quaint simplicity to his lines, might write of the song of birds:

> These sounds are so mournfully sweet
> That mirth is unpleasant to me

and Tannahill's "The Braes o'Gleniffer," his most popular poem, was even more remote from the weaver's shed:

> Naw naething is heard but the wind whistling drearie
> And naething is seen but the wide spreading snaw.
> The trees are a' bare, and the birds mute and dowie,
> They shake the cauld drift frae their wings as they flee;
> And chirp out their plaints, seeming wae for my Johnnie;
> 'Tis winter wi' them and 'tis winter wi' me.

[*48*]

Wilson differed from them in one important particular: he wanted to make factory work itself a subject of his poetry. He was the first poet of machine industry who knew what he was writing about in terms of his own personal experience. His factory poems evolved later in his work; in the first enthusiasm over Burns's poems, Wilson felt only an indiscriminate fellowship with all native bards. "Last night I passed almost a whole night with three poets," he wrote to Brodie from near Edinburgh, at the height of Burns's success. "Blessed meeting! Never did I spend such a night in all my life. Oh, I was all fire! oh, I was all spirit!" The three poets were Ebenezer Picken, who transferred from the University of Glasgow to Edinburgh, after a quarrel with his father about publishing his juvenile verse, and James Kennedy, a well-to-do literary amateur of Edinburgh who subsequently gave up poetry and became a manufacturer. The third Wilson identified to Brodie as "the immortal author of the well-known ballad, *The Battle of Bannockburn*" and defies a more positive identification, the most assiduous search among forgotten Scottish writers failing to give a clue to the immortal author of a work of that name.

These raptures quickly passed. Burns's example emboldened Wilson to write in Scottish dialect, and indirectly Burns gave him a subject. Burns was a poet of the countryside, writing in the tradition of pastoral verse, and drawing on the ploughboy's life he had known. Wilson after the age of thirteen lived among factories: he knew very little of ploughing, planting and harvesting, and a great deal about looms, webs, lays, temples, spindles, cords, rods, and all the mechanics of weaving, as well as a great deal about threads, silks, gauzes, organdies, flannels, broadcloths, muslins, and the checkered, ornamented, figured and varicolored lawns that were now being produced in Paisley. Wilson knew about designs, for he sketched his own designs for the cloth he wove. He knew muslins—the white turbans that were now being made for export to Arabia, another Scottish monopoly—and brocaded, corded, checked and flowered cloth to be worked into bonnets, cloaks, aprons and gowns.

Since he also knew weavers, he had a subject in them and their work. Wilson hated the monotony of weaving, and loved the perfection of the craft. His pride in the technical perfection of the weavers was almost fanatical. In 1786 fashions in dress changed overnight, and silk went out of fashion. The Paisley weavers converted to linen, that same year turning out 2,000,000 yards of linen, worth £165,000, a change possible only because the weavers adapted themselves so quickly. Elsewhere the shock was greater. The first recorded strike of weavers took place the next year in Glasgow; the striking weavers tore the webs from the looms of the weavers who refused to join them, and paraded through the city, until the demonstration wound up in a riot in which three people were killed.

The weaving that Wilson learned was entirely hand labor. A semi-automatic operation had been developed, in which the shuttles were mechanically prepared for their return journey. The weaver moved them by means of a string attached to a stick. The spectacle of grown men waving sticks back and forth all day aroused the scorn of Harriet Martineau when she visited the Paisley factories. But the device was labor-saving. Now it had been greatly improved: several shuttles, six to ten at a time, mounted on rollers, were moved simultaneously through the web. To the old weavers the result was magical: the cloth seemed to spring into existence, the work was light and pleasant, and the back-breaking monotony of throwing the shuttle seemed ended forever.

Wilson shared their feeling. Machine industry moved him only to wonder and admiration. Like most workmen, he approved wholeheartedly of all labor-saving machinery. Events led him to experiment with his first poem of factory labor almost as soon as Burns's influence led him to write in the vernacular. When silk passed out of fashion in 1786 every loom in Lochwinnoch became silent. This was because the industry of Paisley was organized like a club: those who belonged were provided for, and those who did not belong were not. In periods of expansion work was farmed out to independent weavers in small shops in outlying towns like Lochwinnoch, and when trade contracted the Paisley mills alone continued to operate. "For her sons," Wilson wrote,

> . . . stern Paisley sole confined
> the web to finish and the woof to wind.

Young William M'Dowell succeeded his father to the immense Castle Semple properties in that same year, 1786. Wilson, like the Lochwinnoch country people, believed that the crisis was artificial—as Wilson wrote, "fools and deep-designing men" (unnamed in his account) wanted to gain control of the countryside for their own unknown ends, and were continuing the economic distress deliberately. Their purpose was to provoke a riot which would provide an excuse for stationing the troops in Lochwinnoch and the nearby towns. The people of Lochwinnoch sent a petition to M'Dowell, who was in London, attending to his parliamentary duties. He was a kind-hearted man, a bachelor, shy and studious, with none of the indifference of his class for the tenants; it was said that his eyes filled with tears because the villagers had appealed to him. He sent money to relieve cases of immediate distress, and began working on long-range plans for the town.

The first power-driven cotton mill had been built in Scotland four years before. M'-Dowell and his brother-in-law, George Houston, together with John Burns, a Paisley engineer of genius, now erected an experimental cotton works at Lochwinnoch. They built a circular dam in the Calder, 20 feet high, 85 feet in circumference, with a 24-foot mill wheel. The stone factory building was a mechanical marvel at the time, glittering with windows, an almost automatic factory in comparison with the shops that had operated in Lochwinnoch before. This formed the substance of Wilson's first attempt at a major poem:

> . . . within, ten thousand ways
> Ingenious Burns his wondrous art displays,
> Wheels turning wheels in mystic throng . . .

The Houston, Burns and Company mill was so successful that the following year the huge Johnston and Company mill was built to use the same power. The first mill employed 140 hands; the second was one of the biggest factories in the world, 5 stories in height, lighted by 192 windows, and employing 650 people. Incidentally, Hugh Orr, now an aged man who was venerated in America, smuggled out of Lochwinnoch two skilled machinists who had worked on the improved textile machinery, the transportation from England of men who knew mechanical secrets having been prohibited.

Lochwinnoch had never been so prosperous as it now became. Wilson's acceptance of machinery was unquestioning: he wrote of the girls singing at their work, and described the new weavers,

> Far from the world retired, our only care
> In silken gauze to form the flowerlets fair;
> To bid beneath our hands, gay blossoms rise,
> In all the colors of the changing skies.

In this poem, also, Wilson first advanced an idea that interested him all his life—rural industry, as he called it, industry in the fields, small factories allied with agriculture, breaking away from the industrial slums of the cities, the men working in the factories in the winter and farming in the summer. M'Dowell had saved Lochwinnoch and Wilson believed he had also pointed the way to a solution of the social and political problem implicit in the restless masses in industrial Glasgow and Edinburgh.

Blest be the arm! Wilson wrote of M'Dowell:

> ...when Famine from his den,
> Led on by fools and deep-designing men,
> Advanced, grim-threatening, to deform these plains,
> Where wealth and peace and boundless commerce reigns;
> Blessed be the arm that scourged him from our shore,
> And bade our hopes to blossom as before.

CHAPTER THREE

First Love

❧❧❧❧ ◉ ❧❧❧❧

IT COULD NO LONGER be said of Wilson that he did not like the lasses. He had a girl in Paisley, Mary Swan, who lived on Storie's Lane, and at intervals in his life, generally to his embarrassment, Meg Duncan reappeared. After separating from old Craig, Meg moved to Paisley. Since the court had ruled in her favor, she was in a position to have taken much of Craig's income, but to the universal astonishment, she was not greedy, asking only £6 a year for the care of herself and her child. The court raised this to £10 a year, and Meg in Paisley lived quietly and respectably. No further scandal was attributed to her. She raised her son with care (he was eventually lost at sea in his young manhood) and behaved so decently that the stories that were told about her at the Tower of Auchinbathie seemed false.

But she continued to seek out Wilson, when he worked in Paisley in a one-loom hut. He was weaving on the half-abandoned property of a Paisley manufacturer who let him operate for a share of his output. The loom was in a dark, isolated, solitary shed, festooned with cobwebs from the rafters, and there Wilson forced himself to remain stoically on the job, launching the murmuring shuttle and guiding the slender thread, with his only care in life the making of enough money to pay his landlady. "I have received several visits from a certain tattered dame," Wilson wrote to Brodie, "whom, however, I do not much regard . . . I often laughed her out of countenance." There was a sequel to the story of Meg and old Craig, told in *The Cairn of Lochwinnoch*. Meg paid Craig a visit, "and they both retired into a weaver's shop on the opposite side of the transe leading to his son's kitchen during the weavers were at their dinner, where they might remain half an hour, Meg Duncan being in Paisley. Some time after this meeting in the weaver's shop she had a wane, a dochter, the paternity of which he denied, but for the support of which he had to pay. Meg, within a few years of her death (which took place on 25 Dec. 1845) stated that auld Craig was truly the father, the child having been begotten in the weaver's shop. At this time Craig was upward of 80 years old and entirely blind."

Wilson's friend Tom Witherspoon married Jean M'Lean. She had an older sister, Martha, a tall, dark and very pretty girl, slightly older than Wilson, well educated, and belonging to a family of considerable prominence in Paisley. The two sisters were the daughters of Andrew M'Lean, who had earlier been a partner of the bookseller and printer Alexander Wier, the signer of Wilson's indenture of apprenticeship. They had all been members of the congregation of the New Church in Dr. Witherspoon's days there.

Martha M'Lean was something of an intellectual, interested in poetry, and a member of the literary circle of Paisley at a social level above that on which Wilson lived. It became a practice for Tom Witherspoon and his wife, and Wilson and Martha, to walk along the banks of the Cart in the summer evenings into the country. Wilson, it was remembered, "had a keen relish for rural scenes, and his spirits brightened as soon as the town was left behind." He wrote a number of poems about these walks with Martha:

> . . . when locked arm in arm we retire from the city,
> To stray through the meadow or shadowy grove;
> How oft do I awaken her compassion and pity
> While telling some tale of unfortunate love.
>
> Her innocent answers delight me to hear them,
> For art and dissembling to her are unknown;
> And false protestations she knows not to fear them,
> But thinks that each heart is as kind as her own.

William Witherspoon had contracted tuberculosis, and had left his family to avoid endangering other members of it. He lived alone in a cottage some distance upstream on the White Cart. William Witherspoon also had a sweetheart in Paisley, and, as was often the case in that time, when illnesses like his were a sentence of death, she was allowed more freedom than was generally the rule, "blushing," as Wilson wrote in a poem, as she "eased his wounding smart." As Witherspoon's illness grew more serious, Wilson became his only visitor. The dying divinity student busied himself planting flowers around his cottage. He discovered he was a gifted gardener, and put in a lawn. He planted pinks and daisies along a pebbled path leading to the door, with rows of carnations and tulips behind them, and so many golden sprays and bushes of glowing roses that he converted the little house itself into a flowering arbor.

In the fall of 1788, Wilson left Paisley on another peddling trip, and when he was nearly a hundred miles away from Paisley received a letter from William Witherspoon that he recognized was a dying message. The letter contained some word from his friend that he said would remain with him as long as he lived, and he came to believe that in some mysterious way Witherspoon's death foreshadowed his own. He hurried back to Paisley, but Witherspoon had died before he reached there. Wilson walked up the Cart to the cottage, but it was already being torn down and the ground taken over for a farm. The day was gray and cold, the door of the cottage hung open, the garden had been torn up and hogs had uprooted the lawn. Wilson built a fire in the fireplace, and thought of his dead friend, living and dying in this wintry cabin, "till by degrees life in me broke."

The farmer on whose land the cabin stood had seen the smoke of the fire, and came across the fields to see what Wilson was doing there. Wilson wrote a poem in memory of his friend, describing the arrival of the farmer:

> ... puffed up with pride immense,
> see he comes stern to command me hence ...
> Thus spake the youth, then rising, ceased his strain
> And, wrapped in anguish, wandered o'er the plain. ...

Soon after Witherspoon's death, Wilson called on Thomas Crichton, the Governor of the Town Hospital of Paisley, who was one of Witherspoon's friends. Wilson and Crichton, somewhat remarkably, had never met, though each had heard of the other. Crichton lived on Sneddon Street, with his wife and two children; he was a highly respected citizen, approaching middle age, in moderate but comfortable circumstances. Wilson called in the evening. "He told me his name," Crichton wrote, "and informed me that he had a volume of poems in manuscript, which he intended for the press, and requested that I look them over at my leisure. He put the small volume, which was neatly written, in my hand, saying he would soon call again and hear my opinion."

Crichton described Wilson at that time as a tall, slender, dark-haired individual of twenty-two, accounted handsome, with an expressive and thoughtful appearance, always neatly dressed, with a manner superior to his station in life. Self-possession was his most unexpected trait: he had moved in so many circles and over such a wide expanse of country that he expressed himself in conversation and writing with considerable ease and correctness. In questioning him, Crichton learned that Wilson knew the work of the more popular English poets, and some of the best essayists and novelists, but that his knowledge of books was far less extensive than that of the educated circles of Paisley. He had, however, made the most of what he read, and gave the impression of being an educated man. Moreover, he was a good musician, had a good musical ear, and employed it to judge the harmony of language, forming pretty accurate opinions on the quality of good writing. The same good taste governed his casual speech, and he made no errors that would have called attention to the deficiences in his background. Insofar as he was known to cultivated circles in Paisley, he was regarded with good will. It was recognized that his family background had been a handicap, far more limiting, Crichton wrote, than Burns's early poverty had been, for Burns's father was an intelligent man who saw to it that he studied under good teachers, while Wilson had found his way to such education as he had solely through his own efforts.

Wilson's poetry impressed Crichton favorably. "For original ideas," he wrote, "a masculine superiority of language, high graphic and descriptive character—particularly his Scottish poems—they will stand a fair comparison with any of our Scottish poets, not even Burns excepted. However, he is far short of that poet in fine poetic imagination.

Crichton was Paisley's leading man of letters. He was a contributor to *The Scots Magazine,* the leading periodical of the country, the author of a poem on curling, "The Sports of Winter," and was perhaps as well informed about Paisley as any writer in its history. But he wrote very little. His total output, in sixty years as a man of letters, consisted of his youthful poems, a number of prayers, some miscellaneous journalism, and two superb biographical essays, one on Alexander Wilson and one on Dr. Witherspoon. They were not widely circulated, his essay on Wilson, enlarged from its magazine serial version, being published in an edition of only twenty-five copies.

In time, Crichton's opinion of Wilson's work grew even more favorable than it had been at first. He was impressed not so much by Wilson's poetry as by the intelligence that it revealed. He came to believe that no Scottish writer of his generation could equal Wilson in strength of intellect, though several were "superior in point of literary attainment." He endorsed Wilson's work to John Neilson, simultaneously encouraging Wilson himself. As a result, Wilson took his manuscript to Neilson, who had only recently set up his shop in Paisley, and Neilson readily agreed to bring out Wilson's poetry.

Financial problems delayed its appearance. As late as November, 1789, Wilson wrote to Brodie from Edinburgh: "I believe I have as many pieces on hand as finish the book, with some themes only in view yet. . . ." Against his better judgment, Wilson was persuaded to collect subscribers for his book of poems while on a peddling trip selling cloth. Neilson was to prepare a very impressive book, consisting of 72 poems, in an edition of 700 copies. There was to be a fine engraved frontispiece, to illustrate Wilson's poem on the legend of the Battle of Larg, dealing with a Norse invasion that had struck Scotland from the west, through the coast beyond Lochwinnoch and Misty Law.

Wilson was reluctant to peddle his own works, but let himself be persuaded from an intense desire to establish himself. From James Kennedy, who had gone into business in Edinburgh, he secured a supply of goods on credit, and Neilson printed an advertisement (in rhyme) for his forthcoming work. Wilson had returned to Lochwinnoch in the summer —he was there when the Bastille fell in July, 1789—and it was not until September 18 that he set out peddling from door to door, calling on village literary men, booksellers, teachers, with the prospectus for his book, while he also sold cloth to housewives. He followed a route from Edinburgh through Musselburgh, Prestonpans, North Berwick, and south to Dunbar; then he took a sloop across the Firth of Forth to Burntisland on its northern shore.

After six weeks on the road he returned to Edinburgh, convinced the trip was a complete and overwhelming failure. He had not taken enough orders to pay Neilson, nor sold enough goods to pay Kennedy. His poems were on his mind: "Every week that passed I found myself sinking deeper and deeper in debt," he wrote. "Little regarding my employment, I often confined myself to writing pieces whole days, or sought the acquaintance of those who professed themselves admirers of poetry, hoping to make them my friends, and by this means soon to have in my power more than enough to pay my debts." He had sold 200 copies of his poems, by no means a bad sale for an expensive book by an unknown workman and peddler, but shattering to Wilson, who thought of his book as his one hope of entering into respectable society.

His love affair with Martha M'Lean had run into trouble. As Crichton wrote: "He was well aware that his unsettled mode of life completely prevented him from making arrangements for entering into the matrimonial state, particularly with one who was brought up in a station rather above his own."

David Brodie, who distrusted Kennedy, advised Wilson to get some additional support in case both his selling trip and his book failed. Brodie had gone into politics in Quarreltown in a small way, and came to know William M'Dowell, who went through the motions of political campaigning for his seat in Commons, though elections were a formality in Scotland, there being only some 2,668 hereditary voters. At Brodie's suggestion, Wilson incorporated his poem "Lochwinnoch" into the volume, including in it a new portrait of M'Dowell which, he wrote to Brodie, he hoped would please both Brodie and M'Dowell.

Wilson returned to Paisley when his book was ready to appear, with the printer pressing him for payment, and Kennedy pressing him for the money owed him for his cloth. Wilson had paid Kennedy nothing, and lived on the piecemeal sale of the goods. All the money he had taken in had gone to bring out his poems. In a vague way Wilson admitted that he could expect nothing "from the merchant way" around Paisley, where cloth was always a drug on the market.

Kennedy threatened Wilson with arrest. This was in January, 1790. Peddlers ordinarily got their goods from merchants or manufacturers on credit and paid when they returned For larger orders, like the one in this instance, goods were shipped on ahead, not carried by the peddler personally, and the peddler was essentially a wholesale agent. Wilson could not pay Kennedy or return his goods. Kennedy himself was a poet; he had only recently started in business, and the dark suspicion formed in his mind that Wilson was deliberately intending to ruin him.

At length Wilson went to the printer and told Neilson frankly where he stood. To his surprise, Neilson was not at all dismayed. He told Wilson to go to Lochwinnoch and apply to William M'Dowell for help. The printed book was not yet ready. The manuscript was scattered. Wilson accordingly made a new handwritten draft. When he had finished it, he wrote a letter to M'Dowell, asking for his patronage. He gave the letter to the printer to read. Neilson barely glanced at it, approved, and Wilson sealed it, starting out at once for Castle Semple.

CHAPTER FOUR

The Patron

A FOOTMAN appeared immediately after Wilson sent in his letter, and asked Wilson to follow him. Wilson was led into a small library, crowded with piles of books. It opened from the dining room. The footman opened the dining-room door, making a signal to M'Dowell, who came in at once.

M'Dowell was friendly and hospitable, asking Wilson to sit down, and questioning him pleasantly about himself. He was in his early forties, twenty years older than Wilson. He was rarely in Lochwinnoch, always seeming a little uneasy in this town, where many of the family servants, and several of the townspeople, were his half-brothers and half-sisters by the old Colonel's impetuous amours.

Wilson answered M'Dowell's questions, and at the first opportunity gave him the manuscript of his book of poetry. M'Dowell also seemed to be a little ill at ease, and glad to have something to turn to. He sat down and began reading the poems. After a time it became evident that he was going to read the whole book. Watching him, Wilson noted that he was carefully going over the poem on Lochwinnoch and its new factories.

The door of the library opened, and the Earl of Eglinton entered. He apologized for intruding, saying he was looking for some pictures. Thereafter, while M'Dowell continued to read, and Wilson waited, the Earl prowled through the stacks of books looking for some illustrations.

The Earl of Eglinton was born Archibald Montgomery; he was now an elderly man, the eleventh earl in this ancient line. He had succeeded to the title when his brother, the tenth earl, was killed in 1769 in a mysterious shooting affray with a customs officer—it was this brother, Alexander Montgomery, who gave Dr. Witherspoon, his niece's husband, the parish at Beith.

Alexander Wilson never revealed much interest in ancestral matters. He wrote only one poem even remotely connected with them, a legend about the Tower of Auchinbathie, long after he settled in America. But there were obscure threads of personal and family fortunes interwoven in this room in Castle Semple, where, in 1810, M'Dowell was to commit suicide, and Wilson sensed them as he waited quietly for M'Dowell to read his poems.

Outwardly the fortunes of the M'Dowells had never seemed so bright. The Ship Bank was so firmly based that its notes were accepted all over the world, and the family capital was now being profitably invested in steam cotton mills. M'Dowell himself, somewhat strangely for a man of his quiet tastes, had become a favorite of the Prince of Wales in London. Nothing to his discredit was recorded against M'Dowell, who, despite his own strong liberal leanings, was on friendly terms with the leaders of all parties, and who conducted both his political and his commercial affairs with integrity.

But under the surface M'Dowell was in a difficult position, despite the immense wealth he had inherited. When West Indian trade failed, his merchant firm, without his approval, tried to run slaves into the southern United States, and lost both ships and slaves. His brother purchased a ship in India, to bring home a shipment of pearls, and was never heard of again. Within two years of the time of Wilson's visit, "the old trading world disappeared in a turmoil of bankruptcies." The final collapse of the M'Dowell companies in 1806 was so monumental a failure that it sent a shudder through the financial houses of the British Empire. M'Dowell's very respectable career in Parliament was nearly finished. He was followed into the House of Commons by a son of the smuggler Alexander Spiers. The brief experiment in social betterment that M'Dowell and his family had tried to bring off was ending, and when Wilson later dedicated his second volume to M'Dowell, he expressed, in addition to the conventional deference of a poet to his patron, a more fundamental human respect, and a kind of sympathy, as if he comprehended that M'Dowell faced conflicts and responsibilities beyond his powers.

M'Dowell read in silence for an hour and a half. The Earl of Eglinton left the room, and after a time came back, saying again that he was looking for some pictures.

M'Dowell at length put Wilson's manuscript aside.

He asked, "Where were you born?"

Wilson told him that he was born in the Seed Hills of Paisley.

"And where do you live now?"

Wilson answered him, and M'Dowell asked, "What education have you got?"

This was a more difficult question, since Wilson had had none since his tenth year. But he answered, and M'Dowell said thoughtfully, indicating the poems, "By what I have seen, they seem not amiss."

Then he told Wilson to push on prudently. He said, "I am your friend." This ended the interview. M'Dowell took two subscriptions to the book at the moment, and told Wilson he would get others. The signs of favor he had demonstrated were sufficient: Neilson went ahead with the publication of the book, and Kennedy, to whom Wilson wrote a long account of the meeting, dropped his threats to have Wilson jailed for debt.

The volumes were printed and bound, but Wilson's own health had now failed. "Having returned to Paisley almost penniless," Crichton wrote, "he devoted his whole attention to the publication of his poems; and attending the press he remained in the town for a considerable time, without pursuing any regular employment, and the pecuniary difficulties which he experienced were, along with other causes, productive of considerable embarrassment."

Among the other causes was his broken love for Martha M'Lean. The happy marriage of Tom Witherspoon gave Wilson a conviction that he had been deluded all his life—Witherspoon had remained at his loom, a sober, unambitious weaver, and had prospered, well known and liked in the town, with property and friends, a home and a wife; he had grasped at every phantom and had nothing.

"During that anxious period he often called upon me, and told me his complaints," Crichton wrote, "and in the spring and early part of the summer of 1790, having some leisure hours at my command, I frequently walked with him a few miles into the country. . . . He often at this time commended his friend Witherspoon for sticking close to his loom." Crichton liked him—"I found him, though a few years younger than myself, an agreeable companion"—and on learning how little Wilson had really read, was proud to be able to put some of the finest books in the English language into the young man's hands. Crichton knew and approved of Wilson's affair with Martha M'Lean, and he knew also of the difficulties they had encountered, but he was entirely unaware of "the painful feelings" that went with their separation, and unaware also of the many painful scenes that had taken place.

Sir William Jardine, who got his information from Wilson's sister Jean, wrote that Wilson had many love affairs in his youth, but it was his love for Martha "that bore an influence on his despondency." It was to her that he wrote love songs, published under pseudonyms or not published at all, in which she was addressed under a variety of poetic names:

> My task to protect and behold her,
> To wander delighted with her all the day,
> When sadness dejects in my arms to enfold her
> And kiss, in soft raptures, her sorrows away.

He wrote of his beloved coming to meet him in the moonlight on a meadow, embracing by the hawthorn as the moonlight brightened, of his rapture as he poured his soul into her bosom again; he wrote of her tall and graceful form, her dark eyes, her low, musical voice, her quaint surprise when she found that a description of so lovely a creature applied to her. The sensuous and erotic verse that Wilson now wrote, testifying as it did to a physical intimacy between them, was a new element in his poetry, different in character from the blunt and often raucous humor of his satires, and at the opposite extreme from his Hogarthian portrait of Meg Duncan.

The fragmentary glimpses of Martha M'Lean that have survived indicate that she was in fact as well as in the eyes of her lover an exceptional person, one certainly possessed of remarkable courage in facing a situation that was hourly growing more desperate. Wilson had nothing to offer her that could in any way have made him an acceptable suitor in the eyes of her family, but in addition to this familiar situation, she was called upon to witness his public disgrace in a melodrama so confused and perplexing that it was a tribute to her that she retained her balance in appraising it, and was one of the few who did so. But by then their love affair had already ended, or nearly ended. Wilson no longer wrote love songs to her, or to anyone.

"His countenance had grown quite emaciated," Crichton remembered of him at this time, "and his friends were seriously apprehensive. . . ." Wilson sent the first copy of his book to Kennedy, on August 6, 1790, and with it a letter asking for another stock of goods on credit. He proposed to advertise himself as a poet and weaver and peddler, and sell his book and Kennedy's cloth on another peddling trip, in addition collecting from the subscribers he had signed up on his previous venture. He wrote feverishly that he had 600 copies and 400 subscribers, but his subscribers were widely scattered. If he had their orders filled, it would cost all that he took in to get the books to them; if he delivered them himself, all the money would be profit.

On second thought, Wilson decided not to wait for an answer from Kennedy, but to go to Edinburgh himself. He was thus away from Paisley when his book appeared.

It would be difficult to find a more peculiarly local work. Wilson's friends were in it, in several poems: the Epistle to D.B.—David Brodie; to T.W.—Thomas Witherspoon; and there were poems to Andrew Clark; to Dr. Taylor; to James Dobie, a bookseller of Beith who later became a prominent Scottish historian and antiquarian; to William Mitchell, the local musician Wilson admired, a son of a Seed Hills tavernkeeper. There were half a dozen works like Wilson's poem "Morning," which was his best poem; among them were "Address to Calder Banks," the first verse to praise the beauty of the country along that river. A third group of poems consisted of isolated sketches of rural life, based on actual incidents or characters around Lochwinnoch, the poem about Craig and Meg Duncan belonging with these, though their tone was generally comic. A few nature poems, among them "The Disconsolate Wren," and a few love poems addressed, under suitable disguises, to Martha M'Lean, made up the remainder of the volume. It was by no means devoid of interest, and the local scenes were pictured with such accuracy it might almost have served as a guidebook, but to a generation that was reading Robert Burns's heady writings, Wilson's work could not make the impression that he wanted it to make, even in Paisley itself.

And in Edinburgh, Kennedy bluntly refused to advance him anything. Wilson had wanted to be on the road when his book came out. Instead he was forced to return to Paisley. There his health gave way completely. He found himself wandering about dazedly, complaining of an "indescribable burning heat in his breast" until he broke down and returned to the Tower of Auchinbathie. He remained there, bedridden, for several months, his illness diagnosed as an inflammation of the lungs, and with his death expected.

It was nearly winter when Wilson left the smuggler's tower—the end of October—and he avoided Paisley. He paid one visit to the town, to explain to Neilson why he could not pay him. The printer, to his astonishment, greeted him warmly, freely excused him, and urged him to be diligent in selling the remaining copies of his poems. Wilson paid his former landlord, and "departed from the confines of that town where, in the short space of seven months, I experienced all the combined horrors of sickness, poverty and despondence."

He again crossed Scotland to Edinburgh, where Duncan provided him with a pack, and he again set out on a peddling trip, trying also to collect from the subscribers to his book. War with revolutionary France was now beginning, and trade all but ended. Wilson kept a diary of his trip, filled with vivid social history at its best—the crowds at the fairs, the talk of the villagers about the French war, the state of the harvest—but characterized also by a rasping bitterness, especially against the provincial intellectuals. On January 5, 1791, he wrote to David Brodie from Edinburgh: "All the stories you have read of garrets, tatters, unmerciful duns, lank hunger and poetical misery, are all sadly realized in me. . . . I find the decree of my fate running thus: renounce poetry, and all its distracting notions, descend to the laborer's role in life, there attend the dictates of prudence, and toil or starve."

CHAPTER FIVE

Poetry Contest

❧❧❧❧ ◉ ❧❧❧❧

HE EVENTUALLY FOUND WORK in Paisley, where he lived as a weaver only, sticking to his loom, seeing only other weavers, and breaking off all contact with people in stations of life above his own. He might have remained there for years, but in February, 1791, he received an invitation to take part in a poetry contest in Edinburgh. It was forwarded to him by his former friend and business associate, Kennedy. The terms of the contest were that compositions in verse had to be read by the authors themselves, but if an author wished to submit a prose contribution, it could be read by someone else for him. Kennedy suggested that he, Kennedy, read Wilson's contribution.

His invitation implied that Wilson should write prose, and Wilson interpreted it as contemptuous. The contest was to be held in the Pantheon of Edinburgh, the literary center of the city. It was to be a formal introduction of the youngest generation of Scottish poets to the literary world. The contestants were assigned a subject, whether Allan Ramsay or Robert Fergusson had done more for the honor of Scottish poetry. The subject reflected the concern of Scottish literary authorities over Robert Burns's growing influence: Ramsay was the household poet of Scotland; Fergusson was Burns's favorite poet, an author who had written only in the vernacular, intelligible only to Scottish readers. Burns's first act when he became famous was to place a marker on Fergusson's grave—Fergusson, a hard-drinking, witty, somewhat disreputable medical student, had died in an Edinburgh madhouse only ten years before, at the age of twenty-four.

Wilson was the only one of the seven contestants to write in praise of Fergusson. He at first ignored the invitation; then his resentment grew at Kennedy's bland or malicious suggestion that he, Kennedy, read Wilson's composition, and, according to Brodie, in one week Wilson wove his 40 ells of cloth, wrote a 210-line composition in rhyme on the relative merits of Allan Ramsay and Robert Fergusson, and walked the 52 miles to Edinburgh, arriving at the Pantheon shortly before the readings began.

Wilson's contribution was an old-fashioned recitation in verse, with gestures. He professed to be an old Scottish farmer who knew nothing about poetry, but had been inspired to enter the contest because he heard a large cash prize was to be awarded. So he had arrived at the Pantheon with his contribution, complaining mightily because he, as a contestant, had been charged admission, and he would now put on his spectacles and read his essay on whether Gin Ramsay or Rab Fergusson war best, in the hope that people would listen to a frank old countryman like himself.

As nearly as he could understand it, back in the days when great English poets like Dryden and Sandy Pope sang ilka bonny morn, poor auld Scotland sat without a song. All the great poets were dead and gone, and all the young ones went to London, till none was left to write about our own sweet lasses and our own green hills. Then up rose Allan Ramsay, oh, blythesome, hearty day! and for sixty years, as nearly as he could make it out, nobody could compare with Allan as a droll, hearty, confoundet queer Scottish poet.

This Allan wrote such a glibly-gabbet that it made the crankiest Scotsman double up with laughter just to read him. The old man himself grew up believing there could never be a poet as good as Allan Ramsay. But then along came this Rab Fergusson. And Rab, when he wrote about graveyard ghosts, made the old man's teeth chatter. When Allan Ramsay wrote about love, he had shepherdesses skipping and dancing over the moors, but this Rab Fergusson, when he wrote a love poem, he pictured poor dazed Sandy weeping for his foolish wife, and he made the picture so clear that the old man found his own eyes filling with tears. So he was forced to conclude that while Allan might have more art in his poetry, poor Rab Fergusson, given his death in his tender years, and setting his youth and inexperience by, was a greater poet. His careless lines jinked like birds, and he made us see our own friends, our own firesides, our thoughts, our hearts and follies. And so, Wilson concluded,

Let ane an a' here vote as they incline,
Frae heart and soul Rab Fergusson has mine.

When Wilson finished his reading he received an ovation. There were 500 in the audience at the Pantheon, admission was a sixpence, each member of the audience had one vote, and the money taken in went to the first prize winner. Not only was the literary society of Edinburgh present, but the aristocracy as well. Robert Cumming, one of the contestants, was the son of a prominent Edinburgh family. His supporters, and the subscribers to his book of poetry, included people like the Duchess of Buccleuch, Lady Semple, the Marchioness of Tweedsdale, the Earl of Aloyn, the Earl of Lauderdale, the Countess of Dalhousie, the Countess of Glasgow, Lord Gifford, Sir William Maxwell, Peggy Brown of London, Sir Harry Moncrief, Sir Alexander Campbell, Lord Hay, Lady Margaret Cameron of London, and many others. Cumming himself was a graceful and unpretending poet of genuine distinction, writing classic English verse which, at its best, had a kind of dusky, mellow charm, but he fell into conventional poetic attitudes and wrote increasingly proper sentimental poems of gradually thickening dullness and monotony. Cumming had brought forty guests with him to the Pantheon, including some of the most fashionable young women of Edinburgh society, who contributed to the literary life that night an elegance rarely found there.

Cumming's poem on Allan Ramsay won the first prize by seventeen votes, Wilson being second. But literary society resented Cumming's action in papering the house with his aristocratic friends, and Wilson became the popular hero of the evening. In the audience was James Anderson, who had started a literary magazine, *The Bee,* four months before. Anderson was one of the most eminent of the reformers and literary men of Scotland, an agricultural chemist, a pioneer in soil conservation, and a friend of George Washington's. Anderson asked Wilson to contribute to *The Bee,* which was challenging *The Scots Magazine* as the first literary periodical in the country. A week later, back in Paisley, Wilson sent Anderson a neat prose essay on an untaught botanist who lived nearby, an illiterate genius who had spent his life experimenting with herbs and plants. *The Bee* also printed a number of Wilson's poems.

Anderson asked Wilson to become assistant editor of *The Bee.* The magazine, however, was not yet ready to build its staff. An Edinburgh hack writer, James Thompson Callender, did the detailed editorial work, but was to be replaced. In the meantime, Wilson continued to work as a weaver, paid his debts, and lived quietly in Paisley. In the summer of 1791 he brought out a second edition of his poems, dedicated to William M'Dowell, and including his long prose journal of his peddling trip. At Thomas Crichton's urging, Wilson also wrote the verses for a book of hymns by Robert Gilmour, a Paisley musician who later became well known for the songs of Burns and Tannahill that he set to music. Wilson's hymns were in this vein:

[*63*]

To Him who bids the tempest roll,
Or lulls the noontide blaze;
In joyful anthems let your soul,
Proclaim His boundless praise. . . .

Simultaneously with this work, he was writing his comic masterpiece, "Watty and Meg," which was on the point of being printed. And he had written other poems, published anonymously, of which the public was soon to hear a great deal. In January, 1792, Robert Burn's friend Mrs. Frances Dunlop wrote to Burns of her admiration of Wilson's poems, saying she was almost sorry to have read them, though the volume "is the only one of the many spurious progeny to which your genius has given existence, that one is not ashamed to hear called poetry. This is the production of a manly mind. . . ." Why, then, did she regret it? "I own myself vext degraded and disappointed when I am led to suspect one must not expect to find high life except below stairs. . . . In short, I do not wish to discover a great many Wilsons among the wabsters of Paisley. . . ."

"Wilson's book I have not seen," Burns replied, "and will be greatly obliged if you will send me a copy."

CHAPTER SIX

The Prisoner

WILSON'S ARREST (three months after Burns's expression of interest in his poetry) provided Paisley with one of the most puzzling of the mysteries that periodically studded its history. As was the case with the Witherspoon scandal, it was a local matter with obscure connections with political disputes that reached beyond Paisley, and as one result of it Wilson left Scotland for the United States to begin the career that made him a pioneer naturalist of the New World. "We have now reached the only period in our author's career," wrote Sir William Jardine, with a quaint air of shamefaced candor, "which is tarnished by the performance of actions discreditable to him. . . . He was prosecuted, and sentenced to imprisonment in the jail of Paisley, and to burn [an] offensive poem with his own hand. It will be sufficient to say, that he deserved the punishment, having behaved with neither propriety nor honor in the transaction."

Jardine's admiration for Wilson was so deep that it plainly cost him discomfort to write these words. Wilson's conduct, he said, was in this instance "totally at variance with his real disposition, and the whole tenor of his former and after life. . . . The general depression of trade, occasioned by the wars incident to the French Revolution, threw into idleness many of the young operatives, who began openly to promulgate revolutionary principles. . . . It was Wilson's misfortune to have formed an intimacy with some of these, who, knowing his talents, prevailed on him to revile and satirize the conduct of those who were most offensive to their view of liberty, or of the propriety of conduct as masters. . . . Ever ready to redress what he imagined wrongs, [Wilson] produced a number of poetical squibs which held up the subjects of popular dislike to contempt and ridicule." Writing as an eloquent partisan of Wilson, Jardine nevertheless felt that he could do no more than acknowledge Wilson's guilt, the result of a departure from his own high standards, and if he felt so twenty years after Wilson's death, it was plainly even more difficult to consider Wilson blameless in Paisley itself at the time that charges were brought against him.

Early on Wednesday morning, May 23, 1792, Wilson left the house in Seed Hills where he was staying and went to Glasgow. This was seven miles by the road, and he walked it often—once he had even run the distance and back, but it so exhausted him that he remained in bed for some time afterwards. What his errand was in Glasgow was not brought out when he was questioned. The authorities believed that he had gone there to prepare secretly to publish another of his poems, and this may well have been the case. He had recently published at least three satires taking the side of the weavers against the Paisley mill owners. They were handbill-like productions, with no author or publisher listed, and were distributed by being placed in weaving sheds when the looms were silent. One of these poems, "The Insulted Peddler," was an unprintable burlesque in rhyme: it told of a peddler who left the road for the woods to answer a call of nature, but was interrupted because he was on an estate, the manager appearing and censuring him severely, the peddler attempting uncomfortably to answer, and their argument turning into a grotesque parody of the debates that were then raging about the rights of property. Wilson was, "I am told," Mrs. Dunlop wrote to Burns, "really in the situation he ludicrously enough describes of a traveling packman." In two other satires, "The Hollander" and "Hab's Door," Wilson attacked two well-known and highly unpopular Paisley employers (though not by name), one a Dutchman who was famous among the weavers for cheating on payment for work done, the other a heartless and petty Scottish manufacturer who delighted in finding non-existent defects in the cloth, peering over his spectacles and saying, "Now, now, my good man, that'll never do," and reducing his payments to his weavers as a result. These works were so topical that they had little significance except to the weavers of Paisley who had personal dealings with the mill owners described in them; they were in effect cartoons or caricatures in verse, gaining their effect when one knew the originals.

While Wilson was in Glasgow that Wednesday, William Sharp and his attorney,

Nathaniel Gibson, appeared at the Sheriff's Court of the County of Renfrewshire and filed a complaint against him. The court was held on the second floor of the Tolbooth, the combined jail and courthouse of Paisley, which stood across the public square from the Cross of Paisley. A four-story building with a four-story bell tower, the Tolbooth was an architectural monstrosity, a sort of police church, resembling a house of worship that had somehow gone astray, with barred windows and whipping posts replacing the more customary objects of worship. Two broad outside staircases led from the flat pavement of the market square to a platform where the pillory was located. From this platform a wide hall led to the Sheriff's Court. Debtors were lodged above the court rooms, women prisoners in the attic of the main building, and criminals in cells that were built high into the bell tower.

Sharp and Gibson had matters of the gravest moment to discuss with Sheriff James Orr. They filed a complaint against Wilson on the ground that he had written a libelous work, composed with a view to extorting money from Sharp. Sharp told Orr that he had received, the preceding day, an anonymous letter, together with the manuscript of a poem called "The Shark, or Lang Mills Detected." As the owner of the Long Mills of Paisley, Mr. Sharp was plainly the person offensively described in the poem, which was in the highest degree incendiary, and traduced in the grossest manner his respectability. The anonymous letter, signed merely "A.B.," informed him that the poem would be published within three days, unless he paid five guineas to suppress it. He was given three hours in which to reply.

Sharp was certain that the poem was written by Wilson—"a person well known for his productions in this way." Orr sent an officer of the court to Wilson's boarding house, in order to question him. He could hardly have done otherwise, in view of Sharp's position in Paisley. Sharp was then only twenty-nine years old, three years older than Wilson, but he was already a successful manufacturer in his own right, a member of the town council, and the city treasurer. Like Wilson, William Sharp had been baptized by Dr. Witherspoon in the New Church in its great days, but his was one of the wealthy families of the city, his father a manufacturer and his mother Jean Paisley, of the family for whom the place was named. Sharp was a contemporary of Thomas Crichton and Martha M'Lean, and a member of the cultivated society of Paisley that they belonged to. He was a handsome man, with light blond hair, sociable and pleasant in his manner, often with a smile on his round and ruddy features. He had recently married Margaret Galbreath, who was to bear him a son later in this eventful year.

When the officer sent out by Orr reported that Wilson had gone to Glasgow, the sheriff immediately concluded, from what Sharp told him, that Wilson's purpose was to arrange for the secret publication of the poem against Sharp. He therefore issued a warrant for Wilson's arrest, and warned all printers to have nothing to do with the offensive poem. Some part of the mystery of Alexander Wilson's arrest came from this circumstance. There was then no organized law-enforcement system in Scotland. The police force of each community consisted in the main of constables who served in rotation, an obligatory duty for all citizens, but in practice left to a few, with auxiliary forces patrolling the streets in times of tension and riot. Ordinarily Wilson would merely have been summoned by a court functionary to appear before Orr and answer the questions raised by Sharp's complaint. But Sharp declared that speed was essential to prevent the publication of the poem. Consequently, the warrant for Wilson's arrest made it possible for him to be taken into custody by private citizens, including Sharp's employees.

The letter that demanded money of William Sharp was dated Tuesday, 11:30 A.M. It called for an answer within three hours—to be exact, by four o'clock Tuesday afternoon. The deadline had thus expired almost twenty-four hours before Sharp appeared at Sheriff Orr's office. When darkness fell on Wednesday night, Wilson was still at large.

He plainly did not anticipate any such trouble as was now to befall him. Wilson had been going daily to Neilson's print shop, where his "Watty and Meg," his one really popular poem, was soon to be printed. It was an altogether blameless work, an amazingly graphic and dramatic account of a lower-class husband-and-wife quarrel and reconciliation, containing nothing whatever to arouse the authorities against its author. Returning from Glasgow, Wilson followed his usual round, and stopped in the print shop again. Neilson's press was on Causeyside, a short distance down the Cart from the New Church where Witherspoon had preached, and only about four blocks from the Tolbooth.

In late May the days were long in Paisley, the twilight lingering until ten o'clock. It was dark when Wilson came out of the print shop. As he did so he was seized by five men. One of the first accounts of Wilson's life said they were "spies"—English agents, in the Scottish meaning at the time. Another early account, perhaps not contradictory, stated that the men who took Wilson into custody were personal employees of Sharp.

The Tolbooth was busy twenty-four hours a day, for there were two small stores, one a restaurant as well, which were kept open to provide food and supplies to the prisoners at their own expense. The jailer operated the concession, and food provided by the county was so bad that it was essential for the prisoners to purchase their own supplies. Nothing in the extensive record of Wilson's case indicates when he arrived at the Tolbooth, or by whom he was arrested. At some period on Thursday he was taken before Sheriff Orr. He was shown the letter addressed to Sharp, and asked if it was in his handwriting. He said that it was. He was then asked if it was written at the request of the author of the poem, and again said that it was. The poem was now given him, and he was asked if it was the poem which he had enclosed in the letter, and he replied that it was.

At this point the proceedings were stopped, and Wilson was asked to write on the letter: *This is the letter referred to in my declaration of this date, emitted before the Sheriff Substitute of Renfrewshire.*—ALEX WILSON. Both Wilson and Orr then signed their names on the poem as being the matter they were discussing, and it was filed in the court.

Wilson was asked to name the author of the poem, and refused. According to the court record, he declared "the letter before alluded to contains his sentiments, or expresses his sentiments, upon the subject matter of the poem." He said he did not possess a copy of the poem, and did not know anyone who had a copy. He admitted that he had a copy in his possession when he wrote the letter. He had copied it from the original; that was why it was in his handwriting. He seemed dazed or incoherent, admitting writing the letter which proved him guilty of blackmail, but refusing to reply when asked about the authorship of the poem, and evidently in terror of making some statement which would involve him in deeper distress than he had already suffered.

Orr asked, "Do you know at whose desire the poem was written?"

Wilson refused to answer. Orr then asked, "Did you ever offer the original poem, or a copy, to any printer to be printed?"

Wilson again refused to answer, and Orr shifted the line of his questioning. "Did you call at the shop of John Neilson and ask if there was any letter addressed to A.B.?"

Wilson said that he had not.

"And yet you have had occasion daily to call at Mr. Neilson's shop about other matters?"

"Yes."

"If you had obtained the five guineas from Mr. Sharp," Orr asked, "would the money, or any part of it, have been given to the author of the poem, or applied to the uses and purposes of the letter-writer?"

Wilson refused to answer. "And this," said the summary of his questioning, "he declares to be truth."

Another of the puzzles of Wilson's case is that it is impossible to determine how long he was kept in jail. In 1848 the *Scottish Register* published what it called a complete transcript of the official records, and these suggested that Wilson was held for only two weeks before being released on bond; but the *Register* was wrong. Many other court records lay in the tower of the courthouse in Paisley, dating in all from May 22, 1792 to January 5, 1794, indicating that Wilson had been imprisoned a good deal of the time in that period. Even the court record, however, leaves it unclear as to the grounds on which he was held, since Scotland had no law of criminal libel, and if the poem libeled Sharp, it was a civil case. Yet Wilson was held on a criminal warrant. Again, it is difficult to see why, if Wilson's first answer to Orr was accepted, he was not immediately sentenced, for in admitting that he had written the letter demanding money he had apparently admitted that he was guilty of blackmail. (See Appendix I.)

Whatever other enigmas the court record presented, then, there was one clear fact in it: Orr did not want to base the case against Wilson on his answers after his arrest. In the background there was the growing tension created by the government's offensive against the Scottish reformers. Wilson was still in jail on June 4, 1792, the King's Birthday. Rioting broke out in Edinburgh before that day; placards were put up warning the citizens not to march in the loyalty parades; the police and British agents were kept busy jotting down the names of people who were heard giving the new toast—"To George the Third and last!"

In Paisley resentment at the repressive acts of the government increased until the Weavers Association suddenly called off the King's Birthday parade. Held every year since 1768, and the biggest celebration of the year except for the annual race day in the fall, the King's Birthday was a Paisley institution. The Weaver's Association itself, the most powerful organization in the city, had been started in 1768 to answer fears that the industrial classes might become disloyal, and began its existence by drawing the whole of Paisley into the annual parade. Now the city authorities could not permit the weavers to call the parade off.

Desperate meetings were called—"Mr. Orr and the magistrates," says the history of Paisley, "were thrown into much difficulty at this time"—and the weavers urged to march again. They divided on the issue. It was then agreed that anyone who wished to march could do so. But when the glorious day dawned there were only a few marchers. The crowd of nonmarchers began to jeer, and then became hostile. Eventually all the law-enforcement forces of the city were required to keep the parade going. The weavers of Paisley never held another King's Birthday parade. So great was the tension that even the annual Paisley race, the Derby of Scotland, which had been held every year for 172 years, was called off.

One reason why Orr was reluctant to prosecute Wilson on the strength of his admission was that the weavers had become exercised in Wilson's behalf, and Orr did not want to irritate them further. In addition to his anonymous poems in behalf of the weavers, Wilson had been attending their meetings, and writing the reports and resolutions that were then a feature of them. These meetings were not yet illegal (though the government had grown alarmed, and was preparing to include them among seditious acts), and it was customary for the members to vote resolutions on anything—principally to express support for the French Revolution, but also to urge universal suffrage, to attack some local official, or to appeal for more frequent sittings of Parliament or to recommend to the government what it should do in foreign policy. It had become the practice, in the very recent past, to print these resolutions as paid advertisements in newspapers; then when this was opposed by the government, to print them in handbills and tack them up on walls and trees. James Paterson, the Paisley poet and weaver of Wilson's own generation, recollected in his old age that Wilson was "the most expert writer of reports and resolutions" he ever witnessed, "and that too in a style of elegance most astonishing to his compatriots. . . ."

Even had the times been calm, however, Sharp would have been aroused by Wilson's poem against him. "The Shark" was a deadly attack. On the surface, it seemed only a poem about hard times for weavers, filled with obscure references to a plotting mill owner. Sixteen stanzas long, written in the Scottish dialect, and abounding in localisms and technical phrases having to do with weaving, it appeared harmless enough, the more so in that it could only be grasped by people who knew weaving terminology—"cork" for a small manufacturer; "harnish" for a particular kind of shawl.

"The Shark" purported to be the warning of an elderly weaver to his young colleagues against the mill owner, Mr. Shark. Mr. Shark is generous and civil on the surface, and secretly plotting their destruction. The poem was a sort of soap-box oration in rhyme, not without an implicit parody of soap-box orations. The old weaver says that for years and years the weavers have toiled to bring their art so near perfection, only to have their work threatened. Mr. Shark has been boozing with the Colonel—not otherwise identified—and he has ingratiated himself to the point where the weavers can expect no sympathy if they complain to the authorities. Who would believe that so neat and proper a young fellow—"a chiel sae trig"—would bother about stealing a penny from a poor weaver? Who would believe that devilish schemes flourished beneath that blond head of hair? Who would believe that his sleekit smile was really like the greedy grin of a crocodile?

True, Mr. Shark's own conscience had bothered him. But after a great struggle he defeated his conscience and sent it away from him forever. "This done," says the old weaver, "trade snoovt awa wi' skill"—and this leads to the dangerous lines of the poem:

> . . . and wonderful extention;
> And widen't soon was every mill,
> (A dexterous invention!)

What this apparently innocuous phrase meant was that Mr. Shark had stealthily lengthened the devices used for measuring the amount of work done. The inches were longer, the yards longer, not so much as to be noticeable, or to be important in the day's output of any one weaver, but a colossal theft when multiplied over thousands of hours at the looms and endless miles of cloth. Mr. Shark was a new kind of exploiter, something never heard of before—not like the old-fashioned crooked boss, cheating a man of a few shillings, but some kind of a monster with far-ranging schemes for robbing ten thousand folk all at once. His elastic inches and feet and yards, to men whose cloth was handwoven by the inch or a fraction of an inch an hour, made a maddening psychological hazard to add to the burden of toil.

The allusions to fraud were in such technical language that the meaning of "The Shark" could not be grasped unless its readers knew how weavers worked and were paid—which everyone in Paisley knew, and few elsewhere. If Thomas Crichton in his old age had not written his memoir of Wilson, and explained why the poem was so damaging to Sharp (Crichton implied that the charges in it were true, and even Sir William Jardine confessed he thought there was an element of truth in them), it is doubtful that later generations could have grasped anything of what was involved in Wilson's trial.

If Wilson believed that he had discovered a peculiarly vicious type of swindle, the information could only have come to him from the weavers. In the atmosphere of Paisley at that moment any such fraud, if proven, would have been catastrophic to the mill owners in general, not to speak of the disgrace to Sharp in particular. But in any event, the curious interplotion of the demand from Sharp of five guineas changed the nature of the case. If Wilson had been arrested for libel, his trial would have involved the questions of the truth or falsity of the charges, but he was charged with sending a letter to Sharp to extort money from him. To heighten the strangeness of his conduct, he confessed writing the letter— "from what motive," he said in his defense, "the *defender* acknowledges himself unable to comprehend."

Among the weavers who could have supplied him with information against Sharp, or evidence of his crooked measuring devices, were James and William Mitchell. "Wilson was much engaged with the Reformers in that period," Parkhill wrote in his history of Paisley, "the two Mitchells in particular." It was a little misleading to call the Mitchell brothers reformers. They grew up in the Seed Hills where Wilson was born, their father operating the first tavern to open there. They were musicians, professional performers at dances, and Wilson had an irrational fondness for them, especially for William Mitchell, which he came to regret. They were hard-drinking, restless, popular young men, and Wilson seemed to enjoy their company because they were so good-natured and irresponsible by comparison with the serious intellectuals who ordinarily gave him companionship. In the first edition of his poems, published in the fall of 1790, Wilson had included one poem addressed to James Mitchell, and three to William. These were, on the surface at least, inconsequential: a description of a trip to the mountains to visit William Mitchell, who was briefly working in a lead mine; an excuse in poetic form for Wilson's inability to write a letter; a program laid down for insuring life-long friendship between them. In the second edition of his poems, which Wilson had prepared in 1791, he removed two of the poems addressed to William Mitchell. He could have removed all three without lessening the merit of the work.

But the times had worked a greater transformation in the history of "these musical brothers," as Crichton bitterly described them, than in Wilson. As political tension mounted, the old conservative leaders of the weaving societies, the men who headed weavers' golf clubs, fishing clubs and literary societies, gradually retired or became ineffectual, and James and William Mitchell unexpectedly emerged as the radical leaders of Paisley. They were leaders in the agitation to prevent the King's Birthday parade, to organize the shops for strike—or "combinations," as strikes were then called—and William Mitchell was the Paisley delegate to the second convention of the Friends of the People in Edinburgh.

Three weeks after the crisis of the King's Birthday parade, Allan Maconochie, the sheriff of Renfrewshire, handed down his decision in Wilson's case. He set damages to Sharp at £50 sterling, fined Wilson £10 sterling, ordered him held in prison until the fines were paid, and to beg the pardon of God and Mr. Sharp in open court.

Sixty pounds sterling was roughly equivalent to a year's income of a good weaver in the best of times; the sentence really meant that Wilson could be held in jail indefinitely. Moreover, the matter had been moved away from the original charge under which Wilson had been held. Sharp's action for libel had become the instrument by which Wilson was identified as the author of the poem. The poem was punishable as a revolutionary document.

Under the original action, Wilson, if guilty, was liable for damages. He now was in danger of losing his life.

Between the time of Wilson's arrest and Maconochie's sentence, the royal proclamation against seditious writing reached Paisley. This decree prohibited the writing, printing and circulation of any work defined as disloyal by the authorities. An emergency measure brought about by the panic resulting from the French Revolution, it provided for transportation to the penal colonies, or death, for persons who wrote, printed, possessed or circulated seditious literature of any kind. "Spies were everywhere," Parkhill wrote. "A nameless terror lay over the weaving district." In the years between 1789 and 1892 the reports of British intelligence agents from Scotland to the Home Office in London filled one volume. They filled three large volumes a year after Henry Dundas became Home Secretary in 1791. In the Home Office Dundas (now known everywhere—in whispers—as King Henry the Ninth) was studying an amazing miscellany of facts and rumors: a story that a retired army officer had broken down in a church in the west of Scotland and confessed that he was a French spy, only to disappear before the congregation could inform the police; a report that Captain Oswald, nephew of Witherspoon's old friend, and the leading American spy, had been seen near Glasgow; vague data on Colonel Hew Semple, cashiered from the Army because he had journeyed to Paris and addressed the Convention in the early days of the French Revolution—and then innumerable reports of the relentless tracking down of men in taverns, who had been heard muttering "To George the Third and last" as they downed their drinks. Even William M'Dowell was the subject of one of these spy reports. But it turned out that he had merely signed a petition which, in advocating a course for the government to follow, asserted that Pitt had been a greater statesman than Lord North.

The chief of British intelligence in Scotland was a man known only as J. B. He was a prominent Edinburgh writer and reformer, happily married, with a large family, and a popular favorite because of his cheerful and sociable disposition. He was courageous, addressing Dundas as an equal, and openly criticizing to Dundas the policy of the government, and his political perceptions were acute. He sent his letters to Dundas through the address of a divinity student in Edinburgh, Patrick Moir, who lived at 17 Thistle Street. He received Dundas' orders there. Once when J. B. irritated Dundas by too frank a criticism, the Home Secretary sent him a personal letter addressed to him at home. J. B. happened to receive it himself; he was so shocked and frightened that he was forced to go to bed, and wrote piteously begging the Secretary never to do so again, as he would be forever ruined if anyone suspected he associated with Dundas.

Wilson probably knew J. B. without knowing his importance; at least he was on good terms with one Edinburgh literary man answering somewhat to his description. But, if so, no report on Wilson appeared in the Home Office correspondence at that time. Dundas' agents came into Wilson's life in a much more intimate sense, and one which he could not have suspected: William Mitchell was also a government agent. It had been Dr. Witherspoon's contention that British intelligence agents were corrupt, that they provided the government with information it wanted to hear, to serve their own interests, and such appeared to follow from Wilson's own experiences with them. He might well have been the first of many victims among the reformers in this period, had it not been for the factor that he was already in the hands of the police when the repression began.

Shortly before Maconochie delivered his decision on Wilson, Orr had released him. Immediately after the decision, he ordered Wilson to appear. When Wilson did not appear, Orr ordered him seized, and fined him £10 Scots (less than £1 sterling) for contempt of his court. When Wilson explained that he had no lawyer, Orr appointed counsel to represent him. His choice was a little singular. He appointed none other than John Snodgrass, the central figure of the famous Witherspoon libel case, the man who had staged the Medmenham Monks ceremony in a Paisley hotel. The answer that Snodgrass and his colleague, James Walkinshaw, prepared for Wilson was far-fetched, evasive, and did Wilson's case no good. It was memorable for only one glimmer of reason to account for Wilson's admission that he had written the letter to Sharp: he could have denied writing the poem and the letter "but the defender had no occasion for any such refuge. The complainer (Sharp) would have been the last person on earth he would ever have attributed such vicious conduct to."

The reply in any event made no difference to Sheriff Orr. For a full year he managed to keep the question of Wilson focused on Wilson's contempt of court, rather than on "The Shark" and the problems it raised. Wilson from time to time was released. On one occasion he went to Edinburgh while free on bond of good behavior. He wandered far into the mountains, to the town of Callander, where he entered a village school. He sat at his desk among the boys, with his slate and chalk, trying to learn arithmetic—a strange task for a man who had accused Sharp of adding fractions of inches to yards. After three days he gave it up, and wandered down to Sterling, to sleep on the battlefield where Scottish independence was decided. Then he went on to Edinburgh, rented a room, and remained indoors a week, until he was down to his last half-crown. When he emerged he found to his surprise that the disgrace in Paisley had not affected his standing in Edinburgh. He visited the Pantheon, took part in a debate, and was cheered. He found some sort of hack work that gave him enough to live on. Though he had once been promised the assistant editorship of *The Bee*, Dundas was now putting *The Bee* out of existence. It had published a caustic historical essay, "The Political Progress of Britain," written by James Thompson Callender. Dundas was convinced that the work had been written by Lord Garden of Gardenstone, the only liberal on the Scottish bench, and destroyed *The Bee* while trying to force the editor, James Anderson, to name Gardenstone as the author of a seditious work.

Wilson no longer cared whether he had a literary future or not. He was a convicted blackmailer, and nothing could restore his aspirations for his work. The charges that had been brought against him in Paisley were of such nature that there could be no question of his association with Martha M'Lean, for example, or, for that matter, with any other girl of respectable family. The charge of blackmail automatically terminated his continued patronage from M'Dowell. In fact, a shadow was cast over all Wilson's satirical writing, from his early attack on old Craig the miser on down to his political poems.

His affair with Martha had, of course, ended. They corresponded secretly for some time, because they were forbidden to meet, and because Wilson realized it was unwise for them to be seen together. They corresponded by way of Thomas Crichton. Crichton wrote that "owing to particular circumstances, they had seldom an opportunity of meeting." The circumstances were that Wilson was so often in jail. Crichton agreed to be the intermediary, and they both addressed their letters to him.

Wilson insisted that Crichton read the letters, which he was reluctant to do. Wilson took this precaution to avoid endangering Martha, since Crichton as Governor of the Town Hospital, and an elder of the church, was an eminently respectable witness in case the inquiry into Wilson's friends should reach to her. Crichton said the letters were touching, very high-minded, full of noble sentiments, and marked by deep affection on both sides. Thinking back upon them, he commented that with all Wilson's expression of undying love, he could not remember that he had at any point made a proposal of marriage.

On New Year's Day, 1793, the government opened a terrific offensive against all reformers, democrats, levelers, revolutionists and, for that matter, against all opponents of Henry Dundas. Suspected printers, ministers, lawyers, weavers and workmen were rounded up; sentences of from three to fourteen years in the penal colonies were handed out for possession of seditious writing; the letter of the law against treasonable practices was enforced with an addled efficiency that suggested an intelligence system that had gone mad. A workman, George Mealmaker, had published a protest which the authorities considered seditious; its language had been corrected by a minister named Palmer, who had tried to prevent Mealmaker from publishing it, and who had, in fact, toned down the language to forestall any accusation of treason. But Palmer was sentenced to seven years in the penal colonies, where he died of hardship trying to escape. Thomas Muir was sentenced to fourteen years in Australia in a midnight trial, in one of the greatest scandals in British legal history. Gerald Maragon and William Skirving, the next two most prominent of the martyrs of the Scottish reform movement, were sent to Botany Bay and, like most of the political prisoners, died of hardships also.

Wilson was unaffected by the roundup because he was already in jail. On January 22, 1793, Orr delivered his decision. In the meantime, printed copies of "The Shark" had been placed in every weaving shop in Paisley, which Orr said aggravated and did not alleviate the contempt. He ordered Wilson to be locked up for fourteen days. After fourteen days he was to be held until someone put up bond for his good behavior for two years. He was to deliver up all copies of the poem in his possession: "And I further order that before the said defender shall be set at liberty, he shall be conducted to the market place of Paisley, and shall there, with his own hands, commit to the flames the whole copies of said publication. . . . The Sheriff will then resume consideration of this process"—in other words, the question of "The Shark" would then be taken up.

CHAPTER SEVEN

Flight

FROM HIS CELL Wilson wrote a note to Dave Brodie, asking him for money, since a prisoner in the Tolbooth was in grave danger unless he could buy his own food. Brodie immediately sent Wilson enough money for his needs. In thanking him, Wilson wrote that only absolute necessity would have led him to ask Brodie for the loan.

Wilson now had another two weeks in his cell in the Tolbooth, which was becoming his only settled residence in Paisley. His poem, "Watty and Meg," was sweeping the country, hawked about by unauthorized peddlers who advertised it as a new work by Robert Burns. Its sale had more than cleared up Wilson's debt to the printer Neilson (it sold in all more than 100,000 copies), and Neilson presented Wilson with a greatcoat in lieu of royalties. In the darkening cold of midwinter, Wilson needed it. He described the Tolbooth as "this new scene of misery, this assemblage of wretches and wretchedness, where the rumbling of bolts, the hoarse exclamations of the jailor, the sighs and sallow countenances of the prisoners, and the general gloom of the place require all the exertions of resolution to be cheerful and resigned to the will of fate."

When the two-week sentence was served, Wilson petitioned Orr to let his brother-in-law, John Bell, be his security for good behavior. Bell was a workingman, a boiler in a bleachery, and Orr might feel he lacked resources to sign the bond. But Bell had expressed his willingness to sign. And, because of Sharp's influence, Wilson said, he could not find security among prosperous people in Paisley who would otherwise willingly assist him. If Orr, at Sharp's insistence, set the bond high, Bell would not be able to be his bondsman.

Orr agreed to release Wilson on a bond of £300 Scot—about £35 sterling—for which Bell could be responsible. But it was not necessary for Bell to sign for him. Tom Witherspoon did so, an act of kindness that Wilson found almost unbearable because Martha

M'Lean was Witherspoon's sister-in-law. In effect, she had signed for Wilson. The bond of caution pledged Wilson to keep the peace for two years. If he troubled or molested any of His Majesty's subjects in that time, if he injured or attempted to injure anyone by writing anything against their good names, character or reputation, Witherspoon forfeited the £300.

The day after he was released, Wilson appeared at court. He said he possessed no copies of the poem and did not know where any were. However, the court order read that Wilson had either to produce and burn the poems or go back to jail. Two copies somehow materialized. There had to be more than one—the court order read "copies." But the court order was amended to mean by "market place" anywhere on the central square of Paisley. The Tolbooth was at one extremity. Wilson could burn his poems on the platform at the head of the outside stairs of the Tolbooth, and not in the square itself, which was always crowded.

At eleven o'clock on Wednesday morning, February 6, 1793, Wilson was led from his cell by John Peers, the clerk. Wilson identified the copies of "The Shark" he had left with Peers, and Peers placed them in his hand. The procession now moved from the courtroom to the broad hallway that opened on an outside platform. From the platform above the double staircase leading to the ground, the gathering looked over the square toward the Cross of Paisley, from behind the whipping post. The prisoner, the court attendants and Sharp's lawyer clustered uncertainly there, not sure of what to do. Wilson burned the poems at the top of the stairs. Peers let him stoop down behind the railing so people would not notice anything. The original edition of "The Shark" was on cheap, thin paper, almost like blotting paper, four pages scarcely larger than the palm of one's hand. At best, the conflagration could not have been great.

In April, Orr announced that he was now ready to go back to the original case of "The Shark." In the middle of May he gave his decision, which was far less severe than Maconochie's original judgment or directive. Orr stated that Wilson's conduct in the past year had aggravated the original charge, and ordered him to pay £5 5s. damages to Sharp. Wilson was also fined £2 12s. 6d., and costs were levied against him. Orr reduced these to £3 10s. Wilson was to be locked in the Tolbooth until these sums were paid. But Orr reserved the right to remit the fine, provided Wilson would "within eight days of this date, give in a letter to [Sharp] containing suitable acknowledgments for the wrong done him." The judgment stated that Wilson was hereby convicted of attempted extortion.

Wilson refused to write the required letter to Sharp. After some ten days in jail he wrote to Brodie that the total he had to pay was £12 13s. 6d., much less than the original £60 sterling that had been levied against him by Maconochie, but it was still beyond his ability to pay. Sheriff Orr had sickened of the whole business. "I had the comfort to be told," Wilson wrote to Brodie, "that Mr. Sharp was resolved to punish me though it should cost him a little money. However, I shall know more after confinement of two days or so."

When Wilson was released from jail, Tom Witherspoon and his wife took him into their home. Misfortune had come the way of the young couple: their first child had died.

Times were hard and the weavers were being reduced to almost plebeian status; it was heroic of Witherspoon to take Wilson in under the circumstances. Wilson was in Witherspoon's care throughout the fall and winter of 1793, when the persecution of the Scottish reformers reached its climax. James Anderson, giving up *The Bee,* settled quietly in London. Lord Gardenstone died in July, 1793, at the height of the repression. The reform movement was destroyed, but the savagery and injustice of the administration caused a revulsion of feelings.

As the year 1794 opened, Wilson was again arrested. On January 4, the officers unexpectedly brought him before Orr's court. The action was not brought by Sharp. The complaint was filed by Edward Jamison, the prosecutor who had previously been the joint complainer with Sharp in the many preceding actions, since if Sharp's claim was granted laws against extortion had been violated. Jamison now emerged with a highly vindictive spirit of his own. He swore out a warrant for Wilson's arrest "for the crime of being concerned in framing and industriously circulating an advertisement addressed 'To the Friends of Liberty and Reform' calling a general meeting of the Friends of Reform to be held this night in Falconers Land on Stories Street at five o'clock," the alleged crime having taken place some six months before. There was no evidence against Wilson. But the bond of caution that Tom Witherspoon had signed for Wilson's good behavior made any such charge a disquieting indication of official hostility persisting after he had satisfied Sharp's complaint.

Wilson was again locked in the Tolbooth. He pled not guilty, denying any connection with the meeting or the advertisement, and petitioned Orr to be released on bail, "which I am ready to produce." Orr at once admitted him to bail, generously modifying it, as he said, to £200 Scot. A remote kinsman, William Wilson, went bail for Wilson. John Peers, the sheriffs' clerk, was Wilson's witness in this application for bail. Nothing more was heard of Jamison's charge; it was not prosecuted.

The following month, twins were born to Thomas Witherspoon and Jean M'Lean, a boy and girl baptized David and Agnes at Dr. Witherspoon's former church. The weaver's house had grown too crowded to contain a convicted blackmailer and a semi-fugitive.

Wilson collected a pack of goods and set out on another winter peddling trip. He crossed Scotland and peddled goods north of Edinburgh. From a fisherman's hut on the shore of the German ocean he wrote to Tom Witherspoon that he was through—there was nothing more that he could do, and despair had murdered his hopes. He felt himself to be a stranger in Scotland, and could never again be at home there. He had determined to emigrate, and as he did so he realized that it would be best if he never saw Witherspoon again, but left their relationship as it stood.

Consequently, Wilson remained away from Paisley. In his absence the town was startled by the news that the Mitchell brothers had fled. In his memoir of Wilson, Crichton asked bitterly how these musicians could have become leaders of the working class at a time when the peace of society was much disturbed. He said that Wilson had been attracted to their company by his love of music. What had happened that forced Wilson to the line of conduct he followed? The Scottish writers who wrote of Wilson as a poet reached different conclusions. Jardine, as has been said, believed Wilson's talents were being made use of by the radicals, which meant James and William Mitchell, who attacked Sharp precisely because he was a superior individual among the mill owners, and had a following among the weavers.

Rev. Alexander Grosart, who collected Wilson's correspondence and poems in Scotland, wrote somewhat later than Jardine. He decided after prolonged investigation that the conflict arose because the original charge in Wilson's poem was true. Grosart wrote that not one line of evidence was ever introduced in connection with the truth or falsity of Wilson's accusation. If the poem had been published, and Wilson then sued for libel, the question of the truth might have been before the court. The last-minute charge of blackmail forestalled any discussion of the truth of the charges made in the poem. Grosart believed that Wilson's attack on Sharp was justified in every line.

John Parkhill, the historian of Paisley, stated that the common belief in the city was that Wilson had taken the punishment for the Mitchell brothers. It was then believed that their lives were in jeopardy because they were revolutionary leaders noted for their inflammatory words. In the light of Wilson's career as a whole, this explanation was most logical. The blackmail attempt of which he was convicted was incredible through its stupidity. Had he tried to raise money by such means he would not have followed the particular course of action that had been followed, for it could only have led to his arrest. Wilson had undoubtedly written a very damaging anonymous attack on William Sharp. It had been published, but not yet widely circulated. Parties unknown demanded money from Sharp in return for suppressing the poem. Wilson was afraid to speak because of his own involvement with the radicals, his authorship of resolutions for weavers' groups, his romantic picture of himself bearing punishment for his fellow rebels, and, more importantly, from the fear of further punishment if he admitted more than he did.

Wilson found work as a weaver, and saved his entire income for four months, spending only sixteen shillings in that period. William Duncan agreed to go to America with him, as the first step in moving the family out of Scotland. All these plans were kept secret. Wilson's sisters Mary and Jean both wanted their children to grow up in the United States. As the time for departure approached, Jean's husband, John Bell, grew irresolute, though in his case there had not been a firm agreement to leave. In the middle of May, 1794, Wilson and Duncan prepared in secrecy to take ship. At the last moment, in a final betrayal of his former apprentice, Duncan decided to stay in Scotland.

Wilson then faced the prospect of leaving alone. Duncan's oldest son, William, was now sixteen. As Wilson left, William decided to go with him. They had barely enough money for two fares. On Tuesday evening, May 15, 1794, Wilson appeared in Paisley for the first time in months. He called on Crichton, and they walked from Crichton's house to the river Cart and then along the bank of the river. Crichton was astonished to learn that Wilson was leaving for America the next morning. Wilson was serious and concerned, and wanted Crichton to understand his motives. He could not explain to Crichton how he felt, saying, "I am bound now, and cannot ruin Tom Witherspoon, and I must get out of my mind."

IV

The Exile

When he first set foot in America, moneyless and unknown, he awakened to an adequate sense of his own powers and resources, and intellectual dignity. . . . The depth, shade and illimitable extent of the American forest, with its fair tenantry of winged creatures, were wanting for the width and range . . . of his adventurous and ambitious spirit . . . and the invigoration of its grasping might.

—William Motherwell, *The Harp of Renfrewshire*

CHAPTER ONE

Moneyless and Unknown

❧❧❧❧ ◉ ❦❦❦❦

EARLY on Wednesday morning, May 16, 1794, Wilson and young Duncan started out, reaching Port Patrick, some thirty miles away, that night. They crossed to Ireland, and at Belfast Wilson went alone into the city. He found the *Swift* of New York was loading, carrying 350 immigrants. There was no space left except on deck. Wilson hurried back to where he had left Duncan and asked if he would sail under those conditions. The boy agreed. They moved their clothing to the ship, remaining aboard five days in port so the space they had appropriated would not be seized by other passengers.

The *Swift* sailed into two weeks of fine weather, Wilson wrote to his father, "and only buried an old woman and two children. . . . On the 11th July (Wednesday) we could plainly see land from the mast-head, but a terrible gale of wind blowing all night from the shore, it was Sunday before we again had the satisfaction of seeing it, scarcely perceptible through the fog; but a pilot coming on board, and the sun rising, we found ourselves within the Capes of the Delaware, the shore on land having the appearance of being quite flat, and only a complete forest of trees. . . . We arrived at Newcastle the next day about mid-day, where we were as happy as mortals could be. . . ."

Since the great yellow fever plague in Philadelphia the year before, all ships for Philadelphia unloaded at New Castle. A fellow passenger named Oliver, learning Wilson and Duncan had no money, loaned them a few shillings. They landed at the Battery after noon on July 14, 1794. A grassy tract of land and old shade trees lay between the Delaware River and the town. Beyond was the Strand, with fine old residences. New Castle was founded by the Swedes, and most of it was older than all except the oldest sections of Paisley.

Wilson and Duncan set out on foot over the Broad Dyke, a causeway built by the Swedes over a marshy stretch for a long distance beside the river. Then the road entered a flat wooded country that looked like a new world to them, lowland thickets, wild grapes growing in abundance on vines that climbed over the trees, strange shrubs and flowers. Wilson carried a gun and his pack, Duncan his clothing.

A mile before Wilmington they climbed out of the lowland on a long hill before crossing the Christina River into the city. Wilmington reminded Wilson of Renfrew in Scotland, not far from Paisley—"or perhaps a little larger," he admitted. There were two silk looms in the city, run by French refugees. They had no work for another weaver. Jacob Broom, a signer of the Declaration of Independence, was starting a cotton mill. He was building the jennies at that time in his machine shop—Wilson saw them in the process of construction. But Broom had too many troubles of his own to give work to anyone. The building of the jennies was going so slowly, Wilson said, "I believe it may be some years before half a dozen looms can be employed."

Somewhat discouraged, Wilson and Duncan slept in Wilmington that night and set out again early the next morning. The road passed the thirteen great flour mills that made Wilmington the greatest flour producer of the New World. Beyond the flour mills a path led to the Old Barley Mill, one of oldest in the country, then out through the woods to the Old Snuff Mill. The country grew wilder, the path along the river overshadowed with trees and vines, the woods on both sides a green maze. The little valleys through which streams tumbled into the Brandywine were like bowers overgrown with wild roses and honeysuckle.

A bird caught Wilson's eye as the most beautiful he had ever seen, brilliant red, white, black and steel-blue, a red-headed woodpecker, *Picus erythrocephalus,* found only in America. Wilson shot it. The head was bright red, the breast feathers white, the wings blue, the tip of the tail black—an alert and quizzical bird so lovely Wilson regretted killing it. Overhead, other red-headed woodpeckers were diving and vociferating, pursuing and playing, rattling on the tree trunks and screaming in the woods, constantly active, gay and frolicsome. Birds were everywhere; even mockingbirds were still frequently encountered in the woods near Wilmington in 1794; it was almost the extreme northern point of their migration.

The golden-greenish waters of the Brandywine sparkled in the early sunlight like mineral waters, foaming and dashing over rocks and low falls, with scarcely a quiet pool in the miles from Chadds Ford to the Christina at Wilmington. Two miles from Wilmington the path entered a glen, with bushes so thick they suggested the entrance to a cavern; then the path emerged on a magnificent height overlooking the woods, a great curve in the river, and mills built along the stream. Here Joshua Gilpin and Miers Fisher—the latter a name of some importance in the lives of both Wilson and Audubon—had started their paper mill five years before. Fisher and both Gilpin and his son were among the first purchasers of Wilson's *Ornithology*. Another paper mill was being built a short distance up the river.

No one had work for Wilson and Duncan. The road now led away from the river, through rolling country, very little of which had been cleared. "The only houses we saw were made of large logs of wood, laid one over another," Wilson wrote. "What crops we could see consisted of Indian corn, potatoes, and some excellent oats." They went into a few farmhouses, "But saw nothing of the kindness and hospitality so often told of them." From Kennett Square, then only a collection of farmhouses, they walked seven miles to Chadds

Ford, where the Battle of Brandywine had turned into a British victory that nearly destroyed Washington's army.

They were now on the Kings High Road, the main thoroughfare to Philadelphia. Another nine miles took them through narrow valleys along a winding creek to Black Horse Tavern, then through rolling country again where a few mills had been built on the streams beside the road. They found the establishment of three weavers, "who live very quiet, and well enough, but had no place for us." Outside Philadelphia, on Crooked Creek, they passed another cotton mill and came into sight of the city about sunset.

From a distance it resembled Glasgow. Philadelphia had 30,000 or 40,000 inhabitants— Glasgow 43,000. But only about half of the refugees from the yellow fever plague had returned. Through the spring the people had waited apprehensively for another year like the preceding, with another plague to follow. But the days were flawless. In the middle of June the wind turned southwest, bringing fine growing weather, with just enough rain for the crops; July was cool and pleasant, with enough sun and enough showers to produce the most abundant harvest. There was an overwhelming spirit of renewed hope in the land, a heady pleasure in the wine of fresh air, the exultant relief of a people who felt they were saved by a miracle.

Both Wilson and Duncan found work almost at once. Wilson wrote a long report home, using William Young's bookshop as his address. There were only twenty weavers in Philadelphia, and these had no provision for journeymen weavers, but Wilson found work at John Aitkin's engraving shop. "It is a little singular," Crichton wrote, "that on his arrival . . . he should have made himself known to a Mr. John Aitkin, a copperplate printer, and that when that gentleman learned of his situation he gave him employment in a business in which he was totally unacquainted." Crichton's suspicion was understandable; the opening of the mint and the monetary problems of the United States, together with the intense clannishness of the early Philadelphia engravers, made Wilson's entry into the craft seem strange.

But Crichton did not know the situation in Philadelphia eight months after the worst plague in American history. Philadelphia was reopening hourly. Grass like the grass in pastures grew in the streets, and the fences that had been built to isolate infected sections were still standing, but the burned and looted houses were being rebuilt, and the shutters were being taken down from closed shops. What first struck Wilson, who was as practical as any Scotsman of his generation, were the high prices. What next caught his attention was the number of refugees from the Negro revolutions in the West Indies. These were everywhere. They appeared to be less susceptible to yellow fever than others, perhaps because of early exposure to it. They had come in such throngs that they drove prices out of all reason. The yellow fever had demoralized the people. It was the eighteenth-century equivalent of an atomic bomb. Andrew Ellicott, the keenest mind among the American intelligence officers of the time, considered the yellow fever plague of Philadelphia to have been a conscious effort to destroy the American republic. He wrote that if these fevers could be generated in the large commercial cities of the United States, the country might find itself destroyed by a domestic enemy while defending itself against a foreign one.

Since the fever was introduced by West Indian refugees, and had cost a hundred lives a day for weeks, there was some substance for such fantastic notions. All Philadelphia papers had stopped publishing during the plague, the shops had been boarded up, the roads were blocked by refugees, a spectral film of yellow dust lay over the town and the countryside, and at least five thousand people died. Only the sudden frost of early fall ended the plague. Oddly enough, the fact that mosquitoes spread yellow fever was suspected at the time, but the theory was dropped, though it was beginning to be suspected also that there was a connection between insects and disease, and that birds entered the equation because they lived on insects.

In the fall of 1794, four months after Wilson's arrival in America, Dr. Witherspoon died in Princeton. A fall on shipboard as he was returning from Scotland had cost the clergyman the sight of one eye, and the other gradually failed until he became totally blind. He remained unbroken by trials as severe as any that came to the Founding Fathers. His home in Princeton was looted by the British during the Revolution. One son was killed in the war, and Frances, his favorite daughter, the wife of a South Carolina physician, died suddenly as peace was signed. As Dr. Witherspoon grew older his thoughts turned more and more on a happier time in his youth in Scotland, and he made it a practice, each night at his evening devotions, to call to his mind the members of the old congregations he had preached to. He found that it calmed his mind and left him rested to remember them. Some of the moral authority of this remarkable political philosopher, religious leader, and first director of American intelligence was lost in his last years. At the age of sixty-eight he married Ann Dill, the twenty-three-year-old widow of a New York physician; it seemed too human an action for one who occupied the moral heights on which he lived. But with his death, recognition of his colossal achievement for the new nation swept over the whole country. It became one of the favorite legends of the time that Dr. Witherspoon had brought about the Declaration of Independence by his stirring words and his powerful resolution in a moment when the delegates were disheartened and afraid.

Wilson's own feeling for Dr. Witherspoon was mixed with family resentments and affections. He had become too much a liberal in religion to share the clergyman's Calvinist orthodoxy, translated though that orthodoxy was through the luminous clarity of Witherspoon's common sense and his pure and mellow prose. Yet the Witherspoons meant much to him. He continued to write regularly to Tom Witherspoon all his life, and on one occasion he wrote that William Witherspoon was the closest friend he had ever known. The one love of his life deepened these feelings. Martha M'Lean was now a part of the Witherspoon family through her sister's marriage. Martha herself, after Wilson's departure, married a well-established Paisley man, bore him several children, and lived a happy and prosperous life.

As the winter closed in on Philadelphia, Wilson found himself suffering from the disorder that was a genuine illness among Scottish immigrants. Homesickness, he wrote to his sister Jean, was a real sickness, and came after a few months' residence in the New World, with a piercing longing for familiar scenes and friends. Wilson left Aitkin's shop to start weaving again.

Northeast of Philadelphia, beyond Frankford, a road branched off the turnpike to Trenton and New York, leading through the village of Bustleton to Bucks County. About ten miles from downtown Philadelphia along this road, beyond the village of Fox Chase, a side road ran through half a mile of woodlands to a settlement called Scotland, from the number of Scottish settlers located there. On the bank of Pennypack Creek, Joshua Sullivan had built a house and mill combined, a gray stone structure, picturesque and isolated, with the stream flowing at one side of the house. It was a superlatively beautiful spot, set in columns of sycamores, poplars and maples, with trails through the woodland leading to a grassy plot beside the mill. Wilson lived with Sullivan's family and wove in the mill built over the river. Sullivan was a man of some substance and with a good deal of energy. He took a liking to both the newcomers, Duncan weaving for him when Wilson went on to other jobs.

When Wilson was apprenticed as a weaver, John Finlayson of Paisley had signed as the co-guarantor with Duncan to keep the agreement. John Finlayson married Margaret Robertson in Dr. Witherspoon's church in Paisley, and her brother, James Robertson, was in Philadelphia. Robertson had done well in the New World. He operated three looms, had a nice farm outside the city, and was raising a pleasant family of three daughters, the oldest then thirteen. Wilson and Duncan spent a Sunday with him soon after they landed. After dinner, Wilson wrote to his father, he and Robertson walked alone in the woods for nearly three hours. Robertson asked him questions about Scotland. "I was sorry there were some things I could not inform him of," Wilson wrote cryptically, "but he will hear for himself soon."

CHAPTER TWO

Schoolteacher

ROBERTSON wanted both Wilson and Duncan to weave for him. Wilson was bent on his own projects, and could not, but it was agreed that Duncan would take one of Robertson's looms. On his part, after weaving with Sullivan, Wilson set out on foot through the mountains south and west of Philadelphia. From the heights there appeared nothing except prodigious declivities, wood-covered, the profound silence among these aerial solitudes impressing him "with awe and a kind of fearful sublimity."

Wilson's destination was Sheppardstown. His early biographers assumed that Sheppardstown was the small Virginia town near Harpers Ferry on the Potomac, which waged a vigorous campaign to be made the new capital of the nation. But there was another Sheppardstown at that time, now a part of Carlisle, Pennsylvania. Dr. Charles Nisbet was established at Carlisle as the president of Dickinson College, and the community was a center for Scottish immigrants. Whichever town was Wilson's home for the next few months, he disliked it. "The habits of the people with whom he was compelled to associate," said a contemporary, "and the general wretchedness of his existence there . . . compelled him to return to Philadelphia."

In the spring of 1795 he set out on a peddling trip through northern New Jersey, carrying cloth he had woven on Sullivan's loom. This trip was profitable. When he returned he taught school on the Bustleton road, between Sullivan's place and the village of Frankford.

Just at this time Miers Fisher bought the farm adjoining Joshua Sullivan's mill, named it Urie, and converted it to a great estate. Fisher was one of the richest Philadelphia merchants. Much of the early industry of the region, especially textiles and paper, was financed by him. He was a Quaker, a follower of the Quaker philosopher Robert Barclay, naming his estate Urie after Barclay's birthplace in Scotland. He was married to Sarah Redwood, a Newport heiress—Redwood Fisher was another early subscriber to Wilson's *Ornithology*—and at Urie he and his wife became famous for their hospitality. There they entertained the leaders of the American government, and visiting dignitaries such as the British Ambassador, with massive provincial elegance combined with simplicity and Quaker friendliness.

Miers Fisher was the American agent of Audubon's father, who owned a little property outside Philadelphia, and trusted its management to Fisher. During the wars following the French Revolution, when Audubon's father, as a French naval officer, was on active duty, he sent Audubon to Philadelphia in Fisher's care. The two great ornithologists, Wilson and Audubon, lived almost as neighbors, although, of course, they had no knowledge of each other.

Wilson taught only one term in the Bustleton school. He moved in 1796 to a better school at Milestown, where he remained five years. His own education was so sketchy that he had to study in order to teach. He told Crichton that beginning in 1795 he studied so hard he injured his health. But he prospered to the point where he and Duncan were now looking for a farm, as their first step in moving the rest of the family to America. His niece Isabel was the first to arrive. In the same period Wilson's stepbrother Robert Urie, twenty-three years old in 1795, and serving in the British navy, visited Wilson.

Aside from such family contacts, Wilson kept apart from the circle of Scottish immigrants, especially the political exiles. James and William Mitchell, the Paisley musicians and radicals, were around Philadelphia for the first two years after Wilson's arrival. In the summer of 1796 they disappeared, to his relief. James Thompson Callender had given the Scottish political exiles a worse name in America than they ever had with the authorities in Britain. He arrived as a refugee, a victim of oppression, trading on his authorship of *The Political Progress of Britain,* which was published in Philadelphia by William Young. When the unjust trials of Muir and Palmer excited great sympathy in the United States, Callender wrote characteristically to Jefferson, "I was their intimate friend, and quite as deep in the unlucky business as they were." Callender listed himself in the Philadelphia directory as James Thompson Callender, corrector of the press, 64 Dock Street. He managed to get himself appointed the shorthand reporter of the debates in Congress, a job that paid $4,000 a year, then a very substantial salary. Callender was not paid by Congress, but by the *United States Gazette.* A superb shorthand reporter, gifted with a sardonic and malicious humor, he soon had the whole city laughing at the pompous or idiotic comments uttered by the statesmen in the heat of debates—a form of attack they could not well answer because Callender reported their words with unfailing accuracy. "Of all the foreigners who were connected with journalism in the United States," says Callender's only biographer, "James Thompson Callender was easily first in the worst qualities of mind and character." Congressmen were afraid of him, and with reason; he was a man "in whose heart vindictive passion raged without control." It was not until the spring of 1796 that Callender was formally expelled, and Congress hired its own shorthand reporter for its debates.

Wilson's school was some distance from these stirring political struggles. Milestown was within the limits of Bristol Township, nineteen miles from the center of Philadelphia. The Old York Road, to Trenton and on to New York, ran through Bristol, which stood on the Delaware River; the ferry to New Jersey crossed the river there. Just inside the Bristol limits was Barkham's Lane, and Wilson's schoolyard beyond it. Wilson had twenty-five to forty students each term in his one-room schoolhouse. Most of the families were Pennsylvania Dutch. For generations they had kept their own customs and continued to speak only German. There had recently been a change in their attitude toward the government, and they were now determined that their children should learn English. Wilson's problems of discipline were consequently simplified: the parents of his students forced them to study. He in turn learned German because the family of Isaac Kulp, with whom he boarded, spoke only that language. They were descendants of old settlers, the parents still living nearby, with three young boys and a girl in the family. After learning to speak German, Wilson was able to talk with the parents of his students—"a hardy, sober, industrious and penurious race of people," he wrote owlishly, "lovers of money and haters of Irishmen."

In studying mathematics in order to keep ahead of his students, Wilson became interested in surveying. He made a set of instruments and surveyed lands for the farmers. Sullivan had bought land in western New York State, as had many of Wilson's neighbors. Robert Morris, the Philadelphia merchant and financier of the Revolution, who lived at Bristol originally, owned almost the entire western part of New York State. After his failure these immense holdings were broken up and sold. Wilson wanted to acquire some of this New York State property, writing to his father: "Every individual who has gone there has prospered."

CHAPTER THREE

New World

IN HIS FIRST DAYS at Milestown, Wilson devoted himself to his school and discouraged visits from Scottish political refugees. American politics, at the moment, had become so melodramatic that all political life seemed suspect. Wilson's fellow refugee Callender had become the central figure in a kind of Gothic romance of politics, something like the novels that young Charles Brockden Brown, then teaching at the Friends Grammar School on Second Street in Philadelphia, was writing to launch American fiction. Ousted from his position as reporter of Congress, Callender claimed to have discovered a gigantic plot, a swindle beyond all belief, the creation of Alexander Hamilton, "that threadbare lawyer," as Callender described him. Callender's story was that when the Federal government took over the state debts, according to Hamilton's program, Hamilton and his Federalist colleagues stole between $40 and $60 million—that debts amounting to $30 or $50 million were purchased by the government for $90 million. Congress had already investigated similar charges, and cleared Alexander Hamilton and the Treasury, but Callender had new and amazing facts to reveal.

The background was this:

One summer when Mrs. Hamilton had taken the Hamilton children out of the city a young woman appeared at Hamilton's residence on the corner of Walnut and Third Street. The young woman, who seemed modest and respectable, appealed to the Secretary of the Treasury for help. She said her husband, a merchant named James Reynolds, was moving his business from New York to Philadelphia. He had been called back to New York and there fallen ill. She had no money for her fare, nor friends in Philadelphia to whom she could apply for aid, and asked Hamilton to loan her enough to enable her to join her husband.

Hamilton had no money in the house. He told Mrs. Reynolds he would bring her money for her fare to New York when he had drawn it. She lived in a decent-appearing boarding house on Water Street, and, when he appeared, led him to her room, where, as he said, it appeared that consolations other than financial ones would be welcomed. An affair began, and was resumed when Mrs. Reynolds returned from New York.

Presently James Reynolds appeared at Hamilton's office and asked for a job in the Treasury; Hamilton had none to give him. He loaned Reynolds money, however, when Reynolds asked for it—small amounts as a rule, $300 the largest loan. Hamilton kept Reynolds' receipts. Mrs. Reynolds wrote Hamilton passionate letters of great candor, and seemed so wildly in love with him, and so careless of appearances, that Hamilton resolved to end the affair for fear that word of it would reach his wife, who had returned to Philadelphia.

Callender was fully informed about Hamilton's affair with Mrs. Reynolds from the start. He had established confidential relations with John Beckley, a former mayor of Richmond who became the first Clerk of the House of Representatives and first Librarian of Congress. For a brief period in 1794 and 1795 Callender edited *The Political Register* in Philadelphia, and in the next two years *The American Annual Register,* which was a partisan account of current political events under the guise of a factual record; Beckley gave to Callender the official papers of Congress on Hamilton's relations with Mr. and Mrs. Reynolds.

These papers came into existence in a curious fashion. A minor Treasury official was discharged as untrustworthy. Hamilton had nothing to do with the matter. He was asked to retain the discharged man in his post. When he refused, Hamilton was warned that his relations with Mrs. Reynolds would be published unless he did so. Simultaneously, an inquiry was asked in Congress about the discharged Treasury official. Hamilton asked his political opponents in Congress, especially Monroe, to come to his home, and there placed before them his correspondence with both Mrs. Reynolds and her husband, insisting that the Congressmen read it. They did so with great embarrassment. Monroe reported to Congress that a private discussion with Hamilton had satisfied them that no public issue was involved, and the Congressional inquiry was dropped.

When Hamilton tried to break off with Mrs. Reynolds, he received a well-phrased letter, signed by James Reynolds, stating he had learned of his wife's infidelity. She had confessed, begged forgiveness on her knees, and he wrote in tears at the ruination of his life. Hamilton asked Reynolds to come to his office, denied anything improper in his relations with Mrs. Reynolds, and loaned Reynolds a substantial sum to leave Philadelphia with his wife and start over. This was precisely what Callender wanted. Shortly after, Hamilton received a letter from Mrs. Reynolds saying her husband had consented to a continuation of her love affair with Hamilton, and they were remaining in Philadelphia.

Hamilton thought he had protected himself against blackmail by admitting to his major political opponents the truth of his affair with Mrs. Reynolds. But James Thompson Callender had never intended merely to publicize a routine case of infidelity. He wrote a history of the United States, selling for three dollars a copy, in which Hamilton and Reynolds appeared as leading characters in a matter of the first historical importance. Callender's version was that the Reynolds case proved Hamilton guilty of the multi-million-dollar swindle previously referred to—of buying depreciated state debts and selling them to the Federal government at face value. The records that Hamilton had so carefully kept of his financial dealings with Reynolds, the loans for unstated reasons, the immediate payments of sums to Reynolds on his request, thus emerged as mysterious financial reflections of the colossal theft which Callender alleged was taking place.

Hamilton was ruined. He could not deny his payments of money to Reynolds. He could not deny an intimate relation with the Reynoldses, for he had shown his political opponents in Congress the wild, pathetic, and often strangely poignant letters in which Myra Reynolds proclaimed her love for him. On the small scale of local intrigue in Paisley, Wilson had found that a satire against Sharp appeared as an attempt at blackmail. On the gigantic scale of national politics, Hamilton admitted his affair with Mrs. Reynolds, and found he gave apparent substance to charges of the theft of public funds.

Hamilton confessed the whole business to his wife and she forgave him. He then wrote and published his famous report on his love affair with Mrs. Reynolds, a sort of Federalist paper on the interaction of sex and political power, and as far in advance of its time in its discussion of human motives as were the Federalist papers in politics. Hamilton printed with Myra Reynolds' letters a detailed report of his financial transactions with her husband, perhaps more damaging to his personal pride, in view of his frequent querulous complaints at loaning a few dollars more to Reynolds, after enjoying his wife, than Callender's accusation that he had stolen millions.

Hamilton's book was a masterpiece, a Gothic novel in itself, but written with an emotional honesty and a lack of pretense unmatched by any American author before Mark Twain. "No anticipation can equal the infamy of the piece," Callender wrote exultantly to Jefferson. "It is worth fifty of all that the best pens of America could have said against him." Hamilton had already resigned from the Treasury. He challenged Monroe to a duel over the Callender blackmail, for he assumed that Callender had received his material from Monroe after the Congressional inquiry. The Jeffersonians on their part felt that Hamilton had confessed to an affair with the wife of a swindler in order to prevent an inquiry into the swindles that Callender charged him with. Hamilton may have been the greatest political philosopher known to history, but he was a child in intrigue compared to James Thompson Callender, the obscure Edinburgh hack writer who ruined him. At the height of the turmoil Hamilton still hesitated to break off with Myra Reynolds; he was afraid she would kill herself. Monroe asked Aaron Burr to be his second in his threatened duel with Hamilton. The final catastrophe did not take place then, for the challenge was withdrawn after explanation, but events were under way that led to Hamilton's death at Burr's hand a few years later.

In a world dominated by political scandals of this character, and with Scottish refugees creating many of them, Wilson remained in obscurity. He was a convicted blackmailer—one who had confessed to blackmail, if his signature attached to the letter to Sharp should be taken at face value—and it behoved him to be circumspect. He rose early every morning, sometimes before dawn, went for a solitary walk, and in the evening walked again before sundown. School occupied him fully. He came into the farmhouse where he boarded, and there Kulp and Mrs. Kulp "were playing with their children and smiling on each other with looks of mutual affection and parental pride."

School was often torment to Wilson, an ordeal whose relief was his solitary study at night. He sat at his desk by candlelight while squirrels scampered on the shingles over his head. Since surveying required advanced mathematics, and Wilson was now able to read Newton for pleasure, he had not exaggerated when he told Crichton his intense application to study had injured his health. He read American history with the same concentration. Every Indian battle or massacre anywhere in the line of his travels was familiar to him, though he was less interested in the battles of the Revolution.

Much of his teaching was elementary. The objective of education so far as the farmers were concerned was to enable their children to read and write. Much of Wilson's time was spent in drilling the scholars in their ABC's, which they repeated by rote, in chorus, the names of the letters the same as those used a century later, except that the letter Z was then called an izzard.

> The endless round of A, B, C's whole train,
> Repeated o'er ten thousand times in vain

was one of the burdens of his work. Indulgent mothers and fathers, dull idlers, the dark, impenetrable skulls of blockheads, the complaints of parents, and the virtual impossibility of persuading the trustees to repair the schoolhouse, ranked higher in his array of troubles.

Wilson was fortunate in that fine weather began as he started teaching in Milestown. In September of 1796 there were three unbroken weeks of warm clear weather, with enough light showers to keep the air pure. Late in the month the blue-winged teal, the first to arrive from the north, appeared in immense flocks, flying fast, and dropping down suddenly to the ponds and creeks in the marshy ground along the Delaware. Wilson was living in one of the greatest flyways known to man, where the flights of all species converged from the north as the birds moved down the Delaware to their winter grounds in Chesapeake Bay. A tension of excitement gripped the countryside when the flights appeared. The blue-wing was considered one of the finest native birds, excellent eating, a beautiful bird with black head, glossed green and violet, its black back waved with large semi-ovals of brownish white that merged with its blue-tipped wings. Bluewings fed on the seeds of reeds and on wild oats, and were shot in vast numbers as they sunned themselves in the mud on the river-banks, the hunters approaching within twenty yards behind boats.

In October came the Canada goose, the bird that people meant when they spoke of wild geese, the most common in the country. They appeared in huge numbers, flying in heavy and laborious flights, V-shaped or in a straight line, each flight led by an old gander hoarsely honking. They roosted in the marshes, and Wilson found that the local hunters hunted them with tamed geese. These were birds that had been wounded and tamed, and answered the flocks passing overhead. One or two domesticated birds were taken to the marshes, the hunters concealing themselves within gunshot. When a flight was seen, the decoys began calling until the whole flock came within gunshot. It was then sometimes possible for a skilled hunter to discharge three loaded muskets before they moved out of range. A Canada goose weighed from ten to fourteen pounds, and they sold for seventy-five cents to a dollar apiece in the Philadelphia markets, with another twenty-five or thirty cents paid for the half-pound of feathers that each bird yielded.

All the month of October in 1796 was fair, with cool nights and rain on only five days. The first frost appeared late in the month, and the blue-winged teal moved to the south. But in mid-October, in countless flights, came the canvasback, the most prized of all American ducks, the favorite of a whole people, the staple fare at political dinners, anniversaries and celebrations. Canvasback passed over Wilson's schoolhouse in their gigantic migration because they were bound for a stretch of the Delaware below Philadelphia, where their chief food grew in abundance. This was a reed with a root that resembled celery. It was considered responsible for the delicate flavor of the flesh of the canvasback, "unrivalled in this," Wilson wrote, "or perhaps in any other part of the world."

They were hard to hunt, extremely shy, very fast, rising suddenly with a noise like thunder. Their cunning and active vigor accounted for the high price they brought in the markets, for they cost from one to three dollars a pair. They were then hunted around Milestown by a practice known as "tolling them in." Dogs were trained to run forward and backward on the margins of the water. Red cloth was sometimes tied around the animal's middle, or to his tail. The dog's movements decoyed the birds in, perhaps through curiosity; they approached within thirty yards of the gunner, who raked them as they rose. But this form of hunting required highly trained dogs, and it was more common to hunt canvasback by moonlight.

Wilson was thrilled by these magnificent birds, which he was the first to describe and to paint. Only a short distance away, the Neshaminy, which flowed past his schoolhouse, emptied into the Delaware, creating the kind of water that canvasback liked. During the day, canvasback were dispersed about singly. Toward evening they collected in large flocks, and Wilson saw them assembling as he went for his regular exercise after school hours. The birds gathered at the mouth of Neshaminy Creek. He saw them there, "where they often ride," he said, "as if at anchor, with their head under their wing, asleep, there being always sentinels awake, ready to raise an alarm on the least appearance of danger."

Their vigilance was uncanny. When feeding and diving in small parties, they never went down at one time, but left some on the surface as lookouts. Moonlight hunting for canvasback was an unforgettable thrill of American boyhood. The skiff was floated toward the flock, kept within the shadow of the bank, paddled silently and imperceptibly to within fifteen or twenty yards of the thousands of sleeping birds.

But by the time canvasback hunting at night began, new arrivals were coming in—the butterball, the fisherman, the water pheasant, the sprigtail, the laughing goose, the bluebill, the baldpate, the oldwife, and the south-southerly, as it was called, because its cry sounded like those words, and because it was said to betoken a fair wind from the south. These were the local names of birds now known by other names: the butterball was the buffle-headed duck, with black wings and back, and a glossy green velvety head with a crest, famous for the extraordinary velocity of its flight. The fisherman was the goosander, which was also called the water pheasant, but not much eaten because of its fishy taste. The bird that local hunters called the sprigtail was really the pintail, brown-headed with a banded violet neck, very numerous, and excellent food, but shy and fast, and haunting inaccessible fresh-water marshes. Wilson discovered that they could be shot with some advantage only when they clustered confusedly together as they mounted.

The laughing goose was the Milestown name for the snow goose, which streamed down from the north in November in almost endless flights, very noisy, its notes shriller and more squeaking than those of the Canada goose—another bird prized for its taste, snowy white except for the yellowish rust color around the eyes, and its nine quill feathers, black shafted with white. It was the curious bill that led the natives to call it the laughing goose, for there were twenty-three teeth on each side, and the tongue was armed on the sides with teeth like a saw, equipment which the snow goose used for rooting up marshes like a hog, but which gave it a curious grinning appearance that led to its common name. The bluebill was really the scaup, a common bird also found in Europe, not much hunted because of its fishy taste, thick around the Delaware, where it was a moonlight feeder on shellfish.

Wilson found that the bird that the people around Milestown called the baldpate was actually the widgeon, a frequent companion of the canvasback, but differing in that it never dove for its food, but stole the stalks that the canvasback brought to the surface. Wilson became fond of these birds, which he was also the first to picture. They fed in company, with a sentinel on the watch, and Wilson found that they fed little during the day. In the evenings they came out of hiding, and he heard their peculiar cry, almost a whistle, which he found he could easily imitate, and by which they were readily traced. It was then a relatively simple matter to entice them into gunshot range by their own call.

The south-southerly was the bird properly known as the long-tailed duck. Around Milestown, these ducks were also called oldwives. In the winter months they fed in the coastal waters, diving for shellfish, passing to and from the bays in vast flocks, their loud and confused noise audible for miles. The black duck or the dusky duck came in their vast migrations to roost in the marshes in winter, so shy that they rose in prodigious numbers at the sound of a gunshot a great distance away. The brant paused for a few days in their journey from the north, rising in extensive spiral courses, miles in extent, to great height, their hoarse cry like the sound of a pack of hounds in full cry. The summer duck, which Wilson considered the most beautiful of all, came in small flocks of three or four, to rest in ponds and muddy creeks and behind mill dams, their cry a faint peet-peet sound, except for the wild crowing of the sentinel at the first sign of danger, oe-eeh! oe-eeh!

When people spoke of wild ducks they generally meant the mallard. These were already so shy in 1796 that they were hunted with difficulty, usually from skiffs hidden in the reeds, or from hogsheads buried in the mud on shore, with carved decoys anchored a few yards away. But on the Delaware, frames holding as many as ten decoys were sometimes fastened around a skiff, the skiff covered with reeds, and the whole set adrift with the current. And when the first cakes of ice appeared on the river, it was possible to approach a flock of mallard if a hunter concealed himself in a skiff painted white and floated within gunshot with the floating ice.

The favorite duck-hunting grounds in the area were on Duck Island in the Delaware, a long, narrow river island that stretched from Bordentown, New Jersey, to the township of Bristol, within which Milestown lay. Duck Island was wholly owned by Joshua Carman, who also had the shad fisheries on the river, as had his father and grandfather before him. During the Revolution the whole Carman family had hidden on Duck Island, in an improvised shelter concealed under boughs, when the British occupied the countryside. Old Caleb Carman, the patriarch of the clan, was the hero of the famous Battle of the Kegs, in which the Americans set gunpowder-laden rafts adrift against the British fleet anchored in the Delaware. His son John, then only a boy, aided him. John married the village school-

From the painting by Rembrandt Peale

Alexander Wilson

The Tower of Auchinbathie, where Wilson lived, has been destroyed, but Barr Castle, the companion tower at the opposite end of Castle Semple Loch, is still standing.

Falls of the White Cart River in the Seed Hills of Paisley. Wilson's birthplace, to the left of the falls, is now the site of the Anchor Mills.

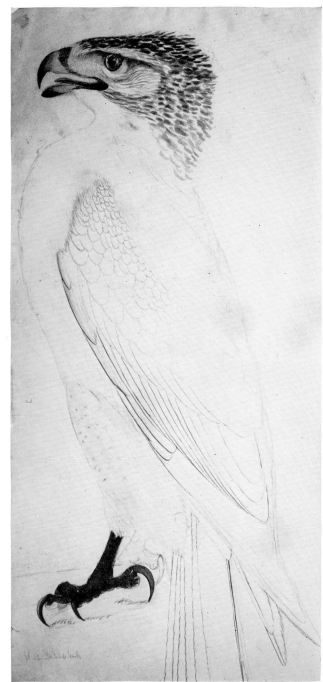

Wilson first sketched owls, like that above, in 1804, when he began his career as a painter of wild life, using a stuffed specimen in his schoolhouse. His extraordinary progress is shown in his rough sketch of a hawk (right), dating from about 1812. *From a collection of Wilson's original drawings in the Museum of Comparative Zoology at Harvard.*

Wilson sketched Niagara Falls (left) during his walking trip in the fall of 1804, and engravings based on his sketches were used to illustrate his poem, *The Foresters*.

A wildly romanticized version of an encounter with a rattlesnake (right), also an illustration for *The Foresters,* contrasted sharply with Wilson's matter-of-fact account of the incident in the poem.

First plate in Wilson's *American Ornithology* was of the blue jay, shown with the goldfinch and Baltimore oriole. Wilson made his own engraving of the jay to see if his project was feasible.

5

Sparrow hawk was pictured with sparrows—"innocent in their habits," Wilson wrote of them, "hopping familiarly about our doors"—in a subtle study of wilderness grays and browns.

Carolina parrot, now extinct, was painted from a pet Wilson captured and tamed on his 1810 journey through the South. Other birds are shy and elusive flycatchers.

Of the ruffed grouse, Wilson in 1812 wrote laconically: "They are pretty hard to kill, and will often carry a large load to the distance of two hundred yards, and drop down dead."

8

Wood ibis (left), which Wilson first saw in the Georgia marshland in 1809 but did not paint until later, with scarlet ibis, flamingo, and white ibis.

Canada goose, largest bird on the plate, was painted with goldeneye and shoveler, left and right above, in flight, and (from left, below) black duck, bufflehead, male and female, tufted duck.

The snow goose (right), whose curious bill led Wilson's neighbors along the Delaware to call it the "laughing goose"; with it are (from left) goosander, male and female, pintail, and blue-winged teal.

Central bird in this plate is the female snow goose; pied duck (extreme left) and hooded merganser (extreme right) were also pictured, with red-breasted merganser (bottom left), widgeon, and scaup duck.

12

Mallard, in flight, and canvasback (second from left, in water), the two most popular waterfowl of Wilson's time, with male and female long-tailed duck, summer duck, green-winged teal, and redheaded duck.

13

Wilson found the gadwall (lower left, in water), then little known, in remote parts of the United States. The eider (above, left, with female, center) was well known in Europe. At extreme right is ruddy duck.

14

Black darters, or snakebirds, male and female (above, left and right), were worked into an intricate design with great northern diver, gull, and little auk.

15

Head of the Pileated Woodpecker size of life.

Head of the Ivory billed Woodpecker size of life.

1. Ivory billed Woodpecker reduced.

2. Pileated W. reduced.

3. Red headed W. drawn by the same scale.

Magnificent ivory-billed woodpecker, with brilliant crest, was twenty inches long. Wilson pictured it life-size, then reduced, with pileated and redheaded woodpecker drawn to the same scale.

teacher across the river from Milestown at Bordentown. His sister Mary married another New Jersey pioneer, John Oliver. There was a network of Oliver and Carman cousins extending all through the countryside, as far south as Great Egg and Little Egg Harbor and Cape May, where Caleb Carman, the founder of the clan, had originally settled, and where his descendants clung tenaciously to the original family holdings, and still dominated the region.

Wilson came to know Joshua Carman, who had inherited the Duck Island property from his father, John Carman, shortly before Wilson came to Milestown. The oldest girl in the Carman family, which had been left fatherless, was Margaret, a dark, shy, and observant girl who was sixteen years old at that time. She was destined to return to Wilson's life in its final years in an extraordinary situation, both for Wilson and for her. But at the time of their first meeting, she could only have been known as the younger sister of the key hunter in the whole countryside. When ducks were honking in the wintery skies there was nobody in the Delaware basin so envied as her brother. The first Philadelphia hunt club built its lodge across the river from where Joshua Carman ruled the whole of Duck Island. He was a hospitable young man, full of information and folklore, and he made Alexander Wilson welcome. But his primary interest was in the shad fisheries on which the family well-being largely depended.

The winter of 1796 was mild until January, with a light snow on Christmas Day, but the new year was wild, cold and stormy, with temperatures of five, ten and thirteen below zero for five days in a row, and two violent snowstorms that blocked transportation. Then the Delaware froze solid. Sleighs ran from Trenton to Philadelphia on the ice all through the next month. The ducks had gone south, though bluebills and baldpates were still commonly seen, and in this frozen world Carman's Duck Island was empty of life of all kinds.

On March 21 the fish hawks appeared. They sailed high in the air, and perched high on the tallest trees, birds whose very presence was supposed to mean good fortune to the farmer whose land they visited. Joshua Carman would not let one be shot on his property. When the fish hawk, or the osprey, to use its real name, suddenly materialized from the south, fishermen knew the shad were running. The birds arrived on the 21st of March no matter what the state of the weather, and regardless of whether the river was free or frozen. If the Delaware was frozen, the ice would break up, and the shad would appear in the immediate future. If the river was clear, the shad would be running only a day behind the arrival of the fish hawks. The birds were broad-winged, noble, fearless, with the unique quality of being savage and beloved. Wilson wrote a poem to them:

> The osprey sails above the Sound,
> The geese are gone, the gulls are flying;
> The herring shoals swarm thick around,
> The nets are launched, the boats are plying. . . .

She brings us fish, she brings us spring,
Good times, fair weather, warmth and plenty,
Fine stores of shad, trout, herring, ling,
Sheeps-head and drum, and old wives dainty.

Yo ho, my hearts! let's seek the deep,
Ply every oar, and clearly wish her
Still as the bending net we sweep,
God bless the Fish Hawk and the Fisher!

CHAPTER FOUR

Exile's Triumph

WHEN WILSON left Scotland he told Crichton confusedly, "I must get out of my mind." In these first months in the New World he had done so, at least in the sense that new interests absorbed him and his old preoccupations had apparently vanished. He was wholeheartedly a republican and a democrat, a wholly uncritical follower of Jefferson, regarding the American Revolution as one of the most remarkable achievements in the history of mankind. His interest in the French Revolution, on the other hand, had largely ebbed with the continuing violence of the Reign of Terror and the warlike policies of the Directory. The feverish tension of the political struggles in Scotland had given way in his mind to a calm confidence in progress which he believed that the American union represented. And in his personal life the ambition that he had placed in his poetry, and the nerve-wracking uncertainty of a weaver's livelihood, had given way to the quiet routine of teaching.

Little by little he was drawn into the life of the community, invited to hunt at Duck Island by Joshua Carman, or asked to a Quaker wedding in the circles of the families of his students. He was now a man of thirty, solitary and quiet, and unaware of how much a stranger and a recluse he seemed to his neighbors. If he did not excite more curiosity, it was because he was by no means the only silent and solitary immigrant then around Philadelphia. He had no contact whatever with the literary society that was growing up in the city around Charles Brockden Brown, though he read its works. He did not criticize them, but he asked why it was that no poet of the wilderness had come into being in this western woodsy region. In Britain there was scarcely a stream that had not been written about, but here there were cataracts that were unnamed and unknown and unsung, and blue wilderness lakes reflecting the sky alone, waiting for the writer who could reflect their glories in verse.

In the spring, teaching became more than ever an ordeal for Wilson, and the outdoors called to him as strongly as to the most restless of his students. In Scotland the woods were quiet, and bird songs relatively rare. Even around farmhouses the evening air was quiet, perhaps a single bird singing in the last rays of the sun, to be answered by another from a different part of the grove, before the long twilight. But in the United States in spring Wilson became aware of a tremendous nation-wide cheeping, twittering, whistling, chattering, rattling and clanging arising from every bush, tree, orchard and field in the country, a chorus that ranged from the clear mellow note of the mockingbird singing its own song, the loveliest in nature, to the melancholy call of the catbird that sounded like the cry of some vagrant orphan kitten bewildered among the briers.

Not only were there more birds in America than Wilson had conceived of—there were more species, more varied and exuberant songs, more dazzling colors. No nation on earth, Wilson felt, could match this rich display of splendid color, the fine shadings of blue of the blue jay, the rich lemon-yellow, the reddish cinnamon of the goldfinch, the orange and lead color of the Baltimore oriole, which the Indians called the fire bird, the rich crimson of the pine grosbeak, with its arrow-shaped spots of black, the marvelous rich vermilion of the summer redbird, the scarlet and jetty black of the scarlet tanager.

Wilson kept birds for pets. At various times he had a jay, a golden-winged woodpecker, an orchard oriole, robins, a pine grosbeak, a redbird, a pair of purple finches, hummingbirds, cardinal grosbeaks, rice buntings, brown thrushes, a sparrow hawk, a scarlet tanager, a Maryland yellowthroat, a house wren, a winter falcon, a mottled owl, and a parakeet in cages in his rooms or in his schoolhouse. But his first acquisitions were unimpressive, a bluejay one of them.

His neighbors had no scientific interest in birds or wild life generally, yet the folklore devoted to both was endless, and every farmer could tell stories of the cleverness of crows or the significance in relation to planting of the migrations in the spring. Wilson's friends were farmers and country merchants. In addition to the Kulp family, there were the Davidsons, who were prominent in the region; the Coryells, the first settlers in the neighborhood of Bristol, who operated the ferry across the Delaware to Trenton; and the Leeches and the Mortons who remained close friends throughout Wilson's life. The most important in Wilson's life, of the Milestown neighbors, were the children of the Miller family. Jacob Miller owned a good deal of property in Milestown as well as in Philadelphia and in Winterton, New York. He was a crusty, somewhat inflexible individual, the father of two sons and five daughters. Sarah Miller, the youngest girl, was sixteen years old at the time Wilson began teaching at Milestown, an heiress, belonging to a family of some social standing, and, like Martha M'Lean in Paisley, occupying a station in life superior to Wilson's own. The Miller home in Philadelphia was on North Second Street, between Arch Street and Race, in a superior residential neighborhood; their Milestown home was a country residence to which they repaired each summer, all Philadelphians since the plague year leaving the city during the hot weather.

When Charles Orr, a Paisley teacher of penmanship who had settled in Philadelphia, sought out Wilson in Milestown and tried to establish friendly relations with him, Wilson did not respond. Alexander Lawson, an engraver, seven years younger than Wilson, born in Lanark, near Paisley, but largely raised in England after the age of sixteen, was another immigrant who made a tentative offer of friendship. Lawson was a big-framed young man, tall and thin, athletic and fond of the outdoors, in temperament apparently ideally suited for companionship with Wilson. But Wilson discouraged Lawson's friendly overtures also.

Wilson broke off contact with potential friends from Scotland, but he hunted with his students and was instrumental in taking boys on their first hunting trips. He bought a horse, and began taking trips into Bucks County north of Milestown, and on to adjoining Northampton County. Then, in his second year at Milestown, his attitude toward the community and his own future suddenly and dramatically changed. He had been content to be known as the solitary schoolmaster, with no life of his own. But he now began almost feverishly to construct a circle of friends. Wilson now overwhelmed Charles Orr with invitations to visit him. Orr was a stiff and somewhat pompous young man, but he was eminently respectable and a gentleman. He taught penmanship in Philadelphia, as he had in Scotland; he was not overly prosperous, but an accomplished teacher in a branch of learning that was then considered an essential to polite society.

When Orr came to Milestown, Wilson made a point of introducing him to his friends. He spoke most warmly of Orr's accomplishments. Wilson asked Orr for small favors that he could easily perform, asking him to secure from Mr. Biggs, an instrument maker of Philadelphia, some material that Wilson needed for constructing a sundial. These tasks Wilson used as occasions for visits or correspondence, and before long a pleasant companionship was built up between the two exiles. Wilson proposed to Orr that they write regularly on philosophy, poetry, politics and kindred matters, to keep themselves in practice and avoid the monotony of teaching. As their correspondence developed, Wilson confided that he was considering marriage.

He dated his letters from "Milestown Monastery," and reported that he was observing the strictest frugality for the future, being absorbed in interesting and secret matters. When he contemplated the luxuriance of nature, the trees in blossom, the birds in pairs, every living thing cheerfully fulfilling the great command to multiply and replenish the earth, "everything I saw seemed to reproach me as an unsocial wretch separated from the great chain of nature, and living only for myself. No endearing female regarded me as her other self, no infant called me its father. I was like a dead tree in the midst of a green forest."

A short time later he wrote:

An old bachelor! . . . and clusters of dimple-cheeked, soft-eyed females in every hut around, and sighing for a husband. We must improve time. . . . We must make advances in one or more of these important duties, which, Mr. Sterne says, devoid of, a human being is undeserving the name of man. That is, write a book, plant a tree, beget a child (I ought to have said marry a wife first), build a house, and learn something every day he did not know before.

Horseback riding, Wilson wrote, was now an unmixed pleasure to him: "I always feel cheerful after it, and can eat confoundedly."

All this was so complete a reversal from his mood of despair after his arrest and the breakup of his love affair with Martha M'Lean that it seemed unreal. And there was a certain unreality, a talked-of, or written-of quality, in Wilson's letters to Orr about his romance. In any event the facetious note ended suddenly.

The second yellow fever plague of 1798 spurred Wilson and Duncan in their plan to buy farmland. They had no savings. Duncan was working as a farm hand. But the dreams of the wilderness held him as it held Wilson, who wrote that he did not know of any more independent life: a farm in the wilderness gradually growing from the woods, the land clearing, a little stock slowly multiplying. When they heard that a tract of land between Cayuga Lake and Seneca Lake in western New York might be within their means, Duncan set out at once.

The distance between the lakes was only 6 miles, and the stretch of land, entirely uninhabited, was 40 miles long. The whole distance, from Philadelphia to the lakes, about 270 miles, was almost unbroken forest. The between-lakes land cost only $5 an acre. Duncan covered the 270 miles in eight days. He spent a week looking over possible sites. When he returned he reported the soil was rich beyond any land he had ever seen, and that deer, bear, turkey and water fowl were abundant beyond belief. He and Wilson decided to buy 150 acres, though a debt of $750, with no farm equipment to begin with, and the land uncleared, was a formidable burden for a twenty-one-year-old weaver and farm worker, as Duncan was, and a thirty-two-year-old schoolteacher earning $10 a month.

Joshua Sullivan loaned them part of the money to get started. Duncan began clearing the land the next spring, while Wilson remained at Milestown, teaching summer school and surveying and doing odd jobs to raise the money to pay for the farm. Their financial problem often became acute. During his second summer in the woods, Duncan urged that they begin distilling. Wilson found that a still would cost about $100, and two would be needed. Moreover the cost of transporting them to the wilderness was a major one. "I doubt if stills could be got up in time to do anything at the distilling business this winter," Wilson wrote. "Perhaps it might be a safer way to take them up, in the spring, by the Susquehanna. But if you are determined, and think we should engage in the business, I shall be able to send them up either way. . . . I want to hear more decisively from you before I determine."

Joshua Sullivan was on his way to western New York to look over his own properties. He visited Duncan, and on his return brought Duncan's instructions for getting the stills to him—briefly, that Wilson should ship the stills to Easton, Pennsylvania, further up the Delaware. Sleds from western New York ran to Easton in the winter with wheat, and often came back to western New York empty, so it would be possible to move the stills cheaply from Easton to a point on the river near where they could be moved to Duncan's farm. Wilson himself could then superintend their transportation the rest of way in the spring, and put them up and begin operations. "I approved his plan," Wilson wrote, "and shall act accordingly."

Now possessed of a large tract of land, though still not paid for, and with a horse of his own and two stills waiting to be put into use, Wilson became more independent in his teaching. At heart he wanted to get away from the schoolhouse and to work with Duncan in the woods, but he feared to do so because the steady income from his teaching alone insured the payments on his land, and Duncan was positive the farm could not yet produce enough to make its own way. In the spring, however, when the question of renewing his contract came up, Wilson was incensed by the attitude of the trustees, and resigned. Wilson had become a favorite with his students. He was responsible, devoted to his task, never drank, and maintained discipline without difficulty. The trustees accordingly retreated, and asked Wilson to reconsider his resignation. Satisfactory terms were reached, and Wilson promised to remain another year.

The political campaign of 1799 likewise increased his confidence, at least enough to end his discreet avoidance of all political disputes. He made speeches for Jefferson and rode about the county in increasing excitement, convinced that only by superhuman efforts could the United States be saved from John Adams' sinister intention of returning it to George III. Wilson wrote a poem, "The Aristocrat's War Whoop," in which Adams and his ilk were pictured boasting that they are going to kick every democratic dog to the devil, and give the country back to England, motivated by their disgust that democrats continue to unmask their thefts and swindles.

Election day, consequently, was an occasion of well-nigh unendurable tension for the schoolmaster, and when he learned of Jefferson's election he wrote another poem. This, he declared, was the long-expected, glorious day, the bright morning after the long night of terror. Now freedom's fabric could be built for millions yet unborn; now no holy bigot's fiery laws would drench our fields in blood; now art, wealth, industry and peace would build great cities where the unbound forest spread:

From Georgia to Lake Champlain,
From seas to Mississippi's shore;
Ye sons of freedom bred proclaim,
The reign of terror is no more.

Observing his deep feelings on the matter, his Milestown neighbors asked Wilson to be the principal speaker at a patriotic meeting on Jefferson's inaugural day. It was not necessary to urge him. His oration showed every sign of having been weighed and pondered with the care given to the Declaration of Independence itself, every phrase radiant with long hours of midnight polishing.

Facing a great crowd, Wilson was conscious of being an alien, and of addressing an audience that contained many veterans of the Revolutionary War. It was one of the greatest events in human history, he began, that a small colony of farmers and woodsmen without a fleet, inexperienced in war, and scattered over an immense country, had defeated a powerful and inveterate opponent, a kingdom of soldiers and seamen, possessing in abundance all the weapons of destruction and provided for every necessity. The concept of liberty brought American soldiers together, created arms, and carried them through every danger to victory and to glory. America had shown that liberty "is a blessed and substantial reality, the great strength and happiness of nations, and the universal and best friend of man."

Carefully distinguishing between liberty and anarchy, and between liberty and a crude equalitarianism, he defined liberty: "the secure protection of persons and property under good and equitable laws—the strict and impartial distribution of justice to all ranks and descriptions of persons—and the free exercise of opinion and religious worship. These constitute true liberty—these are the fountains from whence every blessing flows that renders human life desirable. Nor are they the gifts of man but the birthright of every human being, bestowed on him by his great Creator."

The whole world was watching the fabric of liberty that had been created. "On your success in this grand experiment of representative government, on your established greatness and rising glory, the destinies of mankind, the liberties of the world, are suspended. You have acquired, it is now your great business to preserve and perpetuate to posterity this invaluable treasure. It is, therefore, your deepest interest, as well as duty, to be vigilant and watchful of the prowling enemy of your peace, your prosperity, religion, and happiness. Acquaint yourselves minutely with the true principles of liberty, on which the different state governments, and your great federal compact is founded. . . . Impress these ideas into your children. Cultivate their minds, and enlarge their understanding by education and reading. Set before them in your own persons, examples of firm patriotism and genuine piety. Inure them to habits of industry, economy and virtue, love of country, and gratitude to the Great Giver of all good."

CHAPTER FIVE

Flight and Hiding

❧❧❧❧ ● ❧❧❧❧

WILSON'S SPEECH, characteristically entitled "Oration on the Power and Value of National Liberty," was no mean performance by any standard, and certainly not by the standard of rural speechmaking in his day. Reprinted widely by the Jeffersonian papers, it was later published by Maxwell, a prominent Philadelphia printer. Wilson had become, in a small way, a man of reputation and of standing, and with the promise of a future reaching far beyond his town and his schoolhouse.

But it was the good opinion of Milestown itself that he valued. He remained a boarder at Isaac Kulp's home, and he still walked or rode horseback each morning. He came to know every road and path in the countryside. His trips into Philadelphia were rare, but Charles Orr frequently visited him over the week ends, arriving by the stage which passed through Milestown on its way to New York. Wilson was on cordial terms with the younger generation of Milestown summer residents, with people like young Daniel Miller, the brother of Sarah Miller, who was already established with a business of his own as an iron-monger in Philadelphia, and with Sarah's sister Susannah, who married Nicholas Jones, a bricklayer, the son of a landowner near Gray's Ferry, on the opposite side of Philadelphia from Milestown.

Wilson had, in short, reached a point where he felt confident that he could make his own way without teaching. He resigned, and, as he was determined, refused to reconsider when the trustees asked him to do so. A meeting was held at which he was asked to be present together with the young man chosen as his successor.

Wilson told the trustees that he was fond of his students, and liked the people. But there were many disadvantages. The school building had not been repaired. And it was too small, an important matter to a schoolmaster who was paid according to the number of his students. He was stale with long concentration on his work; if he could ramble around a little, his inspiration might return. The young teacher who was to succeed him inadvertently aided him by revealing he had earned more in the school he left than the Milestown trustees expected to pay. The upshot of the meeting was that Wilson agreed to remain another term.

The trustees agreed to repair and enlarge the school, increased his salary, and extended Wilson's vacation to permit him to ramble around and regain his good spirits.

The decision was costly. On May 1, 1801, Wilson wrote to Orr:

> I have matters to lay before you that have almost distracted me. Do come. I shall be so much obliged. Your friendship and counsel can be of the utmost service to me. I shall not remain here long. It is impossible that I can. I have now no friend but yourself, and *one* whose friendship has involved us both in ruin or threatens to do so. You will find me at the schoolhouse.

Orr found Wilson incoherent. His whole being was obsessed with thoughts of "her who loved me more deeply than her own soul," and who was faced with ruin because of him. But no action was taken by Orr or Wilson at the moment, to avoid contributing to the confusion or the scandal that Wilson was sure was coming. The two friends spent the day together as they had many times previously. Orr then returned to Philadelphia.

At night, secretly, Wilson mounted his horse and rode out of town, never returning. He abandoned all his possessions, taking with him only his greatcoat. He covered his tracks, letting no one individual know his destination, so that no one could communicate with him. He rode first to Wrightstown, about fifteen miles north of Milestown. He stayed there with a friend whose identity he kept so secret that he would not write it to Orr. However, Wilson and Orr had a mutual friend who lived nearby named Archibald Davidson, and Wilson made his presence known to him. He said he was trying to get a teaching post in the local school, but the Quakers who had charge of it could not come to terms.

He then left, without telling Davidson where he was going, again departing suddenly, leaving his greatcoat behind. He had at least planted the idea that there was an intelligible reason for his actions, and that he was trying to find another school, if any question came up. From Wrightstown, Wilson made his way by back roads across New Jersey to New York. He was looking for the Mitchell brothers from Paisley, the radical leaders for whose sake he had taken his punishment in his native city. He had not seen or heard of them for the past four years, and thought of them with a mixture of disgust and hatred. He was dazed, profoundly dejected, and for the first time since his arrival in America let his thoughts turn to going home to Scotland.

In New York Wilson found a hotel within his means, and began inquiring after the Mitchell brothers. James Mitchell, the younger brother, who had signed his peace bond with William Duncan at one of Wilson's arrests, had started a music school in the city. It had only recently closed. Wilson was told that James Mitchell drank to excess, and, as his school ran into difficulties, had gambled heavily. It was said that he constantly went to gambling houses "sometimes taking his students with him." As a result, he lost his reputation and his business. Now he was dodging arrest to avoid going to debtors' prison.

When Wilson eventually found James Mitchell, he gave him no indication of his feeling toward him or his brother, but asked for William Mitchell's whereabouts. James Mitchell could not have suspected how Wilson felt, for he communicated with his brother, and presently William Mitchell and a companion turned up in Wilson's hotel room. Mitchell was drunk. His companion was a street magician—"a hocus-pocus man," Wilson called him— and Mitchell's job was to attract crowds to the performances by playing his clarinet. Mitchell had lost all ambition. He was unkempt, swore constantly, was abandoned to wretched companions, and lost to every good purpose in the world.

Wilson was in so agitated a state of mind that, having sent this information to Orr, he repeated it in another letter a few days later. By that time the doors of debtors' prison had closed on James Mitchell. "I have lost all relish for this country," Wilson wrote,

> and, if Heaven spares me, I shall soon see the shores of old Caledonia. . . . I shall arrange my affairs with Billy [Duncan] as expeditiously as I can. In the meantime I request you, my dear friend, to oblige me in one thing if you wish me well. Go out on Saturday to my niece's [Isabel] and try to get intelligence how Mr. Kulp's family comes on, without letting anyone know you have heard from me. Get all the particulars you can, what is said of me, how Mrs. Kulp is, and every other information, and write me fully. I assure you I am very wretched, and this would give me the greatest satisfaction. Davidson will tell you everything, but mention nothing of me to anybody on any account.

Orr paid particular attention to one sentence in this letter: "Get all the particulars you can, what is said of me. . . ." He sent Wilson a stinging report of the gossip going around Milestown about him. Wilson replied:

> As to the reports circulated in the neighborhood of Milestown, were I alone the subject of them they would never disturb me, but she who loved me dearer than her own soul, whose heart is broken for her friendship to me, she must bear all with not one friend to whom she dare unbosom her sorrows. Of all the events of my life nothing gives me such inexpressible misery as this. O, my dear friend, if you can hear anything of her real situation, and whatever it be disguise nothing from me.

Orr again complied. Wilson had left his trunk with the Kulps, and his greatcoat at Wrightstown. He wanted Orr to get them without revealing that he knew where Wilson was. And Wilson would not put in writing where he had stayed in Wrightstown. He therefore told Orr that he had left his coat with an unidentified party. His friend Davidson knew the name. But Davidson did not know that Wilson had left his coat there. And Wilson was insistent that Davidson should not know that Orr was in Wilson's confidence.

Therefore he, Orr, was to see Davidson. Orr was to give no sign of being in touch with Wilson. He was to inquire of Davidson as if in the hope of being able to locate Wilson.

Davidson would tell Orr where Wilson had stayed in Wrightstown. After learning the identity of the party in Wrightstown, Orr was to write to the person named, who would send him the coat. The fact that Orr knew of the coat would in itself warrant the individual's sending it to him. "I owe him nothing," Wilson commented cryptically.

Orr obeyed orders. But he was tired of Wilson's errands. After much urging, Orr went again to Milestown, and arranged to have Wilson's trunk shipped to Philadelphia and held for him there. With the circumspection that was now characteristic of all his letters, Wilson would not write the name of the Kulps. He told Orr bluntly to "go out to the house where I lodged and request them to bring my trunk to Philadelphia."

On August 7, 1801, three months after the scandal broke, Wilson again wrote to Orr, saying,

> Can you not spare *one* day to oblige me so much? Collect every information you can, but drop not a hint that you know anything of me. If it were possible you could see *her* or any one who *had,* it would be an unspeakable satisfaction to me. My dear Orr, the world is lost for ever to me and I to the world. No time nor distance can ever banish her image from my mind. It is for ever present with me, and my heart is broken with the most melancholy reflections. Whatever you may think of me, my dear friend, do not refuse this favor to know how she is. Were your situation mine, I declare from the bottom of my soul I would hazard everything to oblige you. I leave the management of it to yourself. But do not forget me. . . . Before you write, take a walk up to my niece's as if to inquire for me, and try if you can get any information there. I know that she used sometimes to go and see her. Forgive me, my dear friend, if in anything I have offended you. The more of mankind I see, the more sincerely I value your friendship, and trust it shall only dissolve when time to me shall be no longer.

Wilson's past had caught up with him. He was not altogether unprepared for the disclosure. His elaborate flight, his insistence that Orr go to Milestown and inquire as to his whereabouts, all proved he had anticipated something of the sort. Still more the fact that his own family did not know how to reach him showed how carefully he had prepared to hide out, for they could not be questioned about him. William Duncan could only write to him in care of Duncan M'Inness, a grocer on Chestnut Street, where Orr could pick up his letters and enclose them to Wilson with his own. Wilson himself believed that he could never again live in Philadelphia. The assertion has been made by writers on Alexander Wilson, from Rev. A. B. Grosart to Dr. Elsa Allen, that he had become involved in a love affair with a married woman of Milestown, and was discovered, or feared discovery. The letters of Wilson that have survived virtually say as much, yet they can scarcely be said to provide an explanation for his mysterious conduct on that ground alone. Wilson was concerned about Mrs. Kulp, but in view of his caution in writing any name in his letters, his expressions of anxiety about her meant above all that she could hardly have been the woman in question. In her case he was disturbed by the possibility of gossip about his flight reflecting on her, or by the knowledge that the manner of his leaving would wound her.

The erotic and sensuous notes vanished from Wilson's poetry after the long ordeal of his imprisonment and the painful scenes of his separation from Martha M'Lean. He wrote no love poetry, and his letters did not mention any friendships with women. When he began to write from Milestown to Charles Orr, he mentioned in a rather arch and flustered way an affair of the heart that engaged him, a great disclosure in store, and wrote of his plans to marry—facetiously, to be sure, yet hardly without concrete meaning. Almost immediately thereafter he wrote incoherently of his fears of scandal and exposure, of someone who loved him dearer than her own soul, and of his own hectic flight. It was Thomas Crichton who pointed out that there was something false and unreal about Wilson's communications to Orr. And it is true that the talk of impending marriage sounds strangely remote when along with it Wilson described himself as a dead tree in the green forest, a broken link in the chain of nature.

So while Wilson's letters and his flight do suggest a love affair, they also suggest a romantic debacle, a fiasco, something so humiliating that it was blurred and obscured even in his own thought. Much of his life after his imprisonment might be characterized as dominated by a fear of impotence. After his flight from Milestown he wrote that no human companionship was possible for him, with a poignancy whose origin could only have been in genuine distress. The love of his early years was Martha M'Lean—who most certainly, in Sir Willaim Jardine's phrase, "bore an influence on his despondency"—and in his later years, Sarah Miller, whose father Jacob Miller was a neighbor of Isaac Kulp. Martha M'Lean and Sarah Miller were not unalike: Martha was an intellectual, a literary bluestocking, and an emancipated young woman of a station in life considerably above that of Wilson; Sarah Miller was a daughter of wealth, or of a family that was rapidly progressing from comfortable to wealthy circumstances—and in fact, after Wilson's death, she married Nicholas Rittenhouse, and became connected through the Astors and the Willings with some of the wealthiest families in America. She was a sixteen-year-old girl when Wilson met her, so much younger than he as to be almost of another generation—she was a light-hearted, sympathetic young miss, with fashionable and intellectual interests.

After a long period in which he was in hiding, and saw no one, Wilson again formed contacts with her family, and thereafter until his death his life was always, in some fashion, linked with hers. His final testimony was that she meant more to him than anyone else, and he trusted her more and was more deeply indebted to her than to anyone. Whatever scandal threatened him at the time of his flight, it had not been of such nature as to separate him permanently from her family, or from her. Yet the care with which he concealed his movements when he left indicated a genuine hazard. And to add to the mystery, his life later became involved with that of another young woman living nearby at the time of his flight. This was Margaret Carman, whose brother owned Duck Island, and who reappeared in Wilson's life as he began to be known. She was the most enigmatic of the girls who appeared and vanished in Wilson's story—one certainly on the scene at two of the great crises of his life, though these were separated by many years, and certainly possessed of considerable knowledge of Wilson and his friends.

Whatever the precise occasion for his flight, Wilson never returned to Milestown. He came to be on intimate terms with both Sarah Miller and Margaret Carman, and with other Milestown citizens as well, but he would not go back to the town itself. He lived quietly in New York City, and, in the fall of 1801, when he began teaching in Bloomfield, New Jersey, he let the story be spread in Milestown that he was in New York. His school was in a hundred-year-old log cabin, on a sandy plain sparsely covered with grass. He received a shilling a week from each of his thirty-five students. He paid twenty shillings a week for board, laundry, and the care of his horse.

He was profoundly discouraged, unable to force himself to rebuild in another and poorer community the type of life he had created for himself, with infinite pains, in Milestown. He did feel a brief revival of his interest in natural history at the vast salt marshes of New Jersey, and noted the discovery of the bones of a mammoth in an excavation being dug for a new paper mill. And he wrote a satirical poem, "My Landlady's Nose," which was printed in the Newark *Centinel,* and followed it with another, scarcely more felicitous, on a schoolmaster's hard life.

He found a friend in Bloomfield, though he did not mention him in his frequent letters to Orr. James Gibbs, an artist and a teacher, was born in Paisley. He had married a Lydia Ward, and now, aged twenty-six, was beginning a quiet and respectable career in Bloomfield where he and his wife remained throughout their lives, and were both buried in the local cemetery. Gibbs was the only person in the town for whom Wilson felt any regard, or even much human interest. He left one other note of his presence there, for he lost a pocketbook containing his poems on the road from Newark to Bloomfield, and published a notice in the *Centinel,* asking that the finder leave the poems in a Newark barbershop.

This was the gloomiest period that Wilson had experienced since he came to the United States, and his state of mind was akin to the dark melancholy he had known in Scotland. At mid-term he gave up his school and returned to Philadelphia. Wilson was surprised to find Orr reserved and distant. He was alarmed also, for he had unburdened himself too freely to Orr to permit him to become an enemy. He wrote that he understood that certain people (unnamed in his letter) had given Orr an unfavorable account of him. He would not try to answer his detractors. He said he would be as indifferent if they had spoken well of him. The difference with Orr became a quarrel. Wilson wrote him a formal note asking Orr to "banish all suspicions of disesteem. I entertain none."

Whatever Orr's connections were with Paisley, he did not intend to be publicly associated with Wilson. Wilson confessed that he had no longer any hope of prospering in America, and suggested that he and Orr go back to Scotland together. Orr did not respond to this. Wilson then suggested they start a school in America together. He would sell his horse to provide his share of the capital. Orr retreated into formality and evasion.

V

The Hawk and the Oriole

Amusement blended with instruction, the correction of numerous errors that have been introduced into this part of the natural history of our country, and a wish to draw the attention of my fellow-citizens, occasionally, from the discordant jarrings of politics, to a contemplation of the grandeur, harmony and wonderful variety of Nature, exhibited in this beautiful portion of the animal creation, have been my principal, and, I might say, almost my only motives in the present undertaking.

—Alexander Wilson: Introduction to the
American Ornithology

The humming birds and orioles fly by me as I write.
—Emily Dickinson, May 21, 1883

CHAPTER ONE

Wilderness Vision

꙳꙳꙳ ● ꙳꙳꙳

THE TEACHER of a school beyond Gray's Ferry, across the Schuylkill from Philadelphia, was a fat old sea captain of an educator, constantly and ineffectually bawling out orders to his students. On an emergency basis, the school was offered to Wilson, who was living in seclusion in Philadelphia.

Wilson was suspicious and uneasy. Ten months before he had vanished from Milestown at night, like a thief, or like a highly trained conspirator. He considered himself disgraced, or, if that conviction had ebbed, he now considered himself a failure in life at everything he had ever undertaken.

He visited the school, and conferred with the trustees. The Union School of Kingsessing stood beside the main highway leading south from Philadelphia, one of the busiest thoroughfares in America. Leaving downtown Philadelphia, travelers passed along Market Street, with nearly a mile of roofed markets in the middle of the street, the traffic passing on both sides. At Ninth Street the mellow brick houses and paved sidewalks gave way to fields and rail fences. The streetlights, three to a pole, ended at Ninth Street. Beyond lay ten acres of nurseries and greenhouses, the first seed garden in America, and then the eastern landing of Gray's Ferry. Beyond Gray's Ferry was Gray's Garden, a fashionable restaurant, with an exotic garden behind it. Beyond Gray's Lane and Bartram's Lane there stood a row of frame houses hastily erected during the plague, then an ancient Swedish church—for this part of the country had been settled by the Swedes long before William Penn arrived—and Bartram's Garden, with a collection of botanical specimens from the forests of eastern America.

The countryside was noted for its famous taverns, like the Rose Tree, the Blue Bell, and the Rising Sun. Directly across the road from Wilson's school was one of the more famous, the Sorrel Horse Inn, with a blacksmith shop beside it. A row of poplars screened the schoolyard from the road. The school grounds were large, and covered with a lawn, with old oaks and cedars providing shade. The school building was a square stone structure that looked uncomfortably like a jail, a resemblance that could not have failed to impress Wilson, after his own prison experiences and in the psychic solitary confinement in which he lived.

It was on a Thursday, February 25, 1802, that Wilson agreed to take the school. He visited the classes in session, and noted with dismal foreboding that the students paid no more attention to the teacher's shouted orders "than ducks do to a stream under them." Over the week end he moved his possessions, including the trunk which had caused so much conspiratorial activity after he left Milestown. And on Monday, March 1, 1802, his first day of teaching, he went to his classes with the air of a condemned man mounting the scaffold.

But the move turned out to be a happy one. Wilson read, worked on some poems, and tried to forget the girl in Milestown whose life had become entangled with his own. His students were American boys and girls, not primarily from Pennsylvania Dutch families, and teaching was easier. His salary was $100 a quarter, far more than he had ever earned, and he was promised there would not be more than fifty pupils. His boarding house was friendly. He lived with the family of William Jones, a famous character in Philadelphia, a gigantic man, six feet six inches tall. The home was a big yellow-fronted farmhouse, poplars, catalpas and willows shielding it from the road, rosebushes growing in the front yard, and plum trees and honeysuckle beside the house. Jones's son Nicholas, as mentioned earlier, became the husband of Susannah Miller, the sister of Sarah and Daniel.

After Wilson was established in his school, Orr replied to his peace-making letter with a long explanation. Wilson then wrote back, "It is too much. I cannot part with you after what you have said. I renounce with pleasure every harsh thought I hastily entertained of you. From this moment let all past grievances be eternally forgotten." Their relationship settled into a curious pattern in which Wilson spent his Sundays, after Orr had promised to visit him, waiting for Orr who never appeared. Letters and explanations followed. The next week Wilson again walked down to the bank of the Schuylkill to greet his old friend. But something else had happened. Wilson was undisturbed by these broken engagements. He wrote to Orr that he no longer had a single friend, but it no longer mattered: "No friend on earth can remove my source of misery." Friendship with him only distressed the people who became friendly with him. Wilson did not fear any mysterious influence poisoning his relations with the people in his new surroundings; if every human contact that he formed was to be destroyed, he would form no more. And he bore Orr no bitterness. He wrote a poem, "The Invitation," addressed to him, a fulsome description of rural joys, urging Orr to pay him an extended visit and comparing the simplicity of country life to city trials—a poem eventually published in the literary magazine Charles Brockden Brown had started. But Orr did not visit him. He went back to Scotland. "He has never written to me," Wilson wrote to his father, "so I have no idea where he is, or whether he be alive or dead."

Streams ran on both sides of the house where Wilson lived. They bubbled through a vale into laurel thickets, and a silent oak woods. The water slept in a deep pool, overhung by a dark brown cliff. On its crest Wilson rested each morning and evening. He read Milton, Goldsmith, and Bruce, the Abyssinian traveler who lived near his old home in Paisley. He slept or dozed, or watched the sunlight checkering the leaves of the beech branches overhead. He noted how woodbines had made their way through every chink in the cliff, and how the roots of the beeches twisted around the rocks, the shape of the columbine flowers and elderberry bushes, and the glossiness of the leaves of the laurel.

The thicket was alive with birds. They were more brilliantly colored than wild flowers. Wilson's great work had its origin in those solitary hours. Perhaps a third of all the data in his nine volumes lay directly before his eyes in this glade a stone's throw from his house, and within walking distance of the city. The simplest natural phenomenon inspired him. Owls screeched and hooted all night, the cardinal sang its tremulous notes in the first light of dawn, the great belted kingfisher uttered its hoarse metallic shout as it dove over the rivers, and woodpeckers began pounding on trees and fences. The song of the robin, distinguished by zeal rather than talent, rose as the day warmed, and the chorus swelled with the songs of the goldfinch and bluebird, the chat, redstart, pine creeper, indigo bird, and a vast assemblage of nuthatches, uttering their peculiar *quank-quank* sound as they traveled upside down on the trunks of trees. In the hot afternoons when all other birds were silent there were still the soft indolent notes of the flycatcher, and the strong sonorous whistle of redbirds. Twilight fell, and millions of swallows swarmed around every village and farm in the country. Wilson watched them and tried to calculate how far each bird flew in its brief life. The darkness grew deeper, and whippoorwills began their mysterious calls, and the wild yelling of owls—"hoolats" to the Scottish people—broke from what Wilson called "these grave and antiquated wanderers of the night."

Wilson had reached a point where everything he had tried to do had failed, involving the people he loved in his ruin, and he could no longer endure the collisions and shocks of ordinary social life. He was a spiritual convalescent as he lay on the moss above the pool, drained of any emotional life, exhausted and beaten—or, in the simple and old-fashioned phrase of the time, heartbroken. His thoughts continually went back to his early years, gray Scottish mountains, wonder about his parents' lives and their plans for him, puzzlement as to what had made him the kind of person he had become. And in his imaginative inertia and torpor, from his almost passionate loneliness, the wild life of this tiny fragment of wilderness before his eyes grew into a concept of the life work he might yet do.

Not only birds, but the wilderness itself inspired Wilson's work. He wrote that the old gray rocks overhanging the stream, the nodding flowers, the plants, birds and insects, had become intellectual feasts for him, however obscure, deformed, minute or huge they seemed. How many birds were there? Where did they come from? At one moment the woods were nearly deserted; at the next birds were everywhere, diving and vociferating, pursuing and playing, singing and flying with an intelligence more than human. Orioles, jays, goldfinches, nuthatches, thrushes, buntings, larks, yellowthroats, grosbeaks, creepers, hummingbirds and countless others, unknown and unnamed, filtered through the leaves, a fragment of the original wildness of America, elusive and brilliant, diffusing a peculiar radiance in its intangible and constantly shifting pattern of vivid and vibrant life. The weather determined the time of their arrival, yet not always, for sometimes the birds arrived in advance of the outward signs of spring. When the woods were far advanced early in April there were still no summer birds; but when spring was late, they were present in numbers, though there might be scarcely an expanded leaf to conceal them. Some individuals of some species flew ahead of their mysterious schedules, or, as was the case with the towhee bunting, the males arrived well in advance of the females. At one moment, even though vegetation was advanced, there were few birds, at the next the woods abounded with nesting wrens, orioles, warblers, robins, catbirds, flycatchers, sparrows, pewits, yellow-breasted chats and purple grackles, as well as jays, hummingbirds and scarlet tanagers.

Goldfinches came in February, and robins in March, the prelude to the grand general concert about to burst from the woods, field and thickets, whitened with blossoms and breathing fragrance. The dusky brown wood thrush arrived about April 20, its clear, bell-like song heard in the low, thick-shaded hollows beside streams, or in elder bushes mantled with wild vines. Evenings in April were made audible by the hammering of golden-winged woodpeckers, building their nests, so intent on this employment, as Wilson said, "they may be heard till a very late hour in the evening, thumping like carpenters." After mid-April the weather grew pleasant and warm, and hummingbirds arrived about April 25, darting and circling, their wings invisible, or only like a mist, the males teasing kingbirds and fleeing from bumblebees, and quarreling and battling around tulip trees and larkspurs, and over their favorite flower, the yellow *Balsamina noli me tangere*.

The ruby-crowned wren appeared with the apple blossoms in April. The yellowthroat could be found living in peace and obscurity in its favorite thickets in the middle or the last week of the month. Baltimore orioles were in the weeping willows, or the walnut and tulip trees in May, and in the first week of that month the orchard orioles arrived. They built their nests in the suspended twigs of apple trees, using a particular species of long, tough, flexible grass. This they knit through and through, in a thousand directions, as if the work had actually been done with a needle. Wilson found in examining a nest that a single thirteen-inch fiber had been hooked thirty-four times by the bird, which wound it around and around with an ingenuity that Wilson, as a professional weaver, could only admire.

In forty days the feathered invasion was complete. Its laws were absolute. When the pewit flycatcher appeared, it was safe to plant peas in the open ground. There would be no more frost. The farmers knew this, just as the fishermen knew that when the first fish hawk was seen over Duck Island in the Delaware, its great arched wings bowed in motionless flight, the shad run on the river would begin in a few days. These matters were not speculation or folklore. They were elemental truths of nature, helping to guide the people in taking their livelihood from the earth. There was an almanac of nature, independent of the division of the year into days and months, a continental calendar, based upon terrestrial patterns formed before the land was settled, fragments of the world that had existed before the coming of the white man.

One evening in Wilson's woodland retreat he heard a bird he had never heard before singing with thrilling intensity, a few clear, musical notes, repeated over and over. The bird was the size of a jay or a wren, dusky brown, of a pale, almost transparent flesh color, singing in a large oak tree. He listened until the night began to gather in the woods and the fireflies to sparkle among the branches. Later he heard its bell-like song very often, rising at the earliest dawn, and he found that there was rivalry among different birds of the same species, one striving to outsing another, and that the voice varied with individuals. They were mute in the heat of the day, but sang again in the evening until after sunset, and could be heard in the dripping woods after rain. It was a bird that frequented low, thick-shaded hollows, and after inquiring about it, Wilson at length concluded the bird was one called the wood thrush, known and recognized for its song, but rarely seen in those days though subsequently it became used to civilization and familiar around towns and farms. The song of the thrush ceased, and Wilson thought the bird had moved on; but then he found fragments of the wings and broken feathers of a wood thrush that had been killed by a hawk, and concluded that a hawk had plunged into the thicket after the bird. These were the fragments of the vision of the wilderness that inspired his work. He began his study passively, enjoying the varied and colorful scene before him.

Wilson could not, however, remain a passive spectator and a philosopher, for the same social force that had moved him in Scotland in his days as a peddler now operated again— the need of his sister's family. In the summer of 1802, when his school was out, he received word that William Duncan was coming to America, as the first step in bringing his family over. Duncan was to arrive in July, and would go directly to the farm in New York State where young Duncan was clearing land, and putting in his first crops. Mary and the children would follow later. Wilson visited the farm that summer to carry the news to young Duncan, and to help prepare for the arrival of the family. The farm was near the present town of Ovid, New York. The route lay through Bucks County to Easton, at the junction of the Lehigh and Delaware Rivers, a two-day walk. Beyond Easton the trail led through wilderness all the way, with stops at hunters' cabins, or an occasional forest inn, almost a week up the Susquehanna to a point near the New York State boundary, from which flatboats set out each spring to take the year's accumulated produce down the river to market. Here Wilson pushed north across an open plain, the watershed between the St. Lawrence and the Chesapeake, to the lower end of Lake Cayuga, from which another day's walking through wild and swampy forest took him to the farm.

The house was only a hut in the woods. But Duncan had cleared a good deal of land, and put it in wheat, and expected a good crop. Wilson hunted on the way to the farm, and the trip restored his ambition: he began to make notes for a book of wilderness poems based upon it. He was still in the lake country in July, but the elder Duncan did not arrive. The summer waned, and he did not appear. Back at Gray's Ferry to open his school, Wilson found his sister Mary and six children, the youngest her first grandchild. Duncan had gotten as far as Belfast, and there he remained. He drank up his passage money, and when last heard of was living "with guilt, poverty and infamy," as Wilson wrote bitterly to his father. The consciousness of Duncan's betrayal grew slowly on his family. He had literally rid himself of them all by starting ahead of them, and doubling back from Ireland, while they continued to America. And as far as he was concerned, they were left in a foreign land to perish—he had no intention of going to the United States.

Together with his niece Isabel, Wilson got Mary and her children to the farm before the winter closed in. He then returned to Gray's Ferry to his school.

Tragedy struck almost at once. George Duncan, Mary's younger son, left the farm and set out on his own. Three weeks later he was dead of fever in Norfolk, Virginia. Some time passed before the family knew of his death. Then there was no indication of how he had died, or where he was buried.

Young William Duncan wanted to come to Philadelphia at once and get some kind of cash income as a weaver. Wilson said the problem was to keep the family together through the winter. Mary was dismayed at the hut in the woods, and by her own lack of health and the collapse of her family hopes. Wilson begged Duncan to stay on the farm, to put in a fireplace at once and make the house secure, building the fireplace himself if he could not find a mason. If he spent time looking for work, he could not earn as much, with the cost of his board, as he earned on the farm.

Meanwhile he urged Duncan to teach the younger children. "Be the constant friend and counsellor of your little colony. . . . Do everything possible to make your house comfortable—fortify the garrison at every point—stop every crevice that may be in that chilling devil, the roaring, blustering northwest—heap up fires big enough for an Indian war-feast—make the loom thunder and the pot boil; and your snug little cabin re-echo nothing but sounds of domestic felicity."

Wilson himself added night-school classes through the winter to add to his earnings and support Mary's family. When the sleds went down to Easton in December, Duncan had only a hundred bushels of wheat to send to market; he was in despair. But the account of this family's titanic struggle to remain together had impressed people. Joshua Sullivan made a trip to the lake country and returned filled with pride at the way young Duncan had taken hold of things. A family from Scotland, the Purdys, with children the age of the Duncan children, arrived unexpectedly from Paisley. "The two Purdies popped into my school this afternoon," Wilson wrote to Duncan on December 23, 1802, "as unexpected as they were welcome." The Purdys settled near Duncan's farm, the children intermarried, and subsequently became prosperous farmers in Michigan. Young Duncan became a good teacher in educating his brothers and sisters.

Wilson wrote constantly to his sister Mary, to Duncan, and to the younger children in an effort to keep their spirits up. Alexander, the second son, then sixteen, was already a weaver, and wanted to search for work. However, he could barely read and write, and Wilson wanted him to be educated. "Accustom yourself, as much as you can, to working out,"

Wilson wrote to Alexander. "Don't despise hagging down trees. It is hard work, no doubt; but taken moderately it strengthens the whole sinews, and is a manly and independent employment. An old weaver is a poor, emaciated, helpless being, shivering over rotten yarn, and groaning over his empty flour barrel. . . . But perhaps weaving holds out advantages that farming does not. Then blend the two together; weave in the depths of winter, and work out the rest of the year. We will have it in our power, before next winter, to have a shop, looms, etc., provided. Consider all I have said, and if I have a wrong view of the subject, form your own plans and write me without delay. . . ."

"I seem to gain in the esteem of the people about," Wilson wrote in mild surprise to Duncan.

CHAPTER TWO

The Predators

WILSON'S NEIGHBORS were generally substantial citizens. Down the river was Woodlands, the estate of William Hamilton, an aristocrat who had been accused of treason during the Revolution, and who lived in lordly isolation, building up his botanical garden, where he planted the first Lombardy poplars and ginkgo trees imported to America. In the opposite direction were the farms of the Gibson family, rich Quakers, and the home of General Muhlenberg was just across the river. But Bartram's Garden contained the most influential of Wilson's neighbors. It had become one of the intellectual centers of the nation. John Bartram bought the land at a tax sale in 1728, built a stone house with his own hands, and began to study botany from his interest in the unknown wild plants of America. Called by Linnaeus the greatest natural botanist in the world, Bartram freely provided specimens of American plants to naturalists all over Europe, traveling to the Gulf of Mexico, to the headwaters of the James River, and to the Great Lakes and the Catskills, his last journey a walking trip through Georgia and Florida at the age of seventy. The cypresses that he planted in his early years grew to great height; the pear trees sent to him by the brilliant English naturalist, Lord Petre, became renowned; exotic Oriental plants given him by Peter Collinson, an English merchant, were still growing; and trumpet vines from North Carolina, tulip trees, silver-bell trees, azaleas, and the cucumber tree which Bartram himself discovered were features that attracted almost every foreign visitor to his acres. John Bartram had been appointed royal botanist by King George II, and at his death during the Revolution, as the British were advancing on Philadelphia, he was principally concerned lest the soldiers destroy his gardens as they passed through. But the British spared them. The management of the gardens passed to Bartram's younger son William, the companion of his exploring trips, and the author of *Travels*.

At the time Wilson moved to Gray's Ferry, William Bartram was sixty-three years old. His wife had died, and he was cared for by his niece Nancy Bartram. A friend of Thomas Jefferson, William Bartram had inherited much of his father's genius, though he possessed a certain literary quality in place of his father's transparent honesty and his quaintly guileless poetic prose. Wilson came to haunt Bartram's Garden, as did the Philadelphia intellectuals generally, but almost two years passed before he was on anything like close terms with Bartram himself. Wilson merely wandered through what he called Bartram's woods as through all the woods around. His hesitancy in approaching Bartram revealed his uneasiness. His school and family matters occupied Wilson throughout 1802, yet in the summer of 1803 his project for his great work was already clear in his mind. On June 1, 1803, he wrote to Thomas Crichton in Paisley that he was beginning his work of drawing "all the finest birds of America." But years passed before he told Bartram what he meant to do.

Wilson principally practiced sketching a small brown owl, which he had shot, stuffed, and mounted on a miniature stump, keeping it on his desk. Among the early scraps of his drawings, this item has been preserved: it is an awesome-appearing creature with a huge head, beady eyes, and stiff feathers projecting out like an Indian's headdress. "I declare the face of an owl, and the back of a lark, have put me to a nonplus," Wilson wrote. Another problem was the breast feathers. Wilson drew his birds in profile. When he drew the line from the throat, the soft down of the bird vanished in a hard outline; it looked like a bird wearing armor. When he looked at a bird, no line was visible there, the tiny feathers shading away without a break. He tried to get around the difficulty by making tiny dots to represent each feather in the profile, but the result was merely an unfinished-looking piece of work, as if the bird had feathers on its back and tail, and speckles over the rest of it.

Word of Wilson's interest in birds had spread through the community, and in the summer of 1803 a nest of young hummingbirds was brought to him, the young nearly ready to fly. He kept them in his room at the Jones farmhouse. Each morning Wilson gave the hummingbirds fresh flowers on which he had sprinkled water in which sugar had been dissolved. A caged hummingbird was a rarity, and "numbers of people visited it from motives of curiosity." After three months the bird had grown so accustomed to its quarters that Wilson decided to try to keep it through the winter. He had not yet reached he point where he could paint anything so evanescent as a hummingbird, but his interest in the subject gave him a point of contact with the artist Charles Willson Peale and with Bartram himself. Peale started Peale's Museum with models built by a gifted clockmaker, Robert Leslie, who died before he could launch his institution. Peale told Wilson that hummingbirds could be tamed: he had once raised two from the nest, and they became so familiar that they perched on Mrs. Peale's shoulder to be fed.

Both Peale and Bartram encouraged Wilson's interest at a crucial stage in his life, though both, at this time, merely extended the natural courtesy of established figures in their field to an intelligent newcomer. The circles of scientists in Philadelphia were stirred by much more momentous developments, and the Scottish immigrants were even more aroused by current developments. James Thompson Callender was the most famous of the ten editors imprisoned under the Alien and Sedition Act. Driven out of Philadelphia, Callender started the Richmond *Recorder,* which soon had a national reputation because of its sensational attacks on Washington, Jay, Hamilton and Adams. The immediate cause of Callender's arrest was his publication of an unsupported charge that President Adams was a murderer. The Sedition Act prohibited the publication of false statements designed to arouse the hatred of the good people of the United States against the President, Congress, or the government. Callender was defended by almost every outstanding lawyer in Virginia, the Jeffersonians having taken the position that the Alien and Sedition Law was unconstitutional. Callender was fined $200, and sentenced to jail, but, as his conviction came shortly before Jefferson's election, he served only a short time.

On gaining his freedom, Callender went at once to the White House, and demanded that Jefferson appoint him Postmaster at Richmond. Jefferson refused. Callender then turned upon Jefferson, who had supported him and given him considerable money almost from the time of his arrival in the United States from Scotland. "The private life of Mr. Jefferson, present and past, was the subject of the closest scrutiny," wrote Callender's biographer, "and whenever he was believed to be vulnerable, no matter for what cause, or upon what evidence, he was unhesitatingly assailed in the grossest and most offensive way."

When Jefferson became President, he appointed Meriwether Lewis, a distant kinsman, his confidential secretary. After serving in the Whisky Rebellion, Lewis entered the regular army, served on the frontier, and became a paymaster—really an intelligence officer—generally stationed at Pittsburgh, but also commanding at Fort Pickering, where Memphis now stands, in 1797, when he was only twenty-two years old. His first important duty as Jefferson's secretary was to silence Callender. Lewis carried to Callender some sort of deal from Jefferson, who had told his Cabinet officers that they were free to act against Callender, that Callender possessed no blackmailing material, and who was disappointed that these Cabinet officers did nothing. Lewis was surprised to find that Callender adopted a superior attitude. He said he had damaging information against Jefferson, and implied that the money which Jefferson had been paying him for the past decade was hush money.

Callender continued his newspaper campaign against Jefferson, though he was now universally detested and his influence was declining, and Lewis' effort in Jefferson's behalf failed. Mrs. John Adams wrote to Jefferson to ask him if he still wished to defend Callender in his freedom to make attacks against him like those which Callender had made against her husband. Jefferson replied at great length, with a long and less than accurate account of his relations with Callender, still maintaining he had assisted him only because he was a penniless refugee from British tyranny, and ending with the observation that Callender's ingratitude represented "human nature in the blackest form."

Now, in the summer of 1803, Meriwether Lewis was given a more congenial assignment by the President, and sent to Philadelphia for intensive study to prepare for an expedition to the Pacific. Meriwether Lewis studied botany under Dr. Benjamin Smith Barton, who conducted his spring classes of the University of Pennsylvania students in the gardens of Woodlands. At Lancaster, Pennsylvania, where the guns to be used on the expedition were manufactured under Lewis' supervision, the explorer studied under Andrew Ellicott. Lewis became acquainted with the scientists and literary men of Philedalphia in these months, returning there when he came back from the Pacific in triumph. There is no indication that he knew Wilson during his first Philadelphia visit, although a meeting, in view of their common friends and interests, was not unlikely, but he and Wilson became close friends after his return. Whatever that date of their meeting, the shy, black-haired and dark-eyed explorer made a more profound impression on Wilson than he recorded of anyone else. Both Wilson and Lewis became frequent visitors at the home of the engraver Alexander Lawson, who built up a circle of artists and scientific figures around him. Malvina Lawson, the engraver's daughter, was a young girl at the time of these gatherings, and in her old age noted in her recollections that Lewis and Wilson were temperamentally alike, Lewis notably silent and observant in company. Wilson she remembered as taller, and added that though she was then only a child, "I remember perfectly his brilliant eye, and hair as black as an Indian's, and as straight."

In June of 1803 Meriwether Lewis completed all the study he had time for, and left Philadelphia. He did not start work on the expedition until the fall. In July, James Thompson Callender was found drowned in three feet of water in the James River in Richmond. The coroner's jury in Richmond returned a verdict of accidental death, saying Callender had apparently tried to go swimming at three o'clock in the morning while intoxicated.

Callender and Wilson were of the same generation, came from the same region, and were both, in their early careers, poets and radical or revolutionary writers. Callender was educated, as Wilson was not, and his family name was an important one in Scotland, but both began their careers in hard conditions of financial need. Callender was a blackmailer; Wilson was jailed and convicted on charges of blackmail. Both were men of genius. Callender possessed an amazingly clairvoyant political insight into the weaknesses of democracy that carried with it a kind of moral obligation on his part to proceed with inflexible destructiveness through the weaknesses he perceived. Wilson possessed a lightning intuitive sense of the kind of contribution to democratic culture that needed to be made, coupled with a simple humility and an elemental practicality, in carrying through his own contribution to the limit of his powers.

The genuine resemblance between them ended with their common possession of uncommon gifts. Callender in Scotland was instrumental in wrecking the careers of James Anderson and Lord Gardenstone, two of the distinguished reformers of his time, and in helping destroy the Scottish reform movement that was the most promising political development in the modern history of the country. He was responsible for introducing yellow journalism into American cultural life. The Alien Law that roused Jefferson to fury was personally directed at Callender. His trial was the cause of the impeachment of Justice Chase, with its consequent antagonism and suspicion between Congress and the Judiciary. Almost Callender's only failure, in the objectives of destruction he set for himself, was his effort to divide Hamilton and Washington.

No doubt Callender's biographer was right in saying no man in American history is less deserving of sympathy than Callender. Yet it was impossible to read his letters to Madison and Jefferson and not feel a measure of sympathy for him. Callender knew that he possessed capacities for greatness—or at least for some place in the world where his energy could be spent to some better purpose than the half-sinister, half-pitiful requests for money that largely filled his prose. When the Hamilton scandal drove him out of Philadelphia, Callender wrote to Madison saying his mistake from the start had been to live in the city, that he should have taught in a country school a few miles in the outskirts, and he begged Madison to help him find such a school. (Madison did not help him.) There was a paradoxical didactic strain in Callender, and it was odd that next to Hamilton the principal target of his most ferocious attacks was Noah Webster, the author of the dictionary, who was trying to codify distinctly American usage and speech as opposed to the King's English.

Callender was sometimes said to have lacked elementary human sympathies. Yet this was not altogether borne out by his letters. He left Philadelphia shortly before the second great yellow fever plague of 1798, and lived in seclusion in Virginia, but he constantly expressed to Jefferson his concern about his wife and children who remained in the city. And that he was not altogether worthless was indicated by the fact that his family became respected and prominent. His son settled in Nashville, Tennessee, and his grandson, an eminent physician, became superintendent of the state insane asylum, and the president of the national association of asylum superintendents, one of the important witnesses on the sanity of Giteau, the murderer of President Garfield. As destructive as Callender's career was, he could not have carried out his appalling projects had the conditions not existed that gave him leverage, and the very power he revealed had the effect of tightening the American social fabric. Even more, the hatred Callender aroused led the Scottish immigrants and refugees to action to dissociate themselves from him. They did not want Callender to be the representative of their race in the new world.

CHAPTER THREE

In the Forest

✦

WILSON had begun to build up a circle of friends, almost against his will. Horace Binney, a famous Philadelphia lawyer, was a young man when Wilson was an occasional visitor to the city; he said that Wilson was really held in great esteem for his probity, gentle manners and accomplishments. Binney described Wilson's appearance as "not decidedly Scotch, but still with a cast of it, more like a Congregational minister in his black dress than any other description I can give."

In the fall of 1803 Wilson attended the wedding of Jemima Walters and James Morton, who was from his old neighborhod of Milestown—the Morton home was in Bristol. Following the Quaker custom, all the guests signed as witnesses of the ceremony, and the list was revealing of Wilson's associates and acquaintances and friends in the Philadelphia of that time—Walns, Drinkers, Fishers, Evanses, Rowans, Biddles, and many others of the prominent families of the city. James Morton, the bridegroom, was the son of a Philadelphia merchant who became a lifelong friend of Wilson. Wilson was partially led to such company also through his friendship with his landlord, William Jones, who was also a wedding guest.

A few days after the wedding of Jemima Walters and James Morton, Wilson was discouraged to find that his pet hummingbird had somehow gotten out of its gauze enclosure, and, in flying about the room, had struck the walls and so injured itself that it died. He had already started intensive work sketching and painting in preparation for his books, and had made quite a point of his success at raising the hummingbird in captivity. His first letters to Bartram that have been preserved are notes asking the naturalist to correct sketches he had made of shrubs, plants and birds. "I have attempted two of those prints which Miss Nancy, so obligingly and with so much honor to her own taste, selected for me," he wrote to Bartram on November 20, 1803. "I am quite delighted with the anemone, but fear I have made but bungling work of it. Such as they are, I send them for your inspection and opinion; neither of them is quite finished. . . . The duties of my profession will not admit me to apply to this study with the assiduity and perseverance I could wish. Chief part of what I do is done by candle light."

Wilson first approached the engraver, Alexander Lawson, to ask his help with his book on March 12, 1804. "I am most earnestly bent on pursuing my plan of making a collection of all the birds of this part of North America," he wrote to the astonished Lawson. "Now, I don't want you to throw cold water, as Shakespeare says, on this notion, Quixotic as it may appear."

Lawson certainly threw cold water on the project; he told Wilson he thought he was crazy. Lawson's first reaction was that it was impossible. A little elementary arithmetic would indicate to Wilson that he was proposing something even a wealthy man could not undertake. Bartram had found more than 200 native American birds, and Wilson believed there were many more than that. The copper for a single engraving cost $5.66. The cost of engravings varied, but ran from $50 to $80 a plate, depending on the picture to be engraved and the reputation of the engraver. Coloring the impressions by hand after they were engraved and printed would cost at least 25 cents for each page. If Wilson drew a hundred birds, the copper for the plates would cost more than $500, the engraving would cost between $5,000 and $8,000, and the hand coloring, if 500 copies of each were painted, would cost about $12,500. Before paper, printing and binding costs were considered for a single volume of 10 colored plates, Wilson would have to spend $2,000. Every copy of an edition of 500 copies would necessarily have to be sold for around $12 apiece to return $6,000 for the edition. A ship or a big farm cost $6,000. And it was highly doubtful if anyone would pay anything for the splintery and amateurish bird drawings that Wilson had produced.

Wilson had not been greatly disturbed by Lawson's frank admission that he considered him crazy; he knew he was not. But while hunting he dropped his gun, and it was discharged as it fell, the bullet nearly hitting him. He reflected that if he had been killed the universal conviction would be that he had committed suicide. He resolved to be cheerful and matter-of-fact, and to stop playing his flute in the woods.

One of Wilson's students caught a mouse in the classroom and brought it to Wilson to kill. The boy wanted Wilson to put the mouse in the claws of the stuffed owl on his desk to make a more realistic picture. It was near the end of the school day, and after school Wilson sat about drawing before he went home. But he drew the mouse while alive. He was drawing with feverish concentration, "while the pantings of its little heart showed it to be in the most extreme agonies of fear. I had intended to kill it . . . but happening to spill a few drops of water near where it was tied, it lapped it up with such eagerness, and looked in my face with such an eye of supplicating terror, as perfectly overcame me. I immediately untied it, and restored it to life and liberty."

He learned that while it was drudgery to paint a dead bird, it was absorbing to paint something alive. His students now brought him live crows, hawks, owls, opossums, snakes and lizards, until his room reminded him of Noah's Ark. A boy brought him a basket filled with live crows, and would have brought him a basket of frogs if Wilson had not issued a formal order forbidding it. Wilson paid ten cents apiece for live bird specimens, and consequently had a classroom full of eager naturalists encouraging his researches. A very hesitant and cautious kind of happiness crept into his life. He found himself moved as he stood in the doorway at the noon recess, watching the boys playing ball in the yard, and the girls skipping rope. He let them play as long as he could. There was no bell on his school. He merely leaned out the door, and said, "Books!"

Soon after school was out, on June 9, 1804, Wilson appeared at the Court of Common Pleas in Philadelphia and exhibited a petition praying to become a citizen of the United States. He had resided within the limits of Pennsylvania for ten years. The court was satisfied that said Alex Wilson behaved as a man of good moral character attached to the principles of the United States and well disposed to the good order and happiness of the same. Wilson thus became a citizen and "then and there declared his solemn oath that he would support the constitution of the United States and entirely renounced . . . all allegiances and fidelity to any foreign Prince Potentate State Sovereignty whatever, and particularly to the King of the United Nations of Great Britain and Ireland, of whom he was before a subject."

A few days later he wrote a little song called "The Beechen Bower," about the small familiar glade where he rested and read. The emotion that he expressed was far removed from his exhaustion two years before:

> O dear to my heart is this deep shaded Bower,
> This snug little seat and this smooth beechen tree;
> These hoary old cliffs through the bushes that lower,
> And bend o'er the pool their resemblance to see.
> The fountain, the grotto, the Laurel sweet to me,
> The streamlet that warbles so soothing and free,
> Green solitude! Dear to the maid of my bosom,
> And so for her sake ever charming to me.
>
> There seated with Anna, what bliss so transporting,
> I wish every moment were ever to be.
> Her taste so exalted, her humor so sporting,
> Her heart full of tenderness, virtue and glee.
> Each evening, sweet Bow'r, round they cliffs will I hover
> In hopes her fair form through the foliage to see;
> Heav'n only can witness how dearly I love her,
> How sweet Beechen Bower thy shades are to me.

Wilson was plainly more happily situated than he had ever been, and his school at Gray's Ferry possessed advantages he had not known at Milestown. His family was also prospering; the second year at the wilderness farm, with Mary's entire family present, had turned out to be surprisingly profitable, and Duncan wanted a vacation as soon as the crops were in. He proposed a trip. Duncan had been living in the wilderness for six years. He was lean, tireless, bronzed and healthy, could find his way through any swamp or thicket, and like an Indian read bear, deer and panther tracks. He and Wilson decided on a trip to Niagara Falls, taking Isaac Leech, a Milestown boy, with them. Leech had never been away from home. He was ruddy-cheeked, beaming, bearing a new light rifle, a knapsack, new waterproofs and oilskins. Duncan carried a knapsack only.

As for Wilson, the schoolteacher decided to write a book in verse about the trip, and this he did, the monumental 2,219 line *The Foresters,* meticulously describing every squirrel, pheasant, canvasback, quail, teal, plover and summer duck he shot on the way. So he was equipped with paints, paper and sketching materials, prepared to report every wonder and curiosity to be met with. He was arrayed in white trousers and boots, and carried a dirk, a double-barreled gun, a leather belt filled with shot, a powder flask containing Dupont's best Eagle brand powder, a package of spare clothing, a notebook, and a knapsack which his friends had crammed with cakes, cordials and spirits.

The three travelers met on the banks of the Schuylkill on the dawn of an Indian summer day in October, shivering with the frost in the air. This, too, Wilson described at length in his poem, for he had pledged himself to exaggerate nothing, "but to catch the living manners as they rose."

> No scene nor character to bring to view
> Save what fair truth from living Nature drew.

Driving clouds of blackbirds wheeled overhead through Germantown and Chestnut Hill, thistledown floated lazily over the lawns, the sounds of the cider press and the buckwheat flail came from the farms of Bucks County, and a monotony of rich farmland, woods, fields, and mountains in the distance seemed to be about all that fair nature brought to view. One day's travel brought them to the Spring House Tavern, where they sat at one of the two long tables for dinner, and listened to the farmers talking Dutch in torrents. They then fell exhausted into bed.

In the morning they set out before dawn. The morning star was still bright. The constellations were palely visible. Wilson was stiff and tired, and conscious of his thirty-eight years and his sedentary life. A sheen of ice on a stream, the hard frost, silence, a solitary light, the barking of a dog, the mysterious renewal of the earth and air in the night, held his imagination. Duncan began to sing. Wilson and Leech walked where he led them, their stiffened muscles easing as they marched. By noon of their second day they had crossed Bucks County, and were far enough into Northampton to take it easy. At sunset the rooftops of Easton, Pennsylvania, came into view, and from a hill they could see the junction of the Lehigh and Delaware, the town lying between the rivers. They were delighted with the neat pavements, the snug stone buildings, and the busy townspeople and chattering Dutchmen on the streets. Hurrying on to a tavern with the picturesque name of Pat's Split Crow they bumped into the first of the many disappointments of their trip, a wretched meal, black wet bread and rancid butter, and, when they stumbled into bed, a night made miserable by bedbugs and fleas. Groaning on their way before morning, they limped over the pavements, and panted up steep slopes, to wild mountain country.

They climbed the highest peak in sight, mounting the rocks hand over hand like sailors on shipboard, wet with dew from the dwarf trees and moss. From the summit they looked over a boundless landscape, awed at the vast colored forests, the mistlike lakes in the valleys, smoke rising from cottages, and the Delaware winding in the distance. They did not travel far that day, down the dark windings of a creek to a hut where a pleasant farmer named Marewine gave them lodging. After eating they sat around the fire and talked about cougars. One had attacked a calf while Marewine's daughter was milking a cow nearby. She thought it was a dog and rushed on it shouting, and the cougar was treed and shot.

The travelers slept well, awoke refreshed, paid Marewine half a crown, and went on over the Pocono Mountains. A bear snuffled into the road directly before them, too suddenly for them to do more than shout, "He's gone." Now they went on silently, aware of every rustling leaf, until the whirr of partridges sounded. Only one was shot in this first encounter, feathers floating to earth as the blue smoke rolled away; but a short distance on, two pheasants, trailing their broad-barred tails, appeared in the road, and Wilson got them both.

From this point on they were hunting constantly, in forests of pine and hemlock, dead and deep, floored with matted green moss. Wilson shot a crossbill in the interests of science, and made a note of the large number of this relatively rare bird to be found there, but most of the time he was hunting for game birds. The party slept in hunters' cabins or in taverns where they were welcomed because they shared their game with the owner.

At deep noon one day, when the path circled under great maples, a nine-foot rattlesnake coiled in the path. Wilson started to shoot it, but Duncan stopped him. He believed rattlesnakes were never the aggressors. Wilson held his fire, and the monster glided into the woods. On the heights above the Susquehanna the travelers loafed and relaxed, rolling rocks down the cliff to watch them splash into the river. Out in the open they sang to keep up their spirits, moving through fog so deep they found their way by the fences along the road. Two pheasants whirred across their path, and were shot; a cloud of quail rose in a tumult, and they had so much game that Duncan had to carry it threaded on a stick over his shoulder.

They were now at the lower end of the lakes where the farm was established. Immense flocks of geese were passing overhead, and more were on the lake. Wilson shot four large canvasbacks, and all around them rising trains of birds broke from the surface, with wild whistling wings and hoarse heavy screams. Wilson hired two country boys with a skiff to row him close to the shore, under the vines overhanging the water, until the uproad subsided. On a flat marsh he saw plovers descending, passing him and Leech and Duncan with a roar like a tempest, rising again at another volley, and leaving enough on the shore of the

Drawn from Nature by A. Wilson.   1. *Roseate Spoonbill.*   2. *American Avoset.*   3. *Ruddy Plover.*   4. *Semipalmated Sandpiper.*   *Engraved by I. G. Warnicke.*   6

Roseate spoonbill, shown here with avocet, plover, and sandpiper, was one of the few birds not painted from living models. Wilson drew this from a specimen sent him from Natchez.

lake to cover the small beach. The ducks that had scattered in alarm collected again on the opposite shore. Wilson crossed by a narrow neck of land, hidden by vines, shooting until he was exhausted. The sun had grown warm, and Duncan and Leech were trudging on far ahead. He cut his way back to shore, carrying his spoils—ducks, plover, teal, snipes, splendid summer ducks, divers, a tawny crane he had never seen before, two snow-white storks, and a white-tailed, dapple-breasted hawk also new to him. It was, he learned later, a white-tailed eagle, prized by Indians from Canada to Mexico for its feathers. Exultant, he paid the youngsters a dollar and set off over the hills after Leech and Duncan.

Where huge fallen trees lay across the path he lost his way, and was presently breaking through tangling brush, the load growing heavier and the day hotter with each step. He shot a tiny bird with a crimson spot on its head, one of a small flock feeding on poplar seeds—a lesser red poll, a relatively common bird which he did not know. Descending by guesswork, he fired both barrels of his gun and there was no answering report. Shouting, and shooting at intervals, frightening the squirrels, he trudged on for ten miles before he heard an answering shot, and reached the road where Leech and Duncan were waiting. They shared his load, praised his shooting, and started on.

It was now sunset, quiet except for crickets and the drumming of pheasants. The woods disappeared in darkness, and a deathlike silence closed in on them. A cougar's scream, hollow, quivering, repeated with heart-sinking terror rose from the deeper shadows nearby, followed by silence so deep they could hear acorns drop from the trees. A wolf howled in the swamp beside the lake. They waited for the cougar, but it did not scream again. Following Duncan, who picked his way unerringly, Wilson and Leech stumbled in exhaustion past pools and swampy ground, lit by the phosphorescent lights of decayed roots and stumps. There was another wild cougar scream, human and inhuman at the same time, the dark woods echoing and again growing still as death while they stood breathlessly trying to locate the source of the sound.

Light like a moonrise suddenly filled the woods as they emerged from the swamp. The forest was afire, with a brush fire on the edge of the swamp. Outlined against the blaze they saw a woodsman, grimy with soot, a pitchfork in his hand, preventing it from spreading.

"What, Johnny!" Duncan cried, as they came into the light.

"Duncan!" said the other. "How glad our folks will be to see you!"

They rested at the home of Duncan's wilderness neighbors, slept late, and set out again by a skiff with a blanket for a sail. Rising thousands of ducks, with a lengthened roar, broke the water before them. When darkness settled, and the stars were reflected on the surface, Duncan rowed, singing "Hail! Columbia!" to the night and the stars. A new bridge, a mile long, had just been built across Lake Cayuga, at a cost of $20,000, a marvel of engineering, with 215 wooden trestles. It was lighted its full length at night. They tied their skiff beneath the bridge and slept.

Beyond the bridge the lake narrowed, like a stream through level woods. Ducks were still whistling past them like meteors. They shot a few, but mostly loafed in the mild sun-shine and floated past pines and sycamores. And still files of ducks in streaming thousands poured from the surface, rising as their boat rounded every bend of the channel. They spent the night in a trapper's cabin, crossed to Lake Oneida, and descended the Oswego River to Lake Ontario. At the rapids of Oswego they nearly lost their skiff, saving it by leaping overboard and holding it by hand before it went over the falls. Resting below the falls, Wilson saw a great snowy owl perched over the water, vigilantly watching for fish. The owl caught them by striking with its foot, and rarely missed. As commonly encountered as it was, the snow owl was always considered rare, and Wilson himself thought of it so. A marvelous hunter, feeding on rabbits, grouse, ducks, mice and squirrels as well as fish and carrion, and hunting in daylight as well as in darkness, the snow owl had a flight as strong and effortless as that of a hawk. Its hideous voice, like the cry of a man in deep distress, created horror in the most desolate regions, and it was a subject of superstitious folklore, hinging on the stories that it could not be killed.

Below the falls of the Oswego the river was matted with weeds, growing so closely that the boat had to be poled through with difficulty. The snow bunting, a very common little bird, tawny brown in summer and white in winter—a harbinger of extreme cold, in the common belief—was feeding on the seeds of these water plants. They floated down the twenty-three miles of the Oswego River to Lake Ontario, past the fort, now abandoned. They hoisted a blanket sail, and made good time. But soon the wind began to blow too strongly for comfort. A sloop saw their sail and bore down on them, seeing their need for assistance. Wilson, Leech and Duncan climbed aboard. The skiff was hoisted to the deck also. It was just in time. The wind grew to a storm, and the storm to a tempest. The wracked vessel staggered, slow-rising on huge, white-crested waves, and plunging headlong again. Darkness fell, and the fury of the storm increased. The travelers lay groaning, seasick and terrified, in the cabin.

In the morning the sloop was racing at thirteen knots. Wilson staggered on deck, watched the sunrise, revived, and made a breakfast of venison and onions, the thought of which sent Leech and Duncan plunging below again. Their first glimpse of Niagara Falls came the next morning after they landed, when they emerged from views of lakeside fields and orchards to see before them a boiling smoke, a profound gulf, and dazzling rainbows playing over the ascending spray.

Drenched to the skin, they descended to the edge of the precipice overlooking the gorge. At that time an improvised ladder had been fastened from the edge of the cliff to the roots of a tree on the ledge below, where the trail ran. But in descending it, the traveler had to move out from the cliff, and look directly down 150 feet. Leech climbed out like a bird, with the whole abyss beneath him, Wilson followed, and Duncan, laughing, started down last. The tree roots yielded, the ladder cracked. Wilson had a momentary vision of their mangled limbs and spattered brains on the rocks. But the roots held, and at last they stood at the base of the cataracts.

The three stupendous falls were before them. Tremendous rocks, that could be rolled like millstones, heaps of driftwood, fragments of logs, trees, and animals, and a curtain of spray, were at the base, and overhead the mighty, resistless mass of water, in a green and still unbroken wall, arched over the brink, then smashed into dazzling hills of boiling spray.

Wilson had one last objective, now that they had come so far. He wanted to get into the cavern behind the falls. They crawled over huge rocks, through caverns and up wet slippery cliffs until they could see the rapids below them, and the resounding hollow above. They clasped hands and groped behind the curtain of water.

There they found themselves in a roaring concave chamber, filled with eternal rain and hurling whirlwinds, the rocks underfoot slippery and treacherous. As they penetrated behind the screen of water, the suction suddenly took their breath away, the darkness was complete, and they staggered toward the water boiling past them. For an instant in their bewilderment and terror, they were threatened with a plunge over the brink; then danger itself gave them a desperate strength and they pushed their way back to the ledge from which they entered. They rested, drenched and gasping. The day was now well along, and in the gorge the light faded rapidly. They picked their way by feeling the rocks, and climbed up to the brink in darkness. A light glimmered nearby. They stopped and found lodgings; the home was owned by a man named Wilson. As weary as Wilson was, he could not sleep. Around them the sound of the falls roared like a tempest in calm air. The house trembled. When he fell into short and broken slumber he dreamed that all three were carried down the rapids, engulfed, helpless.

CHAPTER FOUR

Eagles and Men

WILSON was now constantly searching for new birds. High above Niagara the eagles circled endlessly, in trains that reached to the horizon, majestic birds, unawed by men, watching for the game that was swept over the falls. They descended rapidly, and rose on the boisterous currents above the water, passing in a few moments from the Arctic temperature of the heights to the summer warmth below. On Table Rock above the falls there were also snow buntings, the same inconspicuous little bird Wilson had seen on the Oswego. It seemed that the reputation of these birds as prophets of cold weather was justified. As Wilson and his companions left the falls, the nights turned intensely cold. Duncan left them, to go back to the farm, and when Wilson and Leech began their homeward trip the next day the road was frozen. Parts were muddied and slippery, and walking was exhausting. Wilson carried his own gun, helping Leech by carrying his as well. The boy followed him some distance behind, groaning with fatigue. Thus they covered thirty-five miles, and rose at five the next morning to get as far as they could before the weather grew worse. It was now late in the year—November 22, 1804—and a deep snow fell.

Along the road below the town of Little Falls three or four large blue and white birds were leisurely flitting, staying together, or within a small distance of each other, keeping up a kind of low chattering with one another, and apparently nowise apprehensive when Wilson approached. After some study Wilson decided that these were birds never seen around Philadelphia and the South, and soon concluded that he had made a real discovery. With patience and cunning, he finally shot three of them, and kept them to show to Bartram. They resembled the blue jay, but were larger, some eleven inches in length, but without the crest, so that Wilson thought he had found a new kind of jay, a bird somewhat like a mockingbird, soft and gray, and looking rather like an overgrown chickadee. The next day he found others between East and West Canada Creeks which flowed into the Mohawk.

A boat came down the river through the snowstorm. Leech climbed aboard to ride the rest of the way to Schenectady. Wilson splashed six more miles through mud holes before dark. He set out early again on the morning of November 26, and got to Schenectady ahead of Leech, who arrived in the boat about noon. A stagecoach took them to Albany in one day. They rested two days, then caught a sloop to New York, where they arrived on the first of December. Wilson's shoes were completely worn through. His trousers were in tatters. He had to spend twelve dollars for new articles to replace them. He could not afford stage fare to Philadelphia, and walked, reaching Gray's Ferry on Friday, December 7, after walking forty-seven miles that day. In the two months since he set out he had transversed between 1,200 and 1,300 miles, and was further pleased because, having shot a pine grosbeak north of Philadelphia, he saw another near Gray's Ferry itself.

The wife of a neighbor had given birth to twins, a boy and girl, and the boy was named Alexander Wilson in his honor. On the evening of his arrival home, Wilson called and learned of his namesake; he consequently parted with the last of his money in honor of the infant—six dollars in all, which left him with seventy-five cents. As for the jay, Bartram could not identify it; the naturalists about Philadelphia had never seen its like before. The bird was stuffed and placed in Peale's Museum, and Wilson enjoyed a brief season of self-congratulation as the finder of a new bird.

He had neglected his school, arriving late, and with few students, and overnight destroyed the reputation for responsibility he had built up as a teacher. The winter early in 1805 turned out to be extremely severe; the rivers were frozen, and hard times were everywhere. Wilson had only twenty-seven students, and several of the families that had formerly sent all their children to him were now close to starvation. So far as Wilson's own fortune was concerned, he was almost indifferent to the condition of his school, in his intensity of feeling for his new work. He wrote to Bartram that he wanted to live in the wilderness and become an explorer; he had no family, and no ties except those of friendship, "and the most ardent love of my adopted country." He said his disposition was sociable and open, that he was at home by an Indian fire or in a civilized apartment. "But I am miserably deficient in many acquirements absolutely necessary for such a character. Botany, Minerology and Drawing, I most ardently wish to be instructed in, and with these I should fear nothing. Can I make any progress in Botany, sufficient to enable me to be useful, and what would be the most proper way to proceed?"

On March 4, 1805, Jefferson's second term as President began, an event, as Wilson wrote to Bartram, calculated to cause the heart of "every good man within the immense limits of our happy country" to leap with joy. Upon two large sheets of his finest drawing paper, Wilson pictured the birds he had shot on the Mohawk, with Niagara in the background. A local arist of distinction, Barralet, an eccentric Irishman of French ancestry, made an engraving of Niagara Falls from Wilson's sketch, faithfully showing the eagles overhead. Wilson sent his bird pictures to President Jefferson as a token of his esteem. Jefferson thanked him kindly, replying at length in a letter that was an encouragement to Wilson to write again. The President admitted the jay Wilson had found was unfamiliar, and took the opportunity to ask Wilson to look for a bird he had never seen described, about the size of a mockingbird, thrush-colored on the back, and grayish-white on the breast, sometimes heard singing in the tops of tallest trees, with a song as clear as that of a nightingale. "I have followed it for miles," the President wrote, "without ever, but once, getting a good view of it."

Wilson felt that he had known the same experience, and decided that the President's rare bird must be the wood thrush—so anticlimactic an identification he hesitated to send it to Jefferson. And, in fact, he did not do so, saving the account to be included in his book. Early in the summer he sent Bartram a collection of twenty-eight Pennsylvania birds he had drawn to begin his collection of all found in the state—"I dare say you will smile at my presumption." Some of those he pictured were not in Bartram's collection or in the seven volumes of Edwards' birds. Wilson asked Bartram to criticize them freely: "To your advice and encouraging encomiums I am indebted for these few specimens, and for all that will follow, they may yet tell posterity that I was encouraged with your friendship, and that to your inspiration they owe their existence. . . ."

"Please to send me the names of the birds," he wrote to Bartram on another occasion, enclosing a group of his sketches. "I wish to draw a small flower, in order to represent the Hummingbird in the act of feeding: would you be so good as to send me one suitable, and not too large?" He had no paper to work on, using the flyleaves of old books, or wan sheets of coarse paper pasted together. These he covered with some of his finest work, the deep vermilion and jetty black of the scarlet tanager, the bright flame-color of the golden-crested wren, the deep slate and pale light blue of the cedarbird.

The new species of jay he had found turned out to be merely a Canada jay, a familiar bird as far south as central New York though almost unknown to Pennsylvania. But Wilson was so absorbed with his work that he was unembarrassed by the discovery that his supposed rarity was common as a chipmunk.

His drawing had improved almost magically. Art and science dominated his thoughts, not the search for new species, but delineating and defining them, and discovering their pattern in the whole. He would not now let his school affairs monopolize his energy. When he found that he would clear only $15 for the term, he called a meeting of the trustees and laid the problem before them, willing to stop teaching. But the trustees would not let him go. Two of them pledged $100 on the spot, and a town meeting then guaranteed Wilson 48 students, or $200 a term, if he would remain. He also became the tutor to the two sons of Samuel Bradford, a prominent Philadelphia publisher.

The farm at Ovid was still a financial drain, but it had grown more valuable. Wilson decided the farm should be sold. But Mary's family had grown attached to it. Wilson then admitted he had another reason for urging its sale. It was too far in the wilderness, and he wanted Duncan nearby. The problem solved itself. In October, 1805, Duncan was appointed teacher of Wilson's old school at Milestown. Alexander Duncan also moved to Philadelphia and began weaving and attending Duncan's school. James, their younger brother, kept the farm at Ovid, which continued to prosper, Mary writing to Wilson that she and the younger children were well cared for by the fourteen-year-old pioneer.

Wilson's own ambition had crystallized to an ingenious and practical scheme. Borrowing engraver's tools from Lawson, he etched one of his drawings. He calculated that he could picture all the birds of America in a 10-volume set of books, and that he could manufacture the books for $12 a volume, or $120 for the whole set. He wanted a few plates made, and from these he would get enough subscriptions to pay for printing the first volume. With the first volume in hand, he could solicit subscriptions for the entire set. He would use familiar birds in the first volumes, and then, as the proceeds came in, he would be able to travel around the country collecting rarer specimens for the last volumes, and also selling subscriptions to the whole 10-volume edition. He would need only 200 subscriptions to finance the job.

Everything depended on the engravings, for he could not collect the first subscriptions unless he had some samples to show the quality of the work the books would contain. Both Catesby and Edwards etched their own plates. The process followed in those days was to begin by placing a film of varnish over the polished copper plate. Wilson took his drawing of the blue jay, and transferred it to the film by rubbing, a process no more complicated than using carbon paper. He then used Lawson's engraving tool to cut through the film of varnish along the lines of the jay's feathers and bill, to the copper underneath. Then he put a bank of wax around the whole plate, and poured nitric acid into the space enclosed by the wax. The acid cut the lines of the drawing into the copper, the film of varnish protecting the rest of the plate.

As soon as Wilson had cut his first engravings, he rushed the plates to Lawson and asked him to make proofs at once. He said he was leaving town, and had to see if they were any good before he left. When the proofs were pulled, he knew that his project was feasible. He sent the first proofs to Bartram, saying, "My next attempt will perhaps be better, everything being new to me in this." The copper plates, of course, were merely in black and white. The color still had to be applied by hand. It was washed over the engraving with a brush, the dark lines of the feathers showing through the tints. Wilson hastily colored the plates he had made, finishing them by candlelight.

This was at the end of November, 1805. In January, 1806, he was still making engravings, and coloring them by candlelight. In February he had a hundred drawings finished, and could make any number of copies of his eagle and blue jay to indicate what his book would be like.

On February 6, 1806, he wrote to Jefferson asking for a post as naturalist with Zebulon Pike's expedition into the far West, its ultimate destination the Red River country of what became Oklahoma. The expedition was to set out in July. Wilson gave his letter to Bartram to forward to Jefferson with Bartram's endorsement. Wilson never received a reply. "I begin to think that either Mr. Jefferson expects a brush with the Spaniards," he wrote to Duncan, "or has not received our letters; otherwise, he would never act so impolitely to one for whom he has so much esteem as for Mr. Bartram. No hurry of business would excuse it."

Wilson was guilty of imprudence, at least, an error difficult to account for in one of his background and with his knowledge of conspiratorial techniques. The Pike expedition was a state secret. To the best of Jefferson's knowledge, it was known only to himself, to General Dearborn, the Secretary of War, to General James Wilkinson, the commanding general of the Army, and to Pike. All were aware of its confidential character, since it would necessarily enter Spanish land. Many years later, when Jefferson, an aged man, was attacked for his "contemptuous neglect" of Wilson's application, he became distressed at the accusation, and said he had no recollection of ever having received any such letter from Wilson. He conducted a lengthy inquiry, and concluded that by the time Wilson's letter reached him, it had contained no reference to Pike's forthcoming expedition. He reasoned that he would have been startled had it contained such references, for he considered the whole plan a state secret, and therefore believed the application must have been removed from Wilson's letter before it was given to him.

At the same time that Wilson sent his request for a post with a top-secret government expedition, his nephew Duncan, who was succeeding handsomely at his old school in Miles-town, wrote to Wilson that his friends at Milestown wanted him to return to make a patriotic speech there. Since Wilson had left so abruptly after his previous oration on the value of liberty, he refused, saying dryly that for him to speak in Milestown might arouse long-slumbering antagonisms that would cause trouble for Duncan as well.

On April 1, 1806, Wilson resigned his school at Gray's Ferry. Samuel Bradford, the publisher, was preparing a new edition of *Rees's Cyclopaedia,* and hired Wilson to edit the 22-volume set of books, at a salary of $900 a year. Wilson's title was assistant editor. He was to prepare the articles for the printer, revise and select material, deal with contributors, correct proofs, and supervise the engravings. *Rees's Cyclopaedia,* a standard reference work whose American edition had previously been published by Dobson, was to be made an American production, with articles on all sides of American life and history. These Wilson was to write, or to prepare for publication from the work of authorities. He promptly commissioned Bartram to write the article on botany.

Bradford originally intended to ask Wilson to take over management of his bookstore. He needed a man of steady habits there, and Wilson, while he took an occasional glass of spirits or wine, did not drink. But in offering the job to Wilson, Bradford was impressed by his frank, honorable manner, and the intelligence and integrity that he revealed. He accordingly changed his mind during the interview and offered him the post with the publishing house instead, with a salary far greater than Wilson expected. Wilson's projected *American Ornithology* came into their discussions. Bradford became enthusiastic. It was understood that Wilson's work at the encyclopedia would prepare the way for the publication of the *Ornithology,* which Bradford's firm would bring out. In that early harmonious period of their relationship, Bradford came to believe that Wilson could execute any undertaking that he set himself to, and so he agreed, "in the way of means," he said, "to give every aid and facility which the enterprise might require." Affairs moved so rapidly that Wilson resigned from his school on Tuesday, April 1, and moved into his new office on Market Street the following morning. He had taught at Gray's Ferry for four years; unlike his leave-taking at Milestown, he left with the good will of the community.

Samuel Bradford was thirty-two years old, plump, sociable, enterprising and ambitious. He was married to Abigail, the daughter of John Inskeep, president of the Insurance Company of North America, and the Democratic mayor of Philadelphia. Bradford was the descendant of famous Philadelphia editors and printers. It was his great-grandfather, the first printer in the city, who gave Benjamin Franklin his first job there. In another generation, Thomas Bradford started *The True American,* long one of the most influential American newspapers. It was the firm of Bradford that published Dr. Witherspoon's writings in America, listing him as the author, at a time when his books were still published anonymously in Britain. The firm was traditionally the publisher of controversial works, dating from pre-Revolutionary days, and when Samuel Bradford first entered the business he tried to follow the example of his ancestors, with, however, something less than their genuine grievances to put into print. When Callender's *Political Progress of Britain* was published in Philadelphia it was attacked by the expatriate English editor, William Cobbett, and Cobbett's book, called *A Bone for Democrats to Gnaw On,* was published by another branch of the Bradford family. Young Samuel, eager to make a name for himself in a field where his family was respected, whipped out two characteristic political pamphlets of the time to attack Cobbett—not to defend Callender, but because Cobbett had broadened his attack to include all Democrats. The pamphlets made Bradford a hero for the time being to Callender, Clingman, Reynolds and the political underworld generally, but subsequent events proved Bradford to be mistaken, and his political expressions became more guarded. "That lump of walking tallow, streaked with lampblack, that calls itself Samuel F. Bradford" was Cobbett's terse dismissal of his youthful opponent, and Bradford moved out of the range of these hardened political mudslingers.

As a publisher, Bradford was getting away from politics, and into literary, theatrical and artistic publications. Many of these were of distinction, though it was said that his brother, Thomas Bradford, a more practical and little-known printer, was responsible for the best of them, including Wilson's books. Samuel Bradford at any rate was proud of the work that Wilson did, and wanted to make the *Ornithology* the most beautiful book ever printed in America. A singular mixture of quality printer, political dilettante, and temperamental businessman, Bradford was now buying up printing firms and periodicals on a large scale—the business of the printer Maxwell, who had printed Wilson's Milestown speech, was one of his acquisitions at this time—and he became, in the next few years, far and away the largest and most influential publisher in the United States.

William Jones, Wilson's Gray's Ferry landlord, also had a dwelling at 233 Spruce Street, in a pleasant section of tree-shaded, red-brick dwellings, not far from the Delaware, that still retained, a century and a half later, occasional glimpses of the quiet charm it possessed before warehouses intruded among its residences. Wilson lived there, rising each day at dawn, and made his way along Third Street, passing Alexander Hamilton's old residence, and the house across the street from it, near the intersection of Dock Street and Third, where Callender had lived. Walking a block below Independence Hall, Wilson passed the great mansion that Robert Morris had built, crossed Market Street, already bustling in the half-light, and made his way to the office of Bradford and Inskeep. The trees sheltered birds, and he noted how many of them there were, especially robins, in the earliest dawn in the heart of the city. He was now working on the prospectus for his *Ornithology* at every possible intermission in his work on the encyclopedia. He and Bradford assigned five years for the completion of the set of books. They first prepared a handsome advertisement, with a colored plate to show the quality of the work, to be sent to prominent individuals all over the United States. Bradford and Inskeep underwrote the cost of the first volume, to be printed in an edition of 200 copies, the project to be dropped unless Wilson could secure that many subscribers.

The first volume contained Wilson's pictures and accounts of the blue jay, goldfinch, Baltimore and orchard orioles, wood thrush, robin, black-capped, red-bellied and white-breasted nuthatch, bluebird, shrike, pine grosbeak, the Maryland yellowthroat, the yellow-breasted chat, summer redbird, indigo bird, redstart, cedarbird, black-capped and crested titmouse, the red-banded, golden-winged, yellow-bellied, hairy and downy woodpeckers, the yellow-throated flycatcher, purple finch, brown creeper and ruby-crowned, winter, and golden-crested wren. From two to six birds were pictured on a plate. These illustrations alone cost a fortune, since Wilson himself superintended the coloring, patiently intent on bringing out the tiny breast feathers of the birds, or the delicate overlapping of the scales on the legs, determined to get each individual feather faithfully copied, and the proper shading on each scale.

With every bird he pictured he wove a new strand in a fabric of identification with America. And in Scotland the old order he had known was disintegrating so rapidly he would hardly have known Paisley or Lochwinnoch. The social landmark of his early years, for him or for the whole area, had been the M'Dowell family. Just at this time, in 1806, their West Indies merchant firm failed in Glasgow. Since their firm (Alexander Houston and Company) owned the Ship Bank, the panic radiated out from M'Dowell's office on Argyle Street, "creating consternation," said an old account, "not only in the west of Scotland, but throughout the country." An Act of Parliament was hastily passed, setting up a government administrator to wind up the affairs of the M'Dowell companies and check the panic. Years later, when all the firm's obligations had been met, there turned out to be a large surplus, and Lochwinnoch folk believed the whole crisis was artificial, a device by which the government took control of the company and distributed its assets to political favorites. But by that time all the M'Dowells had long since vanished from the scene.

CHAPTER FIVE

Songs and Colors

THE BERRIES of the sour gum tree were plentiful in Pennsylvania in the fall, attracting huge flocks of robins. The dark blue, acid-tasting fruit was preferred by robins to all other food except worms and caterpillars, and the birds could be shot from a single tree all day long. It was only necessary for a hunter to locate a gum tree, which was not difficult, since they grew fifty feet high, were abundant in swamps, and the lustrous fruit hanging on the bare limbs made them conspicuous in the bare woods. Taking a stand nearby, a gunner could bring down robins with every shot. All that was required was to load, aim and fire, reload, aim and fire again, the birds dropping with every discharge. The surviving robins flew after each shot, but a few moments later another flock arrived.

When the supply of sour gum berries grew thin, the robins dispersed into the woods and over fields, to feed on worms and insects, almost disappearing from the neighborhood of the city, but returning after a week or two in even greater numbers. By the time frosts had killed the insects, it had also mellowed the pokeberries, another favorite food of robins. There were now so many of the birds that hunters swarmed from the city to shoot them for market. In January, 1807, Wilson met two young men who in one brief excursion on a single day had shot 360 robins. Similar reports came in from the whole eastern seaboard, from Massachusetts to Maryland. The juice of the pokeberry was of a beautiful crimson color, and stained the stomachs of birds red. Fortunately, as Wilson reported, someone unidentified planted a story in the newspapers to the effect that pokeberries made the flesh of robins unwholesome. It was, of course, entirely fiction, and there was no doubt but that the individual planting the story was Wilson himself, but in any event the demand for the bird in the markets ceased immediately, and Wilson solemnly congratulated his readers that the instinct of self-preservation in the human race had ended the devastation among the robins.

The date of the incident, which he related in the *Ornithology,* was revealing, for it indicated the rate of Wilson's progress on his book. The first color plate in the first volume was of the blue jay, shown with the goldfinch and with the Baltimore oriole, so called by the first settlers in the country because its colors, black and orange, were the heraldic colors of Lord Baltimore. The second plate contained the robin, the wood thrush, and the black-capped nuthatch. The spring of 1807 was extremely late, and until spring Wilson had no specimen of a nuthatch from which his colorists could color the engravings that had been made. The birds began to arrive from the south on schedule, but the weather was so wretched that it was impossible to go into the woods and observe them. It was on Tuesday night, April 7, 1807, that Wilson saw the finished advertisement of his book, and the weather was still wintry. The printed prospectus was in itself a handsome piece of work. It stated that Bradford and Inskeep were to publish *American Ornithology* by Alexander Wilson, in 10 volumes with 10 color plates in each volume, covering all the land and water birds of America, the books to be sold by subscription only, at $120 for a set of 10. The brochure was sent to 2,500 eminent persons in the United States.

The following day another engraving for the book itself came from the engraver, so the colorists could move on to applying the paint to another illustration. But Wilson still lacked a black-capped nuthatch to be used as a model. He accordingly rose at dawn and started across the fields near the river to look for a bird. Ordinarily they were everywhere, one of the commonest birds in Pennsylvania—an early arrival, a familiar, friendly and quaint little black and white bird, nesting in holes in trees or in hollow fence rails. The bird had no song beyond its quank-quank sound, frequently repeated as it moved up and down, in spiral circles, around the trunk of a tree. And it was inquisitive beyond most birds, frequently growing silent, and dropping, head downward, almost to the root of a tree, to examine a man standing beside it, so Wilson anticipated no trouble in shooting one. The black-capped nuthatch was often in company with the red-bellied nuthatch, a harder bird to shoot because it was smaller—four and a half inches—and with quicker motions; and both often traveled in a sort of squadron accompanied by a titmouse and a small wood-pecker, moving in semi-military order from tree to tree. Then the different sounds of the different kinds of birds in the group, the rattling of their bills, and the rapid motions of the bodies of the nuthatches, constantly thrown like tumblers into numberless positions, con-veyed a notion of happy diligence that Wilson found engaging.

But now he could not find a single nuthatch. He first followed along the fences to the Delaware, climbing over and crossing fields, floundering in ankle-deep mud, and then went into the groves along the river, to the junction of the Delaware and the Schuylkill. He re-turned to William Jones's house at eight o'clock, drenched in perspiration and covered with mud, without having even seen a nuthatch to shoot at.

He got over his irritation by telling himself he felt better for the exercise. He wrote to Bartram that he dared not mention the incident to Lawson, or Lawson would say he was crazy. A week later the weather was still too severe to permit outdoor study, and Wilson's impatience deepened. But now his book received a major contribution. Meriwether Lewis arrived in Philadelphia to prepare for the publication of a comprehensive two-volume ac-count of the Lewis and Clark expedition to the Pacific. Bradford and Inskeep secured the contract to publish Lewis' book. Lewis was at the height of his fame, the leader of one of the most successful and romantic expeditions in the history of exploration, now appointed governor of Louisiana Territory, and scheduled to take up his new post in St. Louis in the fall.

Modest and reserved, Lewis scarcely celebrated his triumph, and refused to be lionized, but started to work at once on his book. The land grants Congress gave him—and all members of the expedition—made him well-to-do, but he lived cheaply at the boarding house of a Mrs. Woods, though he spent money lavishly on the illustrations and the material for the volumes he intended to write—with almost scandalous generosity, in fact, by the standards of payment for literary and artistic works at that time. Lewis hired Barralet to make a drawing of the Great Falls of the Missouri, like the drawing Barralet made from Wilson's sketches of Niagara, paying the artist $40. Lewis hired Frederick Pursh also, the botanist for William Hamilton at Woodlands. Lewis noted in his account book $70, "Paid this sum to Mr. Pursh the botanist in advance for preparing drawings of the plants, for my work." These consisted of the 150 specimens Lewis managed to bring back, only 12 of them previously known, astonishing Pursh with his untaught botanical gift.

The birds he had discovered, Lewis gave to Wilson. The greatest encouragement that Wilson had received up to that time was "the request and particular wish of Captain Lewis, made to me in person, that I should make drawings of such of the feathered tribes as had been preserved and were new." The decision was a natural one for Lewis to make. No one in America had painted wild life with the precision and the feeling that Wilson revealed at the beginning of the great creative period of his life. And Lewis aided Wilson in other ways. Before the essay on the blue jay went to press, Wilson was able to add that Captain Lewis had seen the bird up the Missouri, and references to the findings of the Lewis and Clark expedition were scattered throughout the volumes. The passenger pigeon, for instance, was still seen in the Rockies as far as the Great Falls in what became Montana. Jefferson had ordered the members of the expedition to keep diaries, and Lewis bought that of John Ordway, the best and most intelligent of the hunters on the expedition, paying Ordway $300. He put Wilson in touch with Ordway, and from Ordway Wilson gathered interesting and unstudied lore of all kinds, Ordway telling him, for example, that the magpies in the prairies were so greedy that they descended in flocks and began feeding on animals while the hunters were skinning them.

One of the specimens that Lewis gave Wilson was a small bird, about six inches long, with a black back and tail and wings, tipped with yellow, the body altogether yellow, and the forepart of the head light scarlet. Wilson gave the bird the apt and beautiful name of the Louisiana tanager (later renamed the western tanager). A more striking discovery, since it was purely a Pacific Coast native, was a large black and white bird, found near the mouth of the Columbia River, which Wilson named Clark's crow. The third new bird brought back by the expedition—most of the specimens were lost on the return trip—was a very beautiful and singularly marked woodpecker found in the Rockies, with black back, wings and tail, and the breast and belly of deep vermilion intermixed with silvery-fibered feathers. This Wilson named Lewis' woodpecker, a name by which it remained known.

Wilson was thus the first ornithologist to present any indication of the abundant bird life of the western United States. He noted with evident pride that he was enabled by Meriwether Lewis to introduce these natives "of what is, or at least will be, and that at no distant period, part of the western territory of the United States." But he was finding it difficult to secure specimens of birds nearer home. The weather remained severe; a week after Lewis' arrival in Philadelphia, when Wilson was again scouring the woods, their appearance was wintry and bleak. It was April 20, and there was hardly a leaf on a tree. But there were wood thrushes flitting through the moist hollows. Wilson loafed along the brooks that were the favorite haunts of these songsters, listening to their singing with as great a range in voice, energy and expression, from one bird to another, as was found among human singers. He set himself to try to characterize the song itself in words, listening and writing, listening and rewriting, until he was satisfied.

The prelude to the song of the wood thrush varied, sometimes resembling the double-tonguing of a flute and sometimes with a bell-like, resonant sound; then the bird's few clear, musical notes rose in a kind of ecstasy. The song consisted of five or six parts, the last note of each part in such a tone as to leave the conclusion suspended; "the finalé is finely managed, and with such charming effect as to soothe and tranquilize the mind, and to seem sweeter and mellower at each successive repetition." When a wood thrush was singing it was fairly common to hear another answering from a different part of the woods, the two rival songsters seemingly trying to outdo each other in reaching softer tones and more exquisite responses. They sang when the woods were silent, soon after dawn, or in dark, wet and gloomy weather, and their clear notes thrilled through the dripping woods when no other birds sang.

Spring arrived in May, and Wilson was as exultant as the birds he wrote about. Spring brought "the sweetest songsters earth can boast of," Wilson wrote to Bartram; their arrival never seemed to him so miraculous as it seemed this spring. Leaves, birds and blossoms, and every zephyr breathing fragrance, summed up his emotion as the glowing colors of his bird paintings came to life. Wilson bought a horse in order to be able to get to the woods more quickly. The animal was a blooded horse, very handsome, too much of a horse for show for the purpose for which he needed it, and he used it less than he had expected to. He rode to Bartram's Garden to ask information of its venerable owner, or tramped through the woods studying all birds within range, checking the number of eggs in the nest of the goldfinch (five), or the shaded construction of the nest of the Baltimore oriole, remarkable for its "convenience, warmth and security," and a multitude of similar matters. The amount of bird lore preserved in these notes was remarkable. "The song of the Baltimore is a clear mellow whistle," he wrote, "repeated at short intervals as he gleans among the branches.

There is in it a certain wild plaintiveness . . . the pleasing tranquillity of a careless plough-boy, whistling merely for his own amusement."

At night Wilson returned to the Jones house on Spruce Street, where he was almost one of the family. Nicholas Jones and his wife, the former Susannah Miller, lived in the house adjoining Daniel Miller's home on Second Street, only some five blocks away, and there Sarah Miller often visited with Wilson. Nicholas and Susannah were the parents of three sons and a daughter. Daniel Miller, then twenty-five, was newly married. He was an alert, intelligent and enterprising young man, already a successful ironmonger, and beginning to establish a fortune with a glass works in New Jersey. Daniel was socially ambitious. He became one of the founders of an Episcopal church in his neighborhood, and a member of the vestry—though in this he proceeded without the rest of his family, for Sarah did not belong to his church—a position he held throughout his life.

The social evening depended heavily on music. It was one of the jokes of Sarah and Wilson that Jones's taste in this respect was exceptional, and that he delighted in strange and complicated hymns that nobody else ever heard of. When Wilson discovered a rare and complicated hymn called "The Vicar and Moses," he said it must be one of Jones's hymns. He called Susannah "Sister Jones." Sarah Miller, then twenty-seven, was a modern and intellectual young woman, interested in fashions such as were reported from London and Paris, and in the Gothic romances and horror stories that were then popular—with expensive tastes, in short, which her own family might meet, but which Wilson, either as a village schoolteacher, or an encyclopedia editor, could not expect to provide for. They were friends of such nature, however, that the subject of her expensive tastes and his poverty could be referred to good-humoredly, the informality between them increased by the fact that Wilson was fifteen years older than Sarah.

His financial outlook became less promising as the costs of producing the first volume of the *Ornithology* increased. The problem was the cost of getting the engravings colored satisfactorily. Painters were paid twenty-five cents for each completed page. Well-known Philadelphia artists were used in the beginning, but they were not always satisfactory, and the quality of the plates varied from copy to copy, the colors not uniform. Many of them were the work of Alexander Rider, a Swiss-born painter of considerable reputation, but Rider spoiled many plates, though he continued to be employed throughout the whole series. Wilson found it more satisfactory to use amateur or untrained artists who would work closely under his direction and faithfully follow the model. Henry Hopkins, a Dublin-born youth of artistic talent who was working as a clerk, was hired to color many of the plates, and Nancy Bartram and her friend Mary Leech colored others. Wilson sent some of the plates to Bartram to be used by the girls as guides in doing others. The first colorist had painted the goldfinch too brilliant a yellow, and had not brought out boldly enough the red feathers of another bird. Wilson himself had painted the blue jay, but spoiled the page by streaking the color. "In washing the blue jay," Wilson wrote, "the most difficult part is to lay on the color without being streaked . . . and in giving the true tint, which I think is nearly approached in this specimen. Nothing but a wash is necessary, as the engraving must be seen through the color." Because he found that black ink showed too darkly through the color, Wilson used the appropriate colored ink for each bird—blue ink for the blue jay, red for the cardinal, and so on through the spectrum of nature.

In the midst of these vexations, the *Ornithology* received another magnificent contribution from a wholly unexpected source. The apprentice in Bradford's bookstore was Charles Robert Leslie, an engaging seventeen-year-old boy who had been born in England of American parents. His father, a Philadelphia clockmaker and a close friend of Benjamin Franklin, had taken his family with him to London, where the boy was born. He was brought to Philadelphia when he was five years old. Leslie went to school in New Jersey, and had enrolled in the University of Pennsylvania when his father died. The family was left in poverty, the widow opening a boarding house, and Leslie entering Bradford's bookstore for a seven-year apprenticeship. Charles Leslie and his two sisters, Eliza and Ann, were gifted children, and possessed the good will of the cultivated circles of the city through their father's reputation. Their gift was artistic; they excelled in capturing likenesses in effortless and untrained and good-humoredly satiric sketches. Bradford now assigned Leslie to color plates for the *Ornithology*.

The boy's admiration for Wilson amounted to veneration. In his autobiography, written in his old age, he recalled Wilson as one of the most remarkable people he had ever known, one who somehow communicated more than other people a sense of individuality and distinction. In his own dealings with the schoolmaster, he found Wilson superlatively patient. "He looked like a bird," Leslie wrote.

> His eyes were piercing, dark and luminous, and his nose shaped like a beak. He was of spare, bony frame, very erect in his carriage, inclining to be tall; and with a light, elastic step, he seemed perfectly qualified by nature for his extraordinary pedestrian achievements. . . . I assisted him to color some of his first plates. We worked from birds which he had shot and stuffed, and I remember the extreme accuracy of his drawings, and how carefully he had counted the number of scales on the tiny legs and feet of his subject.

After three years of work on the *Ornithology,* Wilson and a group of Philadelphia friends bought up Leslie's apprenticeship from Bradford, and collected a subscription to send the boy to England for training as an artist. This account belongs later in the story of Wilson's work; for the time being, it is enough to say that Leslie studied under Benjamin West, subsequently becoming one of the most famous of Victorian artists, the court painter to Queen Victoria, one of whose favorites he became. His sister Eliza, following him to London, became successful for her satirical sketches of fashionable life, but soon abandoned art and became a novelist; the younger sister, Ann, then became a successful painter in her

1. *Night-Hawk* 2. *Female*
40

Night hawk, with female. Wilson called the hawk "a bird of strong and vigorous flight . . . diving
perpendicularly with a hollow sound."

own right. They were a remarkable and engaging family, the Leslies, and their influence on the *Ornithology* was considerable. Some of the plates of the first volumes of the work reveal Leslie's art. The velvety texture of the orchard oriole, the unforgettable dull dusky red and bright vermilion of the cardinal grosbeak, the cinnamon color, fawn color, black and golden yellow of the golden-winged woodpecker, and the barely perceptible shadings of the tints of the smaller birds, almost perfectly colored in these plates, combined to produce the most vividly colorful paintings of birds ever created. The best of these, with the truest and most natural colors, were the plates on which Charles Robert Leslie found himself in art, and began the work that led to his own career.

CHAPTER SIX

Birds of Prey

ON ONE of his hunting expeditions Wilson saw a sparrow hawk perched motionless on the top of a tall poplar tree at the edge of the woods. He had not yet secured one of these birds to use as a model, but had not concerned himself about them, as they were one of the commonest hawks. He saw them in his early morning rambles, watching around farmhouses and barnyards for mice and young chickens, and noted their irregular flight, as they hovered over a spot for a minute or two, and then shot off in another direction. Like the one he now watched on the poplar, sparrow hawks often perched on top of dead trees near meadows, folding their wings so suddenly when they landed that the wings seemed to disappear. Wilson had watched the hawks perch almost motionless for as long as an hour before they suddenly plunged toward earth.

He decided to bring down the bird he now observed, and raised his rifle. As he aimed, the hawk dropped like an arrow into a thicket about a hundred feet away, Wilson following it down through his sights. He fired just as the bird entered the briers. He saw that he had hit it, and walked to the thicket, pushing the tangle aside. He had killed the hawk instantly. But at the same moment that his shot struck it, the hawk had killed a field sparrow. The still quivering body of the sparrow was in its claws.

The hawk was about thirteen inches long, with a wingspread of two feet. It was of a reddish bay color, with a head of bluish ash, bearing a red crown, with a white field, marked by seven symmetrical spots of black, surrounding the head, and with eyes like globes of black glass. As Wilson studied the specimen before him, he realized that the hawk did not strike at random, but aimed for a particular prey. There was a flock of small birds in the brush, constantly moving, darting about, leaping from twig to twig, hopping from the ground into the trees in short, irregular flights or in longer flights of dipping and weaving. As the sparrow hawk perched motionless on the poplar high above this scene, it was studying one particular bird it had chosen from the flock to be its prey, following the bird and then striking with unerring and fatal aim.

The bird that it had thus selected was doomed: the eyes of the hawk had concentrated on it until its every motion would be anticipated. So unerring was the hawk's eye and aim that it could veer through the thicket despite its wings' spreading a foot on either side, seize its prey, and emerge from the briers in an instant. The hawk had not been waiting for an unguarded moment, or a lapse of vigilance before it struck; with so narrow a margin of time, there could be no opportunity to turn from one small bird to another within the thicket. As deadly as the sparrow hawk was, it was persecuted by blue jays which set up an outcry whenever the hawk was seen.

In the unending wilderness drama that now opened before him, there were some acts that impressed Wilson strongly, and one was the mystery of the selective destructiveness of the hawk, the obscure destiny of the wren or the sparrow chosen to be its victim. Wilson often hunted now in the space between the Delaware and the Schuylkill Rivers south of Philadelphia, where there were level meadows cut with drainage ditches. He hunted there because it was closer to the city, and he had little time for longer trips. Hawks were numerous, and as the spring advanced Wilson was surprised to note a good many barred owls and a kind of hawk he called the rough-legged falcon, concluding that they were survivors of once-numerous birds that had lived in the area before civilization closed around it. There were twenty or thirty of these falcons, big birds, twenty-two inches long and with a four-foot wingspread, with a slow and heavy flight. He often saw them in the evening coursing low over the meadows, generally in pairs. The shots of hunters and the presence of people had given them some of the characteristics of the prey they hunted. They rarely flew far. They sped from one isolated tree to another, "making a loud squealing as they rise, something resembling the neighing of a young colt, though in a more shrill and savage tone." They hunted in the ditches, flying low and slowly over the very surface of the water where, like soldiers in trenches, they could not be shot from the fields. But more often they perched on detached trees rising from the meadows and, like cats, watched the dry banks for hours on end.

Wilson counted forty barred owls in these meadows that spring. Once he saw a pigeon hawk skimming low over the fields, and shot it to use as a model. The hawk had killed a blackbird, and was carrying it off, its claws driven through the very heart of its victim.

Wilson's shot had only wounded the hawk, but as it was dying it clung to the blackbird with its last breath. On the banks of the Schuylkill, near Bartram's Garden, he saw what he thought was a pigeon hawk, sailing high in the air, noting it particularly because its flight was erratic and unusual. The hawk seemed to throw itself from one quarter of the sky to another with terrific velocity, inclining to earth, yet then dropping in a single plunge into a thicket and emerging with a small bird in its claws. While Wilson watched, the hawk returned to the same hunting ground, and repeated the same maneuver in an adjoining thicket, dropping from great height with startling violence and speed in its wild zigzag plunge. In an instant of terror, with the roar of its wings, its wild appearance, extended claws and its fierce red eyes, the hawk appeared to seize its prey by sudden surprise and the powerful momentum of its descent. At length Wilson managed to shoot the hawk. It was not a pigeon hawk, as he had thought, though much resembling it, and he concluded it was a hitherto unknown variety, to which he gave the name of the sharp-shinned hawk because of a knifelike structure of the leg below the knee, enabling the hawk to hold its prey more securely.

In May, 1807, Wilson shot a summer redbird, the first of these birds that he had ever shot. Still common, in the sense that everyone had seen them, they were rare and shy around towns, so that a summer might go by without one being noted, while a few miles away they were everywhere. Startlingly brilliant with its strong vermilion color, and with a song like a loose trill on a fife, the redbird was a popular favorite, something that everyone noted for its beautiful and surprising appearance in the green forest. Yet it was a source of great confusion. European naturalists in studying the redbird from dead specimens had invented no fewer than four different species. The reason was that the male did not achieve its bright vermilion coat until its second year, and in the meantime there were varied colors believed to be different birds. In August the young male birds, hatched about the middle of June, were olive green, stained with buff color. How could it be guessed that the buff gradually brightened to red? So still another bird was identified from a different stage in the growth of one species. The summer redbird that Wilson shot was green-winged, puzzling him no little. He did not know how to classify it, so he painted it as he found it, green wings and all, but set his painting aside until he could be sure of what it was.

The date revealed the progress on his book. In January, 1807, he was working on robins, the fifth bird he pictured; in mid-May he was engaged on the summer redbird, the twentieth bird of the first volume. It was evident that he and Bradford would be steadily engaged if they were to keep to the schedule they had set for themselves, and finish ten volumes in five years. Moreover, the subscriptions came in slowly. There was a general interest in the project, but $120 was too much of an investment to be made, at least not without the first volume in hand to show what the whole set would be like.

The printers and craftsmen accounted for a good many subscribers—half the Philadelphia buyers were tradespeople and artisans—but subscriptions from prosperous people were needed to establish confidence in the enterprise. Much of Wilson's first support in Philadelphia came from Miers Fisher and his family. They bought five sets of the *Ornithology,* an investment of $600, but what lent their support significance was that the position of the family made their endorsement influential. It was at this time, coincidentally, that Audubon's connection with Miers Fisher came to an end.

Miers Fisher was a lawyer as well as a merchant. His concern with Audubon was a relatively small matter among his many interests. In 1790, as noted above, Audubon's father had placed his American property in Miers Fisher's hands. The property consisted principally of a mill and a lead mine at Mill Grove, outside Philadelphia. The elder Audubon could not himself come to America because he was in active service, first in the French revolutionary government, and later under Napoleon. Financial matters were complicated because Audubon was not sole owner of the property.

Personal matters were even more complicated, so much so they often seemed burlesque. The elder Audubon had also placed his son, born out of wedlock, in Fisher's hands. In 1803, when Audubon was about seventeen, he was living with Fisher's family at Urie. The next chapter in the story depends on Audubon's autobiography. He wrote that Miers Fisher was an excessively Puritanical old Quaker who objected to fishing, hunting, dancing, and other innocent amusements. In addition, Audubon said, Fisher wanted him to marry his daughter, who was a charming girl, but he had taken an instant dislike to her. Miers Fisher had no daughter of an age suitable to Audubon's story. He and his wife Sarah Redwood Fisher had a son, Miers Fisher, who was sixteen years old in 1803. He later became the head of the Russian branch of Miers Fisher's merchant house, with headquarters in St. Petersburg. This son married Helene Gregoroffsky, of a noble Russian family, in a Church of England ceremony, special permission having been given by Emperor Alexander, but the bridegroom was poisoned immediately after the ceremony and was found dead the next morning. This portion of Audubon's account of Fisher, then, was fanciful, and a sophomoric version of matters that were really laden with interest and importance.

After a year Audubon left Fisher's home, and lived at Mill Grove, not far from Valley Forge. The personal and financial relations now became so complicated they could barely be made out. The part owner and manager of the Mill Grove property was a rather sinister character named Da Costa, an associate of Stephen Girard, the banker, and Da Costa endeavored to poison the mind of Audubon's father against Audubon. When Audubon left Miers Fisher's home, he was advanced money for his living expenses by an English merchant named Bakewell, who lived near Mill Grove. For five years Bakewell advanced young Audubon money as he needed it. Audubon was in love with Bakewell's daughter Lucy. As the quarrel with Da Costa continued, Bakewell advanced Audubon money to visit his father in France. Da Costa was greatly agitated, and tried to create dissension between Audubon and his father, saying the boy was claiming in Philadelphia that he was to inherit all Mill Grove, and using this supposed fortune to promote his courtship of

Lucy Bakewell. As the Audubon interests were in the custody of Miers Fisher, the elder Audubon wrote to the lawyer his reasons for opposing the marriage at that time, with the explanations he was to communicate to Lucy's father.

Audubon spent more than a year in France. He studied art under David in Paris, and when he returned to America his father established a partnership in business for him with Ferdinand Rozier, whose father was a merchant of Nantes. Audubon's father also had a merchant house there. The agreement was that young Audubon and young Rozier were to be commercial partners for nine years, to operate the Mill Grove property, or to dispose of it as seemed best, but were to make no decision without consulting Miers Fisher "as a common friend and good counselor." Fisher advised them to sell Mill Grove to Da Costa, which they did for around $10,000, disposing of the mill and mine, but retaining the farm. Audubon then worked for Lucy Bakewell's uncle on Pearl Street in New York.

As for Wilson, he was confined by his work on *Rees's Cyclopaedia* and on his *Ornithology* to the Philadelphia publishing house, the first summer since he arrived in the United States that he had spent in the city. The din, the walls, the chimneys, and finally the books themselves began to wear on his nerves. A doubt began to grow in his mind about his great work, not of its value but of the readiness of the country to accept a work of its magnitude. Each subscription was almost painfully acquired. Subscribers, moreover, did not pay a single penny on the *Ornithology* in advance of publication. The signers merely contracted to buy the set, paying for each volume after it was received. Wilson himself was not being paid for his labor on the *Ornithology;* his income came entirely from his work on the encyclopedia, but he owned the rights to the *Ornithology* and would collect his royalties when the books were paid for. The salary paid him as encyclopedia editor, however, was more than he had ever received, and he was consequently satisfied on that score. But confinement to town became increasingly vexatious. On Sundays he rode into the woods, trying to pack into a few hours the observation that had once been almost his only summer occupation.

There was an almost mysterious co-operation of nature with his effort. Again and again he found the birds he had searched for suddenly appearing all around him. More often, when he looked vainly for some bird he could not find, another more startling specimen sang before him, or some wilderness drama was enacted before his eyes that he could never have anticipated finding. This was the time of the year when the mockingbird would permit no cat, dog, animal or man to approach its nest. They were now only rarely seen around Philadelphia, where they were once common. Bartram could recollect times in his youth when they stayed all winter. Wilson watched these birds darting after an intruder, swift as an arrow, striking violently from side to side, utterly fearless. Once as he rode into the woods he came upon a mockingbird attacking a black snake, the worst enemy to its nest, eluding the snake's attempt to strike it, and hitting the snake repeatedly on the back of the head. After a time the snake attempted to glide away. The mockingbird attacked more fiercely. When the snake's strength began to flag, the bird partly lifted it from the ground, beating it with its wings.

The tyrant flycatcher, the kingbird, only about eight inches long, fearlessly attacked the hawks that he watched sailing above the Schuylkill. They pursued crows and eagles. Riding his horse to the woodlands, Wilson saw a kingbird launch itself into the air at the sight of a distant hawk, mount swiftly above it, and dart down on the hawk's back, as violently and unerringly as the hawk dove into the thicket after small birds. The hawk turned and rolled in the air, trying to rid itself of its merciless adversary. The kingbird mounted higher again, keeping up a shrill and rapid twittering, then descended with greater violence. The hawk now tried to escape, but the kingbird followed, keeping up the attack for perhaps a mile. Before that distance had been spanned, another kingbird had appeared to take up the pursuit.

Yet the kingbird was itself driven to wild retreat by the purple martin, a bird much like the kingbird, but with greater powers of flight, which tormented it in the way that the kingbird tormented hawks. Ordinarily the mockingbird, the kingbird, and the purple martin were pacific; it was only while the young were in the nest that their constant broils kept the woods in an uproar. Wilson came upon a red-headed woodpecker apparently playing a kind of game with the kingbird's fiery temper in this period, merely clinging to a fence rail, and circling around it good-naturedly, while the kingbird swept in frustration around and around, attacking repeatedly, only to find that the woodpecker had merely moved to the other side of the rail.

By midsummer Wilson was almost desperate at the ebbing of the season before he had time to study the birds. Many of the warblers had left, and in the dense heat of the woods most of the birds were mute. He told Bartram that he would become a street musician if he remained in the city—a term of contempt to him since William Mitchell had become one. Wilson gave himself a vacation, and wandered alone into the mountains. He hunted and camped in the forest, avoiding towns whenever possible. It impressed him that red-headed woodpeckers were exceedingly numerous, more than he had ever noted before, on the lower slopes. He found and collected little-known birds, like the great-crested flycatcher, which he never saw except in the gloomiest and least frequented wilderness. In the high, timbered slopes of the Blue Mountains he heard the feeble, plaintive song of the wood pewee, a repeated peto-way, peto-way, pee-way, that at this season was one of the few birds heard. But there were great flocks of cedarbirds feeding on the whortleberries that in places literally covered the slopes. They moved about in compact bodies of twenty to fifty, small, silent and gluttonous birds with feathers of exquisite silky texture, fat from the strawberries of summer, and so numerous that despite their small size they were hunted for market, selling for twenty-five cents a dozen that year in Philadelphia.

The summer redbirds usually left Pennsylvania in mid-August. But some remained this year, feeding on the whortleberries that were exceptionally abundant. It was on this trip that Wilson began to feel a certain sympathy for the European naturalists whose mistakes he indicated throughout the *Ornithology*. He saw a singular bird of a sort he had never seen or heard of before, with greenish-yellow wings, and spotted with red, green and yellow so that it appeared to be sprinkled. It so perplexed him that he followed it through the woods a long way to shoot it, a difficult task because the bird had become alarmed by him. When he eventually killed it, he found that it was also an immature summer redbird, like that curious green-winged bird he had shot in the spring. But now the plumage was further advanced toward the vermilion color that it would eventually wear, and it was easy to see why naturalists working from dead specimens alone were led into error. Wilson himself could hardly believe that it was the same bird, but on returning to Philadelphia compared it with the painting he had made in the spring. He was still not positive enough to write of the bird, however, and it was not until he raised a summer redbird in captivity, and saw the changes of color taking place, that he settled this problem to his own satisfaction.

In the deep timbered hollows he heard an uncouth guttural sound, *kowe-kowe, kowe-kowe-kowe,* beginning slowly and ending rapidly, with the notes running together. This was the song of the yellow-billed cuckoo, called the cowbird, or, in Virginia, the rain crow, because it became clamorous before rain. A big, awkward bird, thirteen inches long, it was remarkable for its ability to act. The male remained near the nest when Wilson approached it. The nesting female remained motionless. Wilson came so near that he could almost touch her with his hand. She then threw herself on the ground, feigning lameness, trailing her wings, and tumbling over. Many other birds employed the same artifice—the woodcock and partridge among them—and it impressed Wilson with its commentary on mankind, that the bird protected her young by offering herself as a larger victim.

Quail were sold in the Philadelphia markets at twelve to eighteen cents apiece. Wilson found a mother quail guiding her young in search of food, with a twittering noise like that of young chickens, and sheltering them under her wings after the fashion of domestic fowls. The bird became aware of his presence. She threw herself on the path in consternation and alarm, fluttering along and beating the ground with her wings. She seemed wounded, and used every artifice to attract pursuit, meanwhile uttering peculiar notes of alarm that seemed to be understood by the young, who scattered into hiding.

And always overhead the hawks were gliding, eyes focused on each square foot of ground. The mysteries of the wilderness and the savage dramas it contained were now constantly in Wilson's mind as he compared the wild birds with the large number he kept in cages. Once when his cages were full he put a newly captured blue jay in the cage of the orchard oriole. "She put on airs of alarm," he wrote, as if she considered herself endangered and insulted by the intrusion; the jay, meanwhile, sat mute and motionless at the bottom of the cage, either dubious of his own situation, or willing to allow time for the fears of his neighbor to subside. Accordingly after a few minutes, after displaying various threatening gestures (like some of those Indians we read of in their first interviews with the whites) she began to make her approaches, but with great circumspection and readiness to retreat. Seeing, however, the jay begin to pick up some crumbs of broken chestnut in a humble and peaceable way, she also descended and began to do the same; but, at the slightest motion of her new guest, wheeled around, and put herself on the defensive. All this ceremonious jealousy ended before evening; and they now roost together, feed and play together in perfect harmony and good humor. When the jay goes to drink, his messmate very impudently jumps into the water to wash herself, throwing water in showers over her companion, who bears it all patiently; venturing now and then to take a sip between splashes, without betraying the slightest token of irritation. On the contrary he seems to take pleasure in his little fellow-prisoner, allowing her to pick (which she does very gently) about his whiskers, and to clean his claws from the minute fragments of chestnuts which happen to adhere to them. This attachment on the one part, and mild condescension on the other, may perhaps be the effect of mutual misfortunes, which are found not only to knit mankind, but many species of inferior animals, more closely together; and shows that the disposition of the blue jay may be humanized and rendered susceptible of affectionate impressions, even for those birds which, in a state of nature, he would have no hesitation of making a meal of.

The wilderness incidents that Wilson noted, commonplace or rare, were mounting up to a treasury of bird lore that no one had recorded. The selective blow of the predatory birds, studying their attack before they made it, the pretense and quickness of the quail or the partridge deceiving its enemy, the exact way in which a snowy owl lifted a fish from the water with a backward thrust of its claw, or the way a nighthawk, flying like a huge bat through the Philadelphia twilight, would fold its wings and drop forty feet to the pavement—these were all aspects of the contemporary scene that Americans recognized, but which had not been recorded. Dozens of incidents in the eventual nine volumes of the *Ornithology* are dated from Wilson's fall expedition of 1807, suggesting the amount of usable material that Wilson accumulated when he was able to leave his daily tasks.

But there were few occasions when he could do so. As soon as he returned to work, he set out for New York and Albany to try to get subscriptions to his books. Fulton was now running his steamboat between Albany and New York, and Wilson was anxious to see him. The inventor was on a trip up the Hudson when Wilson arrived in New York in September and Wilson occupied himself with bird studies and selling attempts. He wanted to get a local bookseller to act as the agent for the *Ornithology*, but the leading booksellers, Brisbane and Brann, refused to have anything to do with it until they saw a copy of the first volume. A trip to Newark and to Long Island produced no orders. In desperation, Wilson called at the house of Dr. Samuel Latham Mitchill, who was perhaps the best-known scientist in America. Dr. Mitchill lived in splendor in a mansion, surrounded by his cabinets of conchology and mineralogy, and with his rooms still further enriched by a great collection of Indian tomahawks. He was renowned for his ability to discourse end-lessly about any subject on earth, and was beginning his life work of a study of all the fishes found in the waters of New York. The good doctor had recently married a rich widow, so he was now able to devote all his time to science and to talk.

Dr. Mitchill was not at home. Wilson returned to the mansion on three occasions, without success. However, he then visited King's College, or Columbia, as it came to be called, and the professors there, looking over his prospectus and his plan for the *Ornithology*, persuaded the college authorities to subscribe.* And in his walks around New York and Long Island, Wilson gathered material. He was surprised to see many indigo buntings, small birds of a rich, sky-blue color, active and vigorous, and what he called "a pretty good songster" when it was in voice. The purple finches were now passing through in great flocks on their way south, hardy, vigorous birds, with deep crimson head and back and breast, and dusky black wing tips and tail, and Wilson secured two of them alive, which he kept as pets. One had been caught in a trap, and the other winged by gunshot. They became reconciled to captivity in a day or so. Wilson then caught an indigo bunting to paint and put it in the same cage with the purple finches. The finches nearly killed the newcomer, suddenly becoming tyrannical and domineering, driving the indigo into a corner, and tearing out feathers as Wilson tried to stop them. The aggressors, Wilson noted, then turned a malicious eye on him, biting and holding on with their bills, and waiting for him to withdraw his hand to begin their outrages again.

On October 2, after the *Clermont* returned from Albany, Wilson called on Fulton, who received him pleasantly. *Rees's Cyclopaedia* was soon to go to press with the article on canals, and as the success of the steamboat had revolutionized thought on canals, Wilson was anxious that Fulton should read it. He also interested Fulton in the *Ornithology*, and Fulton subscribed to the set of books. Fulton agreed to stop by Bradford's office in Phila-delphia the following week to make whatever changes were necessary in the articles on canals.

In Wilson's leisure time he haunted the American Museum, a New York imitation of Peale's Museum in Philadelphia. It was run by a rough diamond named Scudder, who told Wilson that he himself was a greater curiosity than anything in his collections. Scudder had exhibits of natural history, stuffed birds and animals, and all sorts of freaks, but he

---

* The plates in this volume, surely one of the first copies of Wilson's *Ornithology* sold, were used in making the color plates for this biography.

also made waxworks, and told Wilson that his exhibit of Potiphar's Wife took in ten dollars for every dollar that he made on all his birds. In Albany there was a similar institution, Trowbridge's Museum, but of much higher quality. Wilson went on to the New York State capital in an effort to sign up more subscribers; he was befriended by Trowbridge, who admired him and encouraged him—Wilson's own stuffed birds went eventually to Trowbridge's Museum—but who could not help him in the main purpose of his trip, and Wilson returned to Philadelphia without securing another subscriber. However, he found an order had come in meanwhile from a most important one—President Thomas Jefferson, whose order was dated October 9, 1807. Jefferson wrote: "He salutes Mr. Wilson with great respect."

As the winter closed in, Wilson spent all his time working on his drawings of birds, and coloring the plates that were made. He had almost no life apart from his work. From his earliest writing, in his poems as well as in his letters, Wilson delighted in human notations about the people he was with, whether it was a glimpse of David Brodie at his loom, or Meg Duncan sauntering past the Tower of Auchinbathie, or William M'Dowell in his library at Castle Semple, or William Witherspoon tending his flower garden at his cottage beside the White Cart. It was impossible for him to mention another human being and not communicate some item of his individuality. These personal touches now disappeared from Wilson's writing. He left no descriptions or individual glimpses of the people he associated with, with the single exception of Bartram. He did not write a line about Sarah Miller, though he had left many glimpses of Martha M'Lean. He drew no sketch in either prose or verse of Samuel Bradford, though he had once delighted in portraying people like William Sharp. For years Wilson had lived as a boarder in the home of William Jones, but he left few comments on Jones, a picturesque and interesting character in his own right. Nor did Wilson leave a record of Daniel Miller, who was not only the brother of the girl he intended to marry, but the man to whom some of his most revealing letters were addressed. And he did not mention such a figure as Miers Fisher, though he was unquestionably in frequent contact with him.

But it was not the absence of specific people from Wilson's correspondence that indicated the change taking place in his view of the world. He no longer wrote of people because he did not pay much attention to them. He was writing of birds as he had once written about weavers, or about the people to whom he tried to sell cloth. Humanity was disappearing from his vision, to be replaced by winged creatures whose habits and colors and ways monopolized his imagination and his thought.

CHAPTER SEVEN

"Few Americans
Have Seen More of Their Country..."

THROUGHOUT the *American Ornithology* Wilson mentioned specific happenings in connection with the birds he painted. "In the month of July last I took from the nest of the Maryland yellow-throat a young male cow bunting," he wrote, for example, or noted that he had shot three black-throated green warblers in June, trying to get a perfect specimen. Scattered and fragmentary though they were, the notes nevertheless added up to a kind of catalogue and calendar, revealing Wilson's whereabouts and occupations.

But in the period between October, 1807, and September, 1808, these personal experiences almost entirely disappeared from Wilson's writing. He mentioned that in November, 1807, the ruby-crowned wren was numerous around Philadelphia. These beautiful little birds came south from their breeding grounds near Hudson Bay, and Wilson mentioned that he hated to shoot them in order to get specimens, "for they appear so busy, so active, and unsuspecting, as to continue searching about the same twig, even after their companions have been shot down beside them."

That was one of the two personal observations Wilson recorded in eleven months. The other was that in December he noted a good many shore larks, flying in loose, scattered flocks—another winter resident, found in vacant meadows within Philadelphia itself, and in Wilson's opinion a beautiful bird with its rich Naples-yellow color and delicate black markings. In passing, also, Wilson recorded that in March of 1808 he shot and dissected eleven creepers, in order to satisfy himself as to their feeding habits and plumage.

But these were spare and uninformative comments to be spread over nearly a year. Few letters of Wilson remain from that period. The reason was obvious: the first volume of the *American Ornithology* was going to press. From the time of Wilson's return from Albany until June of 1808, he was steadily employed on the endless details of the engravings, the coloring, and the correction of the text. Robert Carr, who was greatly befriended by Wilson, and who came to be deeply influenced by him, was almost as passionately concerned to make the *Ornithology* perfect as was Wilson himself. In that first volume the engravings were made by different men, and the plates were colored by several artists who worked at home. Differences insensibly crept into the shadings of the colors of the feathers, and different styles became evident in the work of the engravers, so that Wilson's life in these months consisted largely of his walk to his office before dawn, the accumulation and correction of the color plates, and repeated trips to Carr's printing shop on Sansom Street. The completion of his own editorial work on the encyclopedia—and attempts to sell sets of the *Ornithology*—took his spare moments whenever any became available, but there were few. For the hand-coloring of the plates meant that each page had to be corrected individually. There were 10 colored plates in the first volume, and from 2 to 4 birds on each plate, or almost 40 separate bird pictures; but an edition of 200 books was being printed, so that there were really 8,000 separate bird engravings to be colored correctly. One of the hazards of the *Ornithology* was that while an artist of Robert Leslie's ability might color accurately the large bird featured on a plate, like the marvelous golden-winged woodpecker shown on the third plate in the first volume, another colorist could ruin a whole page by carelessness or inaccuracy in some detail of color or shading on a small figure, like that of the bunting shown on the same plate with the golden-wing.

When the proofs were finally corrected and the forms locked, and printing and binding started, Wilson could then resume a more normal life, and a more normal life for him meant wandering through the woods with his gun, his paints and his notebook, and reporting on what he saw. But he found he could not return to his former habits now that he had time to do so. The hopes that he placed in the *Ornithology,* the creative fever that had been built up, and his realization that he had created something truly new and wonderful led him to start on the second volume at once. He opened it with the painting and the essay on the red-headed woodpecker, the first bird that he had seen when he landed in America. He wrote with a confident informality lacking in the text of the first volume, proceeding from some inward certainty, with an emotion that would have been exultation had manifestation of it not been inappropriate for such a subject. The red-head's tricolor plumage, red, white and black glossed with steel blue, made this beautiful bird familiar to every schoolchild in America, Wilson wrote in his opening passages, and it was significant that he summoned up an image of nature, color and the youth of the nation at the beginning of his second volume.

He knew that his book was consequential as a contribution to natural history. But he had also set in motion cultural currents that were incalculable. When he began his work, American art was narrowly concerned with portrait painting alone, except for the massive scenes like those painted by Benjamin West, just as American literature was narrowly concerned with the topical patriotic poetry of Freneau and the wild Gothic fantasies of Charles Brockden Brown. Wilson gave to art a new subject in the magnificent color and variety of the American wilderness, leading not only to the work of Audubon and his successors, but turning the imagination of artists to native scenes generally, and in literature Wilson inspired the American bird poetry that was produced constantly and reached its great flowering in the few, unforgettable bird poems of Emily Dickinson.

Apart from Carr and Leslie, Wilson's sense of the potential significance of his work was not shared by the people engaged with him in creating it. Bradford had only committed himself to publishing one volume. If it brought in enough subscribers to make the whole venture profitable, the work would be completed. Bradford not only drew back, as a businessman, from any such visionary effort as Wilson contemplated; he would not have appreciated Wilson's purpose if he had understood it. The repeated question that ran through Wilson's essays, letters and poetry was: Why was there not a literature and art concerned with the American scene? The material in the *American Ornithology* was not esoteric or impractical information on the United States in Wilson's own time. Everyone hunted, and the lore of the forest, from the mystery of the migration of the rail to the habits of cougars and rattlesnakes, was an essential ingredient of popular culture. Woodcocks, teal, Canadian geese, snow geese, red ducks, bluebills, their habits, food, relations to other birds, were part of the unwritten common life of the nation, merging with the folklore of weather, woods and seasons. When Wilson wrote of reddish-tawny woodcocks, of their curious flight, as they rose in a kind of spiral, hovering in a wild irregular manner that made them hard to shoot, or when he wrote of the ground they were found in, called a cripple, a deep mire intersected with old logs, he was putting into prose what farm boys knew, but what the literary men of American had never written about. When he wrote of pheasants, ordinarily so alert and hardy, stupefied and bewildered by dogs, and when he described hunting them, he caught the flavor of common speech as well. "They are pretty hard to kill," he wrote, "and will often carry a heavy load to a distance of two hundred yards, and drop down dead." These were a refinement of the phrases of common speech, as his essays were a scientific study of a common interest.

There was a unique center of American common life, a focal point of popular interest, in the universal appeal of the wilderness. Wilson wrote that it was impossible to be bored with the great volume of nature before one in the American forest. He had felt the magnetic pull of the wilderness from the time he arrived, and in one way or another everyone he knew recognized it—in all walks of life, at all levels of society, in all areas. The substance of a culture that was appropriate to democracy lay in this interest that was stimulated and kept alive by the natural wealth before the eyes of everyone.

In the old countries the ties of race, a common heritage from antiquity, loyalty to a monarchy and its institutions, provided a cultural tissue around the institutions of government. The American government was created with theoretical and intellectually conceived institutions that were far in advance of the popular culture. Hence that popular culture did not nourish a deep inner conviction, a certainty of purpose and loyalty. Its typical product was the patriotic speech, read on an anniversary, rather than something that remained a living part of the ordinary daily existence of everyone. Every philosopher of democracy believed that education, in one way or another, would progressively enlighten the people, until they could appraise the merits of men and issues; but Wilson was a schoolteacher, who knew the reality of education from the schoolroom. And so far as popular education in the broader sense was concerned, Callender's newspapers had shown how the information on which people were to form their decisions could be perverted.

To deny to the people their right to chose, merely because education was inadequate, or their sources of information corrupt, was to deny democracy itself. "You make, or you unmake, laws," Wilson had told his audience at Milestown. "You declare war, or you proclaim peace. Not, indeed, in your own individual persons, but in the persons of your real representatives. You select men to perform the great duties of government. Their term of duty over, if they have shown themselves worthy of your confidence, they are reappointed; if not, they descend again to the rank of a private citizen. In the exercise of this right, by the people themselves, lies the chief excellence of a republican form of government; as it not only makes the representatives responsible to, and dependent on the people, as they ought to be, but provides an effectual remedy for almost every abuse. . . ."

But there was an Achilles' heel of democracy. It was provocation, incitement, distortion, and the inflaming of normal differences of opinion until rational discussion became impossible. The need was for a sustaining vision that would keep political differences in perspective—the quality that religious teachers hoped to gain by moral teachings, and that educators hoped would come from an informed people, and which was actually achieved in democracies in times of crisis, when an elemental love of country swept across partisan disputes. Wilson felt that whatever contribution he could make lay in this area, in the creation of some fabric of common life which could sustain a democratic culture.

The Declaration of Independence did not only hold that men were created equal, and endowed with life, liberty, and the pursuit of happiness. It affirmed the faith of its signers in the "Laws of Nature and of Nature's God." The cleavage in American political life that Wilson saw developing came from neglect of that side of the Declaration. The elemental love of country that came to life in times of crisis was a complex emotion springing from many sources—memories of familiar hills and woodlands, the scent of spring, the driving clouds of blackbirds in the smoky air of Indian summer, the sense of common life which in itself meant that men had turned again to nature's God for the wellspring of their actions. The vision of his masterpiece that possessed Wilson was of a work "not idle or useless," he wrote in his introduction, "but worthy of rational beings, and doubtless agreeable to the Deity."

His tragedy was that concentration on his work, coupled with the solitary habits bred by his Scottish imprisonment, cut him off from human relationships in a period when he needed them. At the time Wilson's first volume appeared, the ill feeling between the United States and Great Britain, growing steadily since the battle of the *Chesapeake* and the *Leopard,* had become critical; war was expected. Wilson was so little known in a personal sense that it was not generally understood that he was an American citizen and a patriot. He made no attempt to enlighten people. It never occurred to him that it was necessary to do so. "Few Americans have seen more of their country than I have," he once wrote in this connection, "and none love her more."

His love of his country was tested at the outset. In September the first volume of the *Ornithology* was ready, and on September 21, 1808, Wilson dropped a note to Bartram: "In a few minutes I set out for the Eastern States, through Boston to Maine, and back through the State of Vermont, in search of birds and subscribers. . . ." His great travels had begun, to carry him more than 10,000 miles in the next few years.

He left his horse with Daniel Miller. It was understood that he would pay for the animal's food and care when he returned, for he needed all his own resources for his journey. He carried a few copies of the *Ornithology,* and such supplies as his gun and his paper, ink, brushes, colors and notebook. He walked to George's Tavern, where the New York stage departed—an inn owned by John Inskeep, the partner of Bradford and Inskeep, publisher of the *Ornithology.* The stage left at eight o'clock, and Wilson's traveling companion was a Colonel Simonds, who was on his way to Fort Oswego on the shore of Lake Ontario.

They rode together as far as Princeton, where Wilson left the stage. Or, more precisely, they rode and walked together: the driver stopped the stage frequently, at one tavern after another for long waits, and Wilson and Colonel Simonds walked on when he did so, to be picked up seven or eight miles along the road when the stage caught up with them. The weather was pleasant, the military man and the ornithologist had a good deal to talk about, and Wilson felt that his trip had started auspiciously. When Wilson visited Niagara, four years before, Fort Oswego had been in ruins. It was now being rebuilt, ostensibly to provide a military post for enforcing the Embargo on the lake.

At Princeton Wilson parted from the Colonel, put a copy of the *American Ornithology* under his arm, stuffed his pockets with copies of the advertisement for the set of books, and set out for Tusculum, the mansion of the late Dr. Witherspoon. He felt that it was fitting to begin his journey by approaching the home of the most celebrated townsman of Paisley. The mansion, looted during the Revolution, had been rebuilt; it was now the home of Dr. Samuel Stanhope Smith, the husband of Witherspoon's daughter Anne and successor to Witherspoon as Princeton's president. Smith was then an elderly man, grave, kindly, somewhat pedantic, with impressive appearance and bearing, whose subject was moral philosophy. He had been a preacher and teacher all his life, Witherspoon's favorite student, the founder of Hampden-Sydney College in Virginia before Witherspoon brought him back to Princeton.

As Wilson approached the house he was stirred by unfamiliar and troubling thoughts. In the best of times he experienced an inward discomfort on these occasions, for they called up the memories of his peddling days in Scotland. Walking into a strange town, approaching people to whom he was unknown, turned him back to his frame of mind when he tramped over Highland roads, "beneath a load of silks and sorrows bent," and an obscure sense of misery and defeat settled on him no matter what reception he received. In this case, however, his thoughts were strong and interesting, and too extended to be put into words, though he said afterwards they might amuse his friends. Wilson was somehow sure that the meeting was an important one to him: it was as if he expected a cordial reception, the solution of his problems, and something in the nature of a homecoming. The long months in which he had worked on the book, seeing no one, had doubtless built up an exaggerated sense of its impact on others; nevertheless, he plainly staked much in his expectations of this meeting, almost as he had two decades before when he made his way to Castle Semple to see William M'Dowell about his book of poetry.

He was bewildered by his reception. Dr. Smith received him in a kindly fashion, but as a complete stranger. Wilson displayed the copy of his book, and Dr. Smith expressed the greatest praise for it. But that was all. Witherspoon's daughter had died not long before, and the household was an empty one. However Dr. Smith directed Wilson, very significantly, to a colleague—the only other Princeton official he found at home. This was Dr. John M'Lean, a physician who had become professor of natural history and chemistry. Dr. M'Lean was thirty-seven years old in 1808, or five years younger than Wilson. He bore the name of the Paisley family which, along with Witherspoon, meant most to Wilson. The orphan son of an army surgeon, M'Lean was raised from childhood in Glasgow with Charles Macintosh, the inventor of waterproof cloth, and was known as an infant prodigy in the scientific circles around the Macintosh family. M'Lean entered the University of Glasgow when he was thirteen years old, and studied science in Edinburgh, London and Paris before beginning the practice of medicine in Glasgow at twenty. In 1795 he left Scotland because of opposition to the government's policy of repression, and after visiting Dr. Rush in Philadelphia, was made professor of chemistry at Princeton. Dr. M'Lean married Phoebe Bainbridge, the sister of Commodore William Bainbridge, the most renowned American naval hero of the time. He was well started on a brilliant career (which was to lead him to the presidency of Princeton after Dr. Smith's death), ended by his own untimely death at forty-three during the War of 1812.

Dr. M'Lean was an agreeable conversationalist, gifted with a Scottish wit and sociability, and a man of fine presence and bearing. His son John (who in turn became president of Princeton) was even then a precocious youngster, subsequently becoming a friend of Wilson's friend Daniel Miller. Dr. M'Lean was consequently the leading spirit, at his meeting with Wilson, and an established, successful, and self-possessed individual as Wilson was not. He asked Wilson to have tea with him, and he tried to make Wilson feel at ease, cheerfully confessing that his grasp of natural history did not encompass the world of birds: he could scarcely tell a sparrow from a woodpecker. M'Lean also tried to ease Wilson's disappointment by asking him to leave some of his material and bird drawings with him so he could begin his own study of the subject.

Drawn from Nature by A. Wilson.   Engraved by A. Lawson.

1. Mississippi Kite.   2. Tennessee Warbler.   3. Kentucky W.   4. Prairie W.

25

One of Wilson's finest plates, his superb Mississippi kite was drawn from a bird he discovered and named.
The other birds are warblers which he also discovered.

When it became evident that neither Princeton College nor either of the two officials would subscribe to the *Ornithology,* Wilson left. He was heartsore. He made perfunctory calls on some of the ministers attached to Princeton College. They could not afford to subscribe for a set of books costing $120. At eight-thirty that night Wilson left for New Brunswick, reaching there at midnight, and spending some of his limited money for a night's lodging.

The next morning he called on the professors of Rutgers College. They had no money for a work so expensive, and the college itself would not buy a set of the books. Wilson went on to Elizabeth and then to Newark, without securing a single subscriber. He reached New York without having received anything except extravagant compliments. He said he would gladly exchange them for a sale.

Now seriously alarmed, Wilson spent a day in his New York hotel room, writing letters to prospects, enclosing the printed prospectus of the *Ornithology,* and announcing his intention to call in person to display the first volume. His first response increased his bewilderment. Catherine Ackerly, the widow of William Cock and the heiress who had recently married Dr. Samuel Latham Mitchill, turned out to be an admirer of Wilson's poetry. When Wilson called at Mitchill's home early in the morning—having made three unsuccessful calls the year before—he was invited to breakfast.

A contemporary and admirer of Dr. Mitchill described what happened in these terms: "The doctor poured out the immense treasures of his prompt memory, and gave ingenious illustrations on divers topics for the mental gratification of Wilson," who, on his part, appeared to be stunned by Mrs. Mitchill's interest in his poetry. "The result of this interview was a promise on the part of the doctor to furnish Wilson with history of the pinnated grouse of Long Island."

There were more immediate results: Colonel George Gibbs, the young son of a Newport merchant, an amateur mineralogist, living on his estate near Astoria, bought three sets of Wilson's *Ornithology.* Rufus King, the last of the great Federalist leaders, became a subscriber, and his nineteen-year-old son Charles King also. The Right Reverend Benjamin Moore, the Episcopal Bishop of New York, who was soon to become president of Columbia (where Mitchill was professor of chemistry and natural history), was another subscriber, as was the Reverend John Mitchell Mason, one of the foremost preachers of his time. Perhaps Wilson's most valuable scientific supporter, apart from Mitchill, was Dr. David Hosack. Three years younger than Wilson, the physician at the duel of Hamilton and Burr, Dr. Hosack was a professor of medicine at Columbia, the founder of the Humane Society, the New-York Historical Society, the American Academy of Fine Arts, and one of the founders of Bellevue Hospital. Now he was starting his Elgin Botanical Gardens, a 20-acre tract crammed with 1,500 species of native American plants.

For a time it seemed as if Wilson might get the subscribers he needed in New York alone. Dr. Mitchill wrote an acute and perceptively enthusiastic review of the *Ornithology,* and De Witt Clinton later published an impressive endorsement of Wilson's work. Wilson said he had become as famous as the town crier. He also made his way to Greenwich Village to interview Tom Paine, the great hero of Scottish intellectuals in his youth. Paine received him in his dressing gown, at a table covered with newspapers and his writing materials. He asked to be remembered to Bartram and to Peale when Wilson got back to Philadelphia, looked over the *Ornithology* with a penetrating and intelligent eye, and signed up for a set of the books, though his death a short time later terminated the contract.

There were the familiar disappointments and rebuffs, however, to temper this partial success. The new governor of New York, Daniel Tompkins, from whom Wilson had expected a favorable response, because they were both Jeffersonians, showed Wilson the door, saying coldly, "I would not give you a hundred dollars for all the birds you intend to describe, even had I them alive." But Wilson had at least a beginning. He felt sufficiently confident to take a day off, looking at City Hall, the most beautiful example of American architecture he had seen, viewing the new fortifications that were being built on Governor's Island (he sent a detailed four-page description to Daniel Miller), and visiting the theater to see Thomas Cooper play Romeo. Cooper, whose career began in Edinburgh in 1792, when Wilson reached his deepest despair there, married Mary Fairley, the most beautiful New York belle of the time, and built a mansion in Bristol, near Wilson's old Milestown school. Cooper too became a subscriber to the *Ornithology*.

In New Haven Wilson sold nothing. Walking twenty miles across country to Middletown, Connecticut, he was cordially received by a wealthy sportsman named Alsop, who cheerfully gave him much information about local birds, presented him with letters to men in Boston, and also freely gave him stuffed birds from his large collection, but did not subscribe. At Hartford, Congressman Chauncey Goodrich sent Wilson to Daniel Wadsworth, who bought a set of books. The Hartford Library also subscribed. But then, all the way to Boston, the towns did not give up a single purchaser.

In Boston itself Wilson was coldly received, and busied himself sightseeing, studying the battlefield of Bunker Hill, and talking with the Revolutionary veteran who acted as guide. Eventually he came in contact with a former secretary of ex-President John Adams, and was directed to circles where there might be more interest in his book on the part of people who also possessed the means to buy it. He then sold a few subscriptions—to Josiah Quincy, the president of Harvard; Israel Thorndike, the wealthiest of New England merchants; Elias Hasket Derby, the great Salem mariner; James Bowdoin, the son of the governor; and John Davis, formerly President Washington's comptroller of currency, an authority on maritime law, with a lifelong interest in science. The ministers Jedediah Morse and the Reverend Dr. Prince subscribed, and the Boston Athenæum bought a set, but only fourteen names from all of Massachusetts was an ominous beginning in New England.

Money had become a pressing problem. Wilson no longer rode stages or packet boats.

He walked from town to town. He could not afford to stay in any one place long enough to discover all its possible buyers, and no one had given him a penny in cash.

When Wilson left Boston he walked to Portsmouth and then to Portland, Maine, without selling any books. The birds had largely left for the south; he found nothing to report except that large numbers of yellow-rumped warblers (later called myrtle warblers) were feeding on the dwarf myrtle berries near the shore, lingering beyond their usual time for departure. On the day he arrived in Portland he happened to pick up a paper in a tavern, and read on the front page his poem, "Freedom and Peace," written under a pseudonym years before, during Jefferson's campaign. He said nothing. The next day Wilson attended a session of the court. There the poem was read before a considerable crowd, and discussed as a very good piece of verse, a good song. Wilson listened, still saying nothing of his authorship. He was puzzled and disturbed when he mentioned the incident in a letter to Lawson.

From Portland he walked west, 157 miles, to Dartmouth College. "Dr. Wheelock, the president, made me eat at his table," he wrote, "and the professors vied with each other to oblige me." Wheelock bought a set of the books for the college library, the New Hampshire Medical Society purchased a set, as did Philip Carrigain, a pioneer mapmaker, and Dr. Nathan Smith, a country boy who had learned medicine after assisting at an amputation, and who became the foremost teacher of medicine in the country. Wilson felt it was revealing that the half-wild regions of New Hampshire produced seven subscribers, half as many as all Boston and Massachusetts combined.

He called at a great number of small towns on his way to Albany, though he was suffering miserably from fatigue and a severe cold. Wilson picked up a few more subscriptions in Albany. It was the home of Simeon De Witt, who owned great tracts of land near the Duncan farm, and who was the brother-in-law of Charles Brockden Brown. Brockholst Livingston, newly appointed to the Supreme Court, and another of Witherspoon's eminent students, also subscribed, along with John Lansing, Chief Justice of the New York Supreme Court; the Reverend Eliphalet Nott, a famous Presbyterian clergyman, the president of Union College, who had acquired a fortune by his invention of stoves and other warming appliances; and Archibald M'Intyre, an early steelmaker who pioneered in developing Adirondack ores. All these pledged $120 each to carry on the *Ornithology*, together with the Reverend Frederick Beasley, another of Witherspoon's outstanding students at Princeton, who had become an Episcopalian and the rector of St. Peter's in Albany.

The weather was now cold, with only winter birds on the scene, and migrating ducks overhead. It came to Wilson that all along the way, from Maine on southward, there had always been snowbirds—"I never passed a day, and scarcely a mile, without seeing numbers of them, and frequently large flocks of several thousands." The name was given indiscriminately to any one of the winter sparrows, and in Wilson's own classification, as he placed it with the finches, it was "by far the most numerous, as well as the most extensively disseminated, of all the feathered tribes that visit us from the frozen regions of the north." Along with his mention of the yellow-rumped warblers, this note was his only ornithological refer-ence in his long journey. Trying to sell his books prevented him from gathering material for the later volumes.

He signed up 41 subscribers. With orders amounting to $4,920, his journey could not have been called a commercial failure. But he was profoundly troubled, and his sense of dis-appointment reached to some misunderstanding within himself that had no relation to his progress in an objective sense. "The book, in all its parts," he wrote, "so far exceeds the ideas and expectations of the first literary characters in the eastern section of the United States, as to command their admiration and respect. The only objection has been the sum of one hundred and twenty dollars. . . ." When he set out he had gone first to the house of the late Dr. Witherspoon, Paisley's greatest man, plainly hoping to find his problems much lessened; when he returned to Philadelphia he asked himself grimly if he had not made the mistake of printing a book that was too good for the country. "If I have," he commented bitterly, "it is a fault not likely to be soon repeated, and will pretty severely correct itself."

VI

And None Love Her More...

My dear Sarah

Do not be alarmed when I tell you I must now either run the risk of losing all or make one last and very long and expensive journey to collect what is due. . . . There is no other choice between this and absolute ruin. You will not therefore my dearest friend object to this as on it my whole hopes of happiness depend. It will be two or three weeks before I think of setting out. I will see you many times before then. I would ask your forgiveness for all these disappointments but I know you are goodness itself and judge my suffering means more than your own—therefore a good heart—

—Alexander Wilson

CHAPTER ONE

Southern Victory

࿓࿓࿓ ❖ ࿓࿓࿓

THE LEGISLATURE of Maryland was in session, and soon after returning to Philadelphia Wilson settled his accounts with Daniel Miller for the care of his horse, and rode off on that unreliable steed to Annapolis. He succeeded in getting a resolution introduced asking the State of Maryland to buy a set of the *American Ornithology*. Rarely had democratic government operated with the efficiency of the Maryland legislature in this instance. Every member, regardless of his previous political record, voted against buying Wilson's books. Even the member sponsoring the resolution voted Nay. Wilson was in the house when the statesmen reached their decision. His confidence in democracy gravely shaken, Wilson rode away muttering his familiar curses against a population too benighted to appreciate his work, and against the demagogues who represented them.

One of the prominent men of Baltimore was Nathaniel Ramsay, a Revolutionary hero. He was the brother of Dr. David Ramsay, the son-in-law of Dr. Witherspoon, and also brother-in-law of Charles Willson Peale, the Philadelphia artist and Wilson's personal friend. But it was Wilson's fate to find that people to whom he had introductions generally did not help him. Ramsay did not subscribe, but to Wilson's astonishment he easily signed up seventeen subscribers, mostly people he had never heard of. St. Mary's Seminary, the famous Jesuit college on Pennsylvania Avenue, bought a set of the books, and as Wilson moved on through town, to the business section and to the merchants' homes on Saratoga Street or St. Paul's Lane, he found buyers in Edward Coale, a city official who was soon to start his own bookstore, Jacob Smith, a stagecoach operator, Thomas Chase, an auctioneer, as well as the cashier of the Mechanics Bank, and five merchants. Dr. Chatard, a distinguished refugee physician from Santo Domingo, signed up for a set of the books, as did Edmund Ducatel, a celebrated Baltimore druggist.

The weather was phenomenally severe in the early winter of 1808, the cold worsened daily, and the road between Baltimore and Washington was almost impassable. Wilson reached the Capital with a feeling that he had nothing to lose. He decided to call on the President personally, on the strength of Jefferson's note at the time he subscribed to the *Ornithology*. When Wilson applied for a post as naturalist on the Zebulon Pike expedition, and Jefferson ignored him, the application had been forwarded to Jefferson by Bartram. Wilson was now determined to stand or fall on his own, and he called at the Executive Mansion, sending in a note: "Alexander Wilson, author of *American Ornithology,* would be happy to submit the first volume of this work to the inspection of Mr. Jefferson, if he knew when it would be convenient for the President."

It was Saturday noon, December 17, 1808. Wilson's misgivings were groundless. Jefferson immediately sent word for Wilson to be shown to his study. He received him cordially, and they examined Wilson's book, Jefferson enthusiastic about it. Nothing was said about Jefferson's failure to reply to Wilson's request for a post, Wilson saying nothing because he was still smarting from the snub, and Jefferson because, as he insisted to the end of his life, he had never received any such application from Wilson.

Jefferson in 1808 was a hard-pressed and stubborn statesman whose interest in scientific and artistic matters increased as political confusions deepened during his second administration. Now sixty-five years old, tall, thin and restless as Wilson himself, and with a mind alert and awake in all directions, he possessed native artistic gifts, a ceaseless inventiveness, and a desire to fuse practical and aesthetic projects—all qualities that inclined him in Wilson's favor. When the government was located in Philadelphia Jefferson's favorite retreat had been Bartram's Garden, across the river from where he lived, and Jefferson had an almost paternal feeling for his kinsman Meriwether Lewis, and the newly discovered birds which Lewis had given Wilson were to be an outstanding feature of Wilson's next volume. The statesman and the penniless ornithologist had a good deal in common. Jefferson prided himself on his knowledge of birds. From the point of understanding that Wilson had now reached, Jefferson's knowledge was superficial and his comments often naive—though he was nevertheless one of the best-informed men in America on the subject—but Wilson had been more naive a few years before in sending to Jefferson as a new discovery his painting of the Canada jay.

Jefferson told Wilson that he knew of a Southern gentleman who possessed a great store of information about birds, so much that Jefferson had hoped some time to be able to take down what he said to preserve it, but now saw that the cares of office would prevent his doing so. To Daniel Miller, Wilson wrote dryly that this unnamed paragon, according to Jefferson, "had spent his whole life studying the manners of our birds. . . . I am to receive a world of facts and observations from him."

By this time he was skeptical of Jefferson's assistance, but he misjudged him. Jefferson had subscribed to the *Ornithology* from the printed advertisement the year before; what was more important was that his Cabinet officers and his close political allies, like his kinsman John Eppes, now followed his lead. John Beckley, the first Librarian of Congress, who had precipitated the Hamilton scandal years before, had died a short time before, and his successor, Patrick Magruder, bought Wilson's work. The Georgetown Library bought a set. Cabinet officers of the standing of Albert Gallatin, James Madison and Gideon

Granger, the Postmaster General, added a good deal of distinction to the growing list of Wilson's subscribers, along with lesser-known Federal officials such as Charles Goldsborough, the Chief Clerk of the Navy, and Benjamin Latrobe, the architect who designed the Capitol. By the day before Christmas, when Wilson ended his labors, he had signed up seventeen additional names; added to those he had secured in Baltimore, he had taken orders of $4,000 in a few days.

On Christmas morning he left Washington and rode steadily south. He paused in Fairfax County to see Jefferson's friend, an amateur ornithologist named Coffer, who raised hummingbirds (and who subscribed to the *Ornithology*), but made as good time as possible. His hopes had taken a bold leap forward, and, simultaneously, he was anxious to get south before the advancing chill. He now kept a log book of the birds he saw, but in the stormy weather there was little to record in it. Near Fredericksburg he saw a few mockingbirds, which gave him almost his only ornithological note in a hundred miles.

The birds were fleeing south in advance of the winds. One exception was the red-winged starling. The whole of winter that for most birds was passed in a struggle to sustain life was a continuous carnival for these celebrated thieves. They were more than numerous in Pennsylvania, sometimes darkening the sky, diving and wheeling over the corn fields. Neither guns nor hawks had an appreciable effect on them. Meriwether Lewis told Wilson they were as numerous in the Missouri Valley. The children of Indian villages were employed to shoot them with bows and arrows, just as farm boys shot them with guns, neither discouraging them. But Wilson had never seen them in such numbers as in the Virginia winter. Sometimes they appeared driving like an enormous black cloud driven before the wind, varying its shape every moment. As Wilson rode along the deserted roads, the flocks that he disturbed in the adjoining fields rose with a noise like thunder. The glitter of the bright vermilion in their wings, in the midst of the black cloud they formed, created an effect that was startling and splendid.

Jefferson's implicit endorsement of his work opened doors for him everywhere. The Richmond Library bought a set of the *Ornithology*. Governor Tyler of Virginia (whose son, the future President, married the daughter of the actor Thomas Cooper) became a subscriber. Almost without effort Wilson sold thirty-four subscriptions. And he had a few ornithological observations to record. The mouselike little bird called the Carolina wren was numerous along the James; he had seen this bird in Pennsylvania in May, and with the pleasure of renewing an acquaintance he now heard its loud, strong twitter, not unlike that of the redbird, a sort of chanting *sweet william, sweet william*. As he cleared Richmond, stopping at Petersburg before going to Williamsburg, he was disappointed at the lack of any but familiar birds in the wintery woods. On January 12, near Petersburg itself, he saw a great many rusty grackles, birds that had left Pennsylvania almost exactly two months before. Because he had so little to hunt for (and because European naturalists had confused matters by listing five separate birds when they were all purple grackles), Wilson shot one, to secure a perfect specimen and to satisfy himself about the plumage that had given rise to the error.

Outside the city of Petersburg itself he was surprised to find summer ducks. In the woods at evening he heard the song of the chuck-will, the bird seeming to pronounce precisely each syllable, *chuck-will's-widow,* leisurely and distinctly, emphasizing the last word. Wilson had never seen the bird in Pennsylvania, or known one to be seen, though its relative the whippoorwill was common there. Silent during the day, the bird sang after sunset, and again at the earliest light of dawn; like the whippoorwill, it was a subject of much superstition, and said to be a harbinger of death. In the evening Wilson sometimes saw the chuck-will's-widow skimming low over the ground, settling on logs, and from these sweeping around after night-flying insects, flying silently and with evolutions in the air almost like bats.

Joseph Prentice, whose resolution in the Virginia legislature led to the calling of the Constitutional Convention, signed up for Wilson's books. And in Williamsburg he was heartened by his meeting with Bishop Madison. This rugged ecclesiastic, who had fought heroically in the Revolution, and who was so staunch a democrat that he believed the Kingdom of Heaven was really a republic, gladly purchased a set of Wilson's *Ornithology* for the library of William and Mary College, and freely gave Wilson such information as he himself possessed about Southern birds. They talked about the migration of the rail, and whether or not the snow bunting was the most widely dispersed of all American birds. And it developed that Jefferson had told Wilson the literal truth about an unknown authority on Southern birds. There lived near Savannah an obscure author and artist who had spent more than thirty years in study of the subject. His name was John Abbot, and no one could possibly know more about the birds of his region than Abbot. His one book bore the uninviting title of *The Rarer Lepidopterist Insects of Georgia.* Published in London twelve years before, it was a beautifully printed collection of colored plates of butterflies, an excessively rare volume, known only to authorities like Abbot himself.

Everything about Abbot was mysterious: his background, for he was a backwoods Georgia planter whose artistry was impressive in London, where he had artistic standing as a boy; his reputation, for he had created a definitive work on a scientific subject in his early manhood in his butterfly book, and published nothing more. As an artist, Abbot resembled Wilson in his independence and in the boldness of his vision, but he had been given excellent artistic training in his youth. Abbot resembled Mark Catesby in the exquisite detail of his work, and also in the abstract, surrealist-like trees and shrubs on which he pictured his birds. Wilson hoped for much from his meeting with Abbot; he turned aside from the most direct route to Savannah, however, for he had a melancholy task to perform for his sister Mary. The grave of her son George was unmarked, there was some uncertainty as to what had happened to the boy and Wilson accordingly proceeded down the peninsula toward Norfolk after leaving Williamsburg.

An old German at Hampton saw his interest in birds, and fell into conversation with him, irritating Wilson by his sober insistence that when the mockingbird sang its own song, rather than imitating other birds, someone would surely die. The depressing character of these stories, and their subtle influence in discouraging popular study of birds, always angered Wilson, and he was now additionally disturbed because his sad errand in searching for a grave had made him too conscious of death. He crossed from Hampton to Norfolk, and entered the city in wretched weather, the streets so muddy it was said the sailors had rowed their boats on them.

Wilson was directed to the naval hospital, where he found that the records stated George Duncan had been taken into the hospital on October 3, 1803, suffering from yellow fever. His death was recorded two days later. Wilson inquired until he located a nurse who had been on duty at that time. She had no particular memory of the boy, because there had been so many who died of the plague at that time. From the hospital, Wilson proceeded to the graveyard. The sexton tried to help him, and they went over the grounds together, but because of the number of victims all the dead of the plague had been buried in one section of the graveyard and there was no way to determine which one of the graves was George's. Wilson wanted to erect a stone on the spot; when he found he could not be sure of the grave, he abandoned the effort.

The weather grew worse. Unexpectedly, as Wilson prepared to move on, he sold two subscriptions to the *Ornithology*, Theodorick Armstead, the naval agent at Norfolk, becoming a subscriber, and George Loyall, then only nineteen, who had just graduated from William and Mary. Wilson rode away from the city on the coldest day he had known since leaving Pennsylvania, riding through flat pine woods to Suffolk. There he stopped in a gray evening at a big plantation, whose owner asked him to spend the night. The planter told him that forty of his slaves were sick. Of the thirteen children that had been born to his wife, only three still lived. Two of these appeared frail, and Wilson felt that the outlook for them, and for their equally frail-appearing mother, was dark in the extreme.

In the morning he struck out across country for the settlement of Jerusalem on the Nottaway River, thirty miles away. The river had overflowed its banks; a flatboat was required to move Wilson and his horse through two miles of flooded woods. The current then carried them far below the road on the opposite side. They picked their way cautiously through the pine trees, where two feet of water covered the forest floor.

The weather had grown so cold that each night thick ice formed, and in the morning these flooded expanses were frozen so that the ice cut his horse's legs and breast. The bridges that had been built over the creeks were too short for the high water; after crossing Wilson had to wade, and sometimes to swim his horse. He made three attempts to cross the flooded Roanoke River before he was able to reach the southern shore near the North Carolina town of Halifax. He made the crossing on January 20, 1809. Riding on, he came on a prodigious flock of purple grackles, rising from the surrounding fields with a clamor as loud as a thunderstorm. Larger than the red-winged starlings that Wilson had seen further north, big birds about twelve inches long, of a rich, glossy, steel-blue color, and with shining dark violet and silky green feathers on the head and breast, the grackles were as numerous as starlings in the Pennsylvania fall. As Wilson stopped his horse to watch them, they descended on the road, completely covering it, and the fences beside it, throughout the expanse that lay ahead. When Wilson rode into them, the grackles rose, and after a few evolutions in the air descended on the woods that adjoined the fields. The trees were bare. When the birds perched they covered the whole grove, from the topmost branches to the lowest, until the trees seemed to be in mourning. And meanwhile their calls sounded like the roar of Niagara, heard a great distance away—though the cry of the birds was in a musical cadence, swelling and dying away according to the fitful movements of the wind.

All the way to New Bern, North Carolina, almost a hundred miles south, there were no further scenes to record. Along the wild river Trent that flowed past New Bern, Wilson found field sparrows wintering in the immense cypress swamps and grassy plains, the great winter resort of all the sparrows that visited Pennsylvania in the summer. The shad were running, six weeks before their arrival in the Delaware, and Wilson wrote to Miller that they were the finest he had ever eaten; he wished Miller could be present to appreciate them. By February 2, 1809, Wilson was in the neighborhood of New Bern, and ran into a flock of doves, flying fast, with quick, vigorous strokes of their wings, which gave a peculiar whistling noise. Wilson applied the Old World name, turtledove, or the local name Carolina pigeon, to what is now commonly known as the mourning dove. In these wintry Carolina woods they were feeding on the berries of dogwood and holly and the small acorns of live oaks; another two months would pass before they moved to the northern woods, where their summer love song would be heard in the deepest and most retired shade, the saddest, most tender and affecting song of all doves' songs.

In New Bern itself, Wilson sold a set of the *Ornithology* to Will Gaston, one of Dr. Smith's brightest students at Princeton, something of a paradox because he was a Roman Catholic officeholder in a state whose constitution barred Catholics from office. New Bern was the home of Dr. Witherspoon's son David, also a lawyer; David had married the widow of General Francis Nash, under whom his brother James Witherspoon was serving at the battle where both James Witherspoon and General Nash were killed. David did not subscribe, but Wilson found another buyer in Robert Cochran, the United States Marshal for South Carolina.

Birds were more numerous, though the weather was still freezing. Thousands of pigeon hawks were visible all along the way, ceaselessly gliding on the currents of air, breaking suddenly into their descent on the thickets where the small birds were hidden. Field sparrows were everywhere also, the birds that vanished with the first deep snow in the north now clustered in bushes so closely together that a dozen might be killed with a single shotgun blast. It occurred to Wilson that no one had bothered to picture this familiar little bird, perhaps because it was so familiar it had always been taken for granted. He accordingly set himself to paint it—a revelation of how barren the bird scene had been—and described it as an innocent, humble and inoffensive creature. "In the dreary season of winter," he wrote, "some of them enliven the prospect by hopping familiarly about our doors, humble pensioners on the sweepings of the threshold."

The plantation country had been temporarily left behind; the country through which he now passed consisted of an immense, solitary pine savanna through which the road wound among stagnant ponds and over dark, sluggish creeks the color of brandy. The high wooden bridges, without railings, were so crazy and rotten they alarmed his horse. The plains ended in enormous cypress swamps, desolate and ruinous. Wilson tried to penetrate some of these, with his gun, searching for specimens, but found it altogether impractical. He was forced to coast along their borders. Here he could see familiar birds like sparrows, and study a profusion of evergreens and berries that he knew nothing of, and sometimes glimpse the wild wealth within the swamps. The ducks that had left the north in the fall wintered here, great flocks of mallard, Canada geese and canvasbacks, the first migrants to start north in another month, and some, like the green-winged teal, to linger until May or June. Occasionally Wilson heard the call of the ivory-billed woodpecker, its cry a single note, repeated every few seconds, like the sound of a trumpet, or the high notes of a clarinet. It was already one of the rarest birds in the New World, a huge, twenty-inch bird, as big as an ordinary barnyard rooster, black and glossy green, with a superb carmine crest and a bill of polished ivory. A century before, Mark Catesby had watched an ivory-billed woodpecker accumulate a bushel of chips at the base of a tree in an hour. But Catesby's account could hardly be believed, so magnificent, daring and little-known was the bird. It fed selectively, eating only the larvae of wood-boring insects, and consequently ranged thinly over tremendous expanses of woodland. The Indians prized it, wearing the bill, an important object in Indian trade, as an ornament, and also as a charm because of the courage and strength of the bird. The ivory-billed woodpecker was becoming extinct, not because it was hunted, but because its food supply diminished with the destruction of the forests. The last was seen in South Carolina in 1904, though several were reported later in Florida, and in 1935 one was discovered in a Santee River swamp, from which occasional reports came of others glimpsed or heard.

Twelve miles outside the town of Wilmington, North Carolina, Wilson was thrilled by the sight of one of these woodpeckers at work on a huge cypress, high among the moss-covered branches, where its blaring notes and loud strokes made it seem the sole inhabitant of the wilderness. He then discovered two more, and shot all three, killing two, and slightly wounding one bird in one wing. Running to the base of the tree where it had fallen, Wilson threw his coat over the woodpecker, which cried out with a reiterated note that sounded like the crying of a young child. Overjoyed with his good fortune at securing it alive, Wilson held the bird, still carefully wrapped in his coat, as he remounted. But it nearly cost him his life, for the woodpecker resumed its violent screaming, and his horse plunged into the swamp with its rider and the bird. By the time Wilson got his horse under control he and the animal were almost as badly shaken as the woodpecker. But he still held the bird. Riding into Wilmington, the woodpecker resumed its piteous cries, so much like the crying of a child that women ran to the doors of the houses as Wilson passed, looking at him with alarm and anxiety.

When Wilson reached the hotel he dismounted with relief, and tied his trembling horse at the piazza. The woodpecker began crying again. The landlord and tavern guests rushed out with expression of concern. Dirty and exhausted, Wilson held the wrapped bird gingerly as he asked, "Can you furnish me with accommodations for myself and my baby?"

The woodpecker let out another series of frightful cries, the landlord looked blank and foolish, and Wilson drew back his coat and revealed the bird. "A general laugh took place," he reported, but it appeared that the townspeople nevertheless regarded him a little uneasily during the remainder of his stay. Wilson left the woodpecker in his room, locked the door, and hurried back to see his nervous horse taken care of. This accomplished, he went back to his captive, before half an hour had passed. His bed was covered with plaster, a square of lath fifteen inches across was exposed near the ceiling beside the window, and a hole the size of a man's fist was opened to the outerwall. In another few minutes the woodpecker would have cut his way to freedom. As Wilson came in, the bird resumed its distressing shout, doubtless, said the exasperated ornithologist, out of grief at having been discovered tearing down the wall.

He managed to get a string tied to the woodpecker's leg, and fastened it to the table. After he had rested a time, he became filled with admiration for his captive, and determined to save and tame it. But there was the question of food. He did not know that the ivory-billed woodpecker ate only insect larvae. Leaving the room for only a few minutes, to scrape up something for it, he was relieved that the bird became silent after he left. "As I ascended the stairs," Wilson wrote, "I heard him again hard at work, and on entering had the mortification to perceive that he had almost entirely ruined the mahogany table to which he was fastened. . . ."

He decided that he had better paint the woodpecker at once, before something else happened, and while gathering his equipment the bird struck him several times with its bill, cutting him severely. He painted several poses, a life-sized head, and the characteristic position of the bird on a tree. To give an idea of the size of the ivory-billed woodpecker, he drew it on the same plate with a red-headed woodpecker, in the same scale, the head and bill of the ivory-billed being almost as large as the whole red-headed woodpecker from head to tail. He was surprised to find that the natives knew little about the bird, and had no stock of lore and legends concerning it. They often confused it with the similar, but smaller, pileated woodpecker, and called it the logcock, the pileated being the lesser logcock. They rarely shot one, observing morosely that gunpowder was too valuable to be used on anything except wild turkey.

Wilmington was a town of some 3,000 people, with scarcely a cultivated field over miles of the loose sandy soil that surrounded it. Wilson had an errand there for Lawson, to search for the will left by one Peter Brados, and he was pleased when he finished with it and moved on to more congenial tasks, hunting in the woods. For birds were becoming more numerous with every mile that he traveled south, and with every day that moved toward spring. The frost ended during the first week of February. There were mild and sunny days, still not warm, but with the promise of spring. On the banks of the Cape Fear River that flowed by the town, and especially in the cypress swamp on its opposite side, there were now Maryland yellowthroats, neat, pretty little green and gold birds that left Pennsylvania in September, deliberate, humble and unsuspicious inhabitants of briers and alder bushes; pewit flycatchers lingering in the low swampy grounds, feeding on smilax berries; tiny yellow-rumped warblers, of the sort that Wilson had seen on the coast of Maine, here assembled in great numbers wherever the dwarf myrtle grew, and known as the myrtle warbler; and the plump and pretty little species called the fox-colored sparrow that could be found everywhere in the South on the borders of the swamps.

For many miles below Wilmington the road threaded over solitary pine savannas and around swamps where Wilson sometimes traveled thirty miles without seeing a house or a human being. He had tried to keep his ivory-billed woodpecker alive, hoping to be able to release it, but it grew steadily weaker, refused all food, and died before it was strong enough to be returned to its native woods. At almost the same time, Wilson discovered another new species, a small zebra-striped woodpecker with a red streak on the side of its head, which he named the red-cockaded woodpecker, and which he was the first to describe and to paint. He hunted them for some time, to secure a perfect specimen, preserving the best to place in Peale's Museum, doubly cautious because he feared the bird might be some familiar species with imperfect plumage.

Over the inland roads the taverns were far apart, and the tavern haunters the most debased and ignorant people Wilson had ever seen. But along the Waccamaw and Pee Dee Rivers were huge plantations of primitive wealth and luxury, where one planter casually mentioned to Wilson that he had more than 600 slaves. The roads were so bad and so hard to find, and the plantation owners so hospitable, that Wilson could scarcely progress southward at all, making long zigzag journeys from one plantation to the next. At almost every plantation he was entertained, sold another subscription, was kept overnight, and so delayed that he was still proceeding along the Waccamaw River on February 10, for on that date he notes whooping cranes flying over it—"the tallest and most stately species of all the feathered tribes of the United States," he wrote.

They were rare birds even in 1809, a thrilling sight—formidable, Wilson called them —and their virtual disappearance could be foreseen. The cranes flew in single file, with a low and heavy flight, only a little above the water. At times they uttered a loud, clear, piercing cry, audible two miles away. Shy and vigilant, they were hard to shoot, and sometimes could be seen rising spirally in the air to great height, as if to reconnoiter the country and select the least inhabited as their own. At these times the confused sound of their voices, reaching earth when the birds were almost out of sight, resembled that of a pack of hounds in full cry.

The woods were swarming with doves, the whistling of their wings heard in every direction. Back from the road the tinny trumpet cry of the ivory-billed woodpecker sometimes sounded plainly, Wilson's horse becoming almost ungovernable at the sound. Kingfishers coursed above the streams, sometimes almost suspending themselves by the rapid action of their wings, sometimes settling on dead limbs overlooking the water, and plunging after fish with their sudden circular sweep. Around the rice plantations near the shore were yellow and brown meadow larks, running about the yards and outbuildings without fear, as if already domesticated. Mockingbirds were singing everywhere, tame and fearless, unafraid of people, or perhaps even with an interest in them, following along the fences beside roads, and keeping up their continual quizzical whistles and parodies.

The hospitality that was offered to Wilson was lavish, the success of his book was now almost assured, but he felt that the interest of the planters was superficial, and the mixed wealth and poverty of the country—the great houses surrounded, as he put it, by villages of Negro slave huts—disturbed him deeply. When he arrived at a plantation house, and his horse was to be taken care of, the planter sent a servant to tell the overseer, who sent a Negro to tell the driver, who sent a slave to do the work. "Before half of the routine is gone through," Wilson wrote to Bartram, an old abolitionist, "I have myself unharnessed, rubbed down, and fed my horse."

Near the South Carolina line, Wilson stopped at the plantation of a man named Vermeer, who did not buy his books, but wanted Wilson's blooded horse. Wilson's horse was giving out, and he proposed a trade. Vermeer offered a big sorrel, if Wilson would also give him twenty dollars. Wilson offered his horse, if Vermeer would give him thirty dollars to boot. They parted with mutual expressions of disinterest, but Wilson was sure Vermeer wanted to trade. He rode on, and Vermeer soon caught up with him under the pretext of showing him the right road. In about three miles they came to the beach, "and there, on the sands, amidst the roar of the Atlantic, we finally bargained; and I found myself in possession of a large, well-formed and elegant sorrel horse, that ran off with me at a canter for fifteen miles. I now found that I had got a very devil . . . the least sound of the whip made him spring half a rod at a leap; no road, however long or heavy, could tame him. Two or three times he nearly broke my neck . . . and at Georgetown ferry he threw one of the boatmen into the river. But he is an excellent traveller. . . ."

On their first day, his new horse carried him fifty-two miles, requiring only a few mouthfuls of straw. He rode into Charleston pleased with his bargain and excited about the

1. *Snow Owl.*

32

2. *Male Sparrow Hawk.*

The snow owl, from one of Wilson's later volumes, was dramatic proof of his growing mastery; it still ranks with the best of American bird paintings. Left above: sparrow hawk.

IV

prospect for his book. The city interested him, with its quiet and shaded streets of brick dwellings with two, three or four balconies, "with a great deal of gingerbread about them," and good shops, and a gay appearance. The great plantation houses and grounds, some within Charleston itself, were magnificent, especially Ashley Hall, with its long avenue of live oaks planted a century before by Mark Catesby. The ladies sauntering along the Charleston streets were beautifully dressed, and often creatures of grace. In the central parts of the city the Negroes crowded the streets, sometimes loudly quarreling with one another to the amusement of the passers-by. On Broad Street itself Wilson was shocked by the slave market. There a crowd of wretchedly dressed Negroes huddled together, people handling them as they might handle cattle, in a corner of the market where there were female chimney sweeps for sale in one stall and roasted sweet potatoes in another. In the evening Wilson wandered to the wharves by the harbor, and there were groups of Negroes also, male and female, sitting around fires, amid heaps of oyster shells, cooking their victuals —"these seem the happiest mortals on earth," he wrote.

He put himself up at a good hotel, and the next day, February 16, 1809, placed in the Charleston *Courier* a large display advertisement for the *Ornithology*. Addressed to THE LOVERS OF NATURAL HISTORY, the advertisement announced a New and Superb Work being published by subscription by Bradford and Inskeep, at $12 the volume, a modest note at the end of 26 lines of text stating the work was illustrated with colored plates drawn from nature by Alexander Wilson.

He then paid a formal visit to Dr. David Ramsay, the leading physician of Charleston, a politician, an historian, amateur ornithologist, and the husband of Dr. Witherspoon's favorite daughter Frances, who was born in Paisley about the same time that Wilson himself was born there. Wilson had been led to believe that Dr. Ramsay would give him a list of possible subscribers in Charleston. Ramsay promised to do so, and Wilson occupied himself with other matters. He had a commercial assignment for the Philadelphia merchant Frederick Foering, one of his subscribers. The Charleston firm of Porter and Drummond owed Foering considerable money, and Wilson had Foering's authority to collect whatever he could on it. When Drummond heard his story, he asked him to return the following day, but when Wilson did so, he found Drummond had gone to the country on a rice-buying expedition. Wilson accordingly looked up Porter, but he found that the two partners were not on speaking terms. To avoid trouble, Porter was willing to ship twenty barrels of rice to Foering to pay the debt, but Drummond's agreement was necessary, and Wilson doubted that the bargain would be carried through.

He returned to Dr. Ramsay, who, however, had not prepared a list of prospects, and put him off again. Wilson therefore returned to Foering's business, and Porter offered him $50 to close out the whole matter. Wilson wrote to Foering that he had decided to accept, saying otherwise they would receive nothing. For the third time he called on Dr. Ramsay, who again put him off. Wilson angrily broke off the discussions. He did not know where to begin on his own, so he walked slowly along the streets, picking out the houses that looked prosperous, and calling on the owners.

He was phenomenally successful. At almost every house he entered he found a subscriber. Gabriel Manigault, the architect whose buildings gave Charleston much of its charm, signed up for the *Ornithology;* he was a wealthy planter, self-taught as an architect as Wilson was self-taught as an artist, and the Charleston homes of his many kinspeople and his new Society Hall remained as remarkable creations by an amateur. Alexander Garden (a distant kinsman of the Lord Garden of Gardenstone who was ruined by Callender), a naturalist living in Charleston, had been a correspondent of John Bartram years before. The most intricate family relationships linked Charleston citizens to each other and to branches of their families that had remained loyal during the Revolution and were now settled in England; they were often associated in business as well, and when one member of a family secured some new ornament to his estate, the others were likely to follow his example. The Manigaults were related to the Izards, and both were intermarried with the Blakes, at whose ancestral home Mark Catesby had lived nearly a century before.

In his travels up one shady street and down another Wilson came to the Charleston Library, which he had rather strangely neglected. The librarian was a Scotsman; he bought a set of the *Ornithology* for the library, and also performed the service for Wilson that Dr. Ramsay had neglected to do. He took the Charleston directory and checked off the names of citizens who might be expected to subscribe. First there was Joseph Blake himself, the great-grandson of Catesby's benefactor, educated at Eton and Cambridge, who had inherited Newington Plantation where Catesby worked, and who now lived largely in London. Then there was Ralph Izard, the son of the American agent in Paris during the Revolution, and Cleland Kinlock, whose grandfather was the second son of Sir Francis of Gilmerton in Scotland. Charles Cotesworth Pinckney, the Vice-Presidential candidate with John Adams, became a subscriber to the *Ornithology,* as did his brother Thomas, who had been governor of South Carolina a short time before. Arnoldus Vander Horst, another ex-governor who had served with Francis Marion during the Revolution, joined the celebrities who were buying Wilson's book. So did General Peter Horry, one of Marion's closest aides, who was living in a house half buried in jasmine and azaleas adjoining the home of Thomas Pinckney.

Judge William James, who had served with Marion when he was a barefoot boy of fifteen, became a subscriber. He was the author of a life of the Swamp Fox, but it had passed into the hands of Parson Weems, before publication, and Weems so romanticized and altered it that the Judge could not endure to look at the book that bore his name. The great military subscriber, however, was General William Washington, a second cousin of President Washington, who had fought valiantly as an infantry captain throughout the Revolution. Unwilling to trade on the name of his famous relative, William Washington was almost unknown except among soldiers, who regarded him with awe. He had fought almost constantly from the beginning of the Revolution to its end, in Virginia, in the battles of Long Island, during the retreat across New Jersey, at Trenton—where he was wounded for the second time—then in South Carolina, where he was sent to the aid of General Lincoln. He fought at Cowpens, Guilford Courthouse, Hobkirk's Hill, Eutaw Springs, a well-nigh uninterrupted schedule of battles, finally meeting in a personal fight on the battlefield Colonel Banastre Tarleton, the leader of the British forces, hated and feared for his savagery. They nearly killed each other, both being borne wounded from the field.

William Laughton Smith, the old Federalist member of Congress who had managed to get James Thompson Callender kicked out of Congress after a terrific struggle, subscribed to the *Ornithology*. He was an official of the Charleston Library, now virtually retired from politics, a native of England who had studied law in London. He, too, was part of the interrelated Charleston family-and-political combine; his wife was Ralph Izard's sister. Another naturalized Englishman, though not so well known, was John Splatt Cripps. Cripps sailed from England with his widowed mother in his early years. A fellow passenger was Alexander Gillon, one of the richest of Dutch merchants, and soon after they arrived in Charleston Gillon and Cripps's mother were married. Gillon later established a trading partnership in Charleston with Cripps, while he himself became an American agent in Europe during the Revolution, securing arms, ammunition and supplies.

Wilson read in the *Courier* that General James Wilkinson had arrived in Charleston on his way home to New Orleans after testifying at the trial of Aaron Burr; he called at the General's hotel and displayed his book. Wilkinson overwhelmed him with friendliness. A remarkably handsome man, well built, with easy manners and an engaging humor, Wilkinson looked and acted the part of a great military man, though he was, in fact, a trained physician, and had been practicing medicine until the Revolution. His outstanding characteristic was charm; there was a natural fluent grace to his most casual actions, whether an invitation to dinner, or, as in this case, a purchase of a book, for he not only signed up for the *Ornithology,* but paid Wilson $12 in cash because he wanted to take a copy of Volume One with him. This was the first money that Wilson had received for the *Ornithology,* after three years of labor. He told Wilkinson as much, and they laughed about it, Wilson saying that when he first felt actual cash in his hands he was convinced of the eventual success of his project.

He saw Wilkinson frequently. Since the sudden death of General Anthony Wayne, in the midst of their quarrel, Wilkinson had been the ranking general in command of the armies of the United States, although the military organization of the time limited his effective command to the West. The trial of Burr, which he had precipitated by his denunciation of Burr to Jefferson, left him disgraced in the eyes of Federalists, tarnished in the opinion of the general public, and a most serious embarrassment to Jefferson himself, for Burr's trial turned into an examination of Wilkinson's own loyalty, and he barely escaped an inquiry by Congress and a court-martial. He was, if not quite without friends, so shaken in his public standing that Wilson's arrival at his hotel was an event he remembered with gratitude. General Wilkinson subsequently wrote to Jefferson that he greatly enjoyed Wilson's company, and "admired his enterprise, perseverance and capacity."

On his part, Wilson was flattered by Wilkinson's friendship. Wilkinson liked to talk about hunting, and fancied himself something of an expert; much of his military experience had been in the West, and he was able to tell Wilson a good deal about the game birds to be found there. It was a common belief that the rail, for example, was a shore bird, found only along the coast. Wilkinson said that there were great flocks near Detroit, where he had shot many, and they were as plump and well-tasted as those of the Carolina rice country, or the reedy shores of the Delaware. When Wilson incorporated Wilkinson's comments into the *Ornithology* he referred to him (not by name) as "a gentleman in whose judgement he could rely." Wilkinson was, or professed himself to be, a follower of Jefferson; Jefferson had given overwhelming proof of his confidence in Wilkinson by publicizing his charge of treason against Burr. To Wilson, whose admiration of Jefferson was fanatical, this was in itself enough to recommend him, and to enable him to dismiss as partisan attacks the denunciations of Wilkinson as a traitor.

Wilson did not know that Wilkinson was, and had been for many years, a secret agent of Spain, Spy Number 13 in the Spanish secret service. Nor did Wilson know the evil reputation that Wilkinson had acquired among well-informed people. Wilkinson's wife, the former Ann Biddle of Philadelphia, had died a short time before. A gracious and intelligent woman whose charm was legendary, she remained loyal to Wilkinson despite his lurid intrigues of all kinds, and the general could not be said to have been crushed by her passing. After vacationing in Cuba, he was returning to New Orleans, to marry a Creole heiress there, and to begin an attack on his personal opponents among the civilian leaders of the city. Proof of Wilkinson's treason had been discovered more than ten years before by Andrew Ellicott. Knowledge of it, however, remained limited to very narrow circles while Wilkinson's every action was studied. The fiasco of the Burr trial had drastically altered Wilkinson's position with the supporters of Jefferson who had previously judged him tolerantly, and the distrust grew stronger in the light of subsequent events.

Wilson did not then share it. Yet he was perplexed by the sudden social chill that descended on him in Charleston. Even in the best homes in the city, he wrote to Daniel Miller, the ladies had a cold, melancholy reserve, and their conversation was stiff and artificial. Beautifully dressed as they were, and graceful in their movements, the young ladies of the South were pale in their features and languid in their movements. They seemed unhappy. On the other hand, Wilson wrote confidentially to Daniel Miller, "The Negro wenches are all sprightliness and gayety." He concluded that their accessibility had, in effect, left the white girls the sexual orphans in a slave-owning society. "If report be not a defamer," he went on . . . But here his letter was cut to remove his too-frank comments, not to be continued until he had delivered himself of a characteristic phrase, "which render the men callous to all the finer sensations of love and female excellence."

Whatever this odious condition could be that had so disastrous an effect on Southern manhood, Wilson did not recover a happier view of the society. He had been more successful there than anywhere he had been, and more warmly received, yet it was true that a chill had fallen over him, and he did not know the reason for it. When he left Charleston to go to Savannah, and added up the work he had done, he found that he had sold 125 subscriptions to the *Ornithology*. This was all but incredible, $15,000 in orders for a book about American birds, sold on the basis of his own dedication to the task, and the sample that his first volumes provided. He had not only met Bradford's demand for 200 subscriptions, but provided for an edition of 400 copies. Nevertheless, he was uneasy. His disquiet soon had an outward justification: at a place called Two Sisters Ferry his horse became frightened and leaped overboard, and was being carried downstream until Wilson dove after it and swam with it to shore.

Not far beyond the shore lay the city of Beaufort, which was the botanical boundary line of North and South, the extreme southern limit of many Northern birds and plants, the northern limit of many Southern species. The city of Beaufort itself, as if conscious of its strategic location, was hospitable to all growth from the tropical and temperate zones, a mellow and well-tended country of placid rivers and white shell roads, with a Mediterranean scent in the air, great gardens filled with huge blossoming shrubs, tranquil avenues of live oaks, and everywhere fig trees, date palms, crape myrtle, Mexican agaves, English ivy, japonicas, oranges, lemons, oleanders, jonquils, blackberries, wild roses, magnolias and flowering dogwood. The nights were haunted, magical under the solemn starlight or in soft gray mist, frogs croaking and mockingbirds singing on the edge of the cypress swamps or the sullen bayous or the glimmering shore of the sea. "I am utterly at a loss in my wood rambles," Wilson wrote to Bartram, "for there are so many trees, plants, shrubs and insects that I know nothing of."

In the evening he saw flights of crows leaving the river to fly into the interior, and at dawn he saw them return. They flew like ravens rather than crows, sailing often and not flapping their wings, and their voices sounded like a crow with something caught in its throat. There were many beautiful little painted buntings in the thickets, with their warm red and blue feathers, and towhee buntings, the bird that was called the bullfinch in Virginia and the chewink—from its call—or the swamp robin—from the locale where it was generally found—in the Pennsylvania summer. When Wilson saw these birds at home they were invariably red-eyed, the iris itself was dark red, and the Linnaean name for the species meant red-eyed. But here the iris of the eye was white. He was at a loss to know what to make of such contradictions, and at the time his book went to press speculated that perhaps the color of the eye changed.

His guide through such perplexities was Stephen Elliot, a distinguished amateur botanist who had a residence near Beaufort, though his country home was in Georgia. Elliot had long before seen the importance of the area as the botanical watershed between North and South, and devoted his leisure to classifying and cataloguing its inhabitants. He received Wilson with the courtesy of the planters, subscribing to the *Ornithology* as a matter of course, and insisting that Wilson use his house as a base for his hunting trips into the woods. Wilson had so long worked in seclusion that he found it difficult to accept these invitations at face value, fearing they were merely expressions of formal politeness, but in this instance he was certainly mistaken, Elliot becoming profoundly interested in him and his work, and aiding him throughout his life, though his natural reserve somewhat cloaked the friendliness he demonstrated. In any event, Wilson hunted around his home, and also in the Georgia woods, for Elliot owned a plantation on the Ogeechee River. The last two weeks of February were warm and sunny, with ten brilliant days in a row, and the flowering wilderness was as dazzling to Wilson as the grounds of Castle Semple had been to him in his boyhood. He wrote to Bartram that he had accumulated a great store of information about birds that were never seen in the North at all, additional facts of importance regarding birds that were familiar, and had also found species that he could not locate in Linnaeus—so much new material that it must wait classification until he and Bartram could study it together. Elliot was a botanist, rather than a student of birds, but he was also, Wilson said, a really judicious naturalist, and on some questions readily set Wilson right. The problem of the color of the eye of the towhee bunting was one instance, for Elliot was convinced the color of the eye changed. He had shot one not long before with one eye white and the other red.

In the grounds of Elliot's plantation there were the guttural-voiced crows Wilson had observed further north, here keeping apart from the common crows, and occasionally perching on the back of cattle, like magpies in Scotland. The bird was the fish crow, Elliot told him, and, oddly enough for so common a bird, had never been pictured or described. Smaller than the common crow, the fish crow fed on marine life largely, small crabs, minnows, carrion, together with the eggs of herons and rails, though it also haunted barnyards in settled territory. It was one of the paradoxes of Wilson's Southern visit that exotic birds were now everywhere around him, the magnificent wood ibis that Elliot later sent him, the white heron and yellow-crowned heron, and even an occasional scarlet ibis, but he continued to concentrate his attention on warblers, creepers and finches, and even this new species of crow. The reason was that he planned to cover the water birds in the later volumes of the *Ornithology,* and he dared not burden the work at this stage with more material than he could assimilate. He now merely noted his first sight of them, or items of folklore. The great white heron, with the long, yellowish-tinted plumes flowing down its back, he first saw in Georgia, haunting inundated land, conspicuous at a great distance because of its size and color. The great heron—not to be confused with the great white heron—with its fine bluish ash and black and white coloring, he saw flying up the rivers, a sign of rain, according to the natives, as its flight downstream indicated dry weather. Another item of local lore was that the heron was fat during the full moon, and lean at other times, because its hours of eating were lengthened. Standing five feet, four inches high, the heron stalked slowly along deserted stretches of the seacoast, or uninhabited riverbanks, stately and suspicious, and with such powers of flight that it was rarely shot. Even more rarely shot was the brilliant yellow-crowned heron (so called because of an error by Mark Catesby, the crown being white), a black and light ash-colored bird with a jet-black head crowned with two long tapering plumes of pure white—another nocturnal heron, reposing in low swampy woods during the day, rarely seen even by great observers of the woodlands like Stephen Elliot and John Abbot.

Abbot lived not far from Elliot's country place on the Ogeechee, a leathery-visaged man of fifty-seven, with a large Roman nose, stiff dark hair, and abundant crow's-feet wrinkled about his dark and penetrating eyes. Almost mysteriously modest and obliging, Abbot had long lived well as a planter on land awarded to him for his services in the Revolution. His experience was so extensive, his knowledge so great, and his artistic ability of so high an order that it was mysterious also that Wilson and Bartram and the Philadelphia scientists had never heard of him. "There is a Mr. Abbot here who has resided in Georgia thirty-three years," Wilson wrote to Bartram. "I have been on several excursions with him. He is a very good observer and paints well. He has published, in London, one large folio volume of the Lepidopterous insects of Georgia. It is a very splendid work. . . ."

These few lines communicated volumes. John Abbot was born in 1751 on Bennet Street, St. James, London, the son of an attorney. The family spent its summers at Turnham Green, where the boy collected butterflies. He painted and sketched his finds. His parents were art collectors, and to further encourage the boy, Lady Dorothy Honywood, whose family were among the patrons of Mark Catesby, gave John Abbot a set of Catesby's invaluable *Natural History of the Carolinas*. While studying law Abbot was given lessons in art at home, and exhibited his landscapes, which were favorably received, in a London gallery. He was able to earn substantial fees by painting collections of rare insects for wealthy collectors, the study of natural history then being fashionable. Among those for whom Abbot worked was Dru Drury, goldsmith and silversmith to the King and Queen—posts worth £6,000 a year—a collector of butterflies and a backer of expeditions that searched for rare specimens in Africa.

When Abbot was twenty-two years old he struck out on his own, intending to go to New Orleans. He had arrangements with the Royal Society, with a library in Manchester, and with collectors and dealers, to picture American birds and insects. Complications about his passage led him to go to Virginia instead, where he landed in 1773, just as the political crisis became acute. Nevertheless, he made warmer friendships in two years in Virginia than he had made in his entire life in England. But he was unready to fight against his King. At the Declaration of Independence he migrated with a few Virginians into Georgia, which was expected to remain neutral ground. In the War itself, however, he fought with the Americans, receiving a land grant of 575 acres for his services. He married a Virginia girl, Penelope Warren, and for more than twenty years lived comfortably as a planter while he worked at his paintings. Extremely accomplished, and a craftsman of unparalleled industry, Abbot made at least 700 bird paintings for English collectors, sent abroad innumerable stuffed birds and mounted insects, and prepared for a collection that went into the British Museum thousands of drawings and paintings of American insects—one of his collections of insects alone filled 17 volumes and included 1,833 separate works. Sir James Edward Smith, the wealthy and rather eccentric founder of the Linnaean Society of London, who had produced a magnificent catalogue of the flowers of Great Britain (painted by James Sowerby), also published in 1797 John Abbot's two-volume work on rare Georgia butterflies, as his own product, though it was, of course, almost wholly Abbot's work. He was credited with assisting Sir James. These beautiful books, in which Abbot pictured the insects on the same plates with Southern flowers, after the fashion of Catesby's book, represented John Abbot's one bid for public attention. He published nothing more. Whether his experience of publishing with Sir James Edward Smith had discouraged him beyond all measure, or for some other reason, he was thereafter content to work in complete obscurity.

Such was the extraordinary individual Wilson met in the Georgia backwoods. No trace of professional jealousy appeared in Wilson's comments on Abbot's work, though he certainly recognized the quality, and it could not have escaped him that the finish of Abbot's painting was superior to his own. If Abbot did not know everything that was to be known about Southern birds, he knew enough to confer a good deal of authority on the remaining volumes of the *Ornithology* by the material that he freely handed over to Wilson. Abbot knew the time of the year the herons came in from Surinam and Cayenne, that the painted bunting arrived in Georgia about April 20, from some place further south, that only two species of sparrows spent the whole summer in the Georgia heat, and that the nest of the pine creeping warbler was built of grapevine bark, rotten wood, and caterpillars' webs. He had watched the hummingbirds arrive in Savannah about March 23, and two weeks later he had noted the first arrivals at his place in Burke County, sixty miles north—a rate of travel which would leave them far south of the Pennsylvania woods that they usually reached in the last weeks of April.

Wilson had drawn the yellow-billed cuckoo—the rain crow, it was popularly called— and Abbot told him there was another common bird, very like it in appearance. It was usually considered the same by naturalists. A distinguishing mark was a patch of bare wrinkled skin, of a reddish color, about the eye. Observation as exact as this impressed Wilson, who pictured the bird that Abbot had found, and gave it the name of the black-billed cuckoo. In the *Ornithology* Wilson gave Abbot full credit for having spotted the bird. But such was the curious fate of both Abbot and Wilson that Wilson received credit in ornithological literature for having distinguished a new species, though in the very essay in which he reported it, he gave the credit to Abbot.

Abbot was not accustomed to receiving much money for his bird paintings. A few pounds a year were sent to him by English scientists. So long as his plantations were profitable, Abbot did not need other earnings; now, however, his income had declined, and it was unquestionably generous of Wilson to pay him well for the specimens that he sent him after he returned to Philadelphia—$45 for one shipment, as much as Abbot received over a long period from his English customers. Wilson generously credited Abbot for his help throughout the *Ornithology,* and could with justice have said more than he did. He paid to the secluded artist the only tribute he ever received, however, in the United States, and it was understandable that Wilson said no more than he did, for he made arrangements with Abbot to send him Southern birds in the future, and he had no way of knowing how reliable a correspondent Abbot would be. He was an amazingly reliable one, and his contribution to the *Ornithology,* in the long run, ranked with those of Bartram and Charles Leslie.

"This has been the most arduous, expensive and fatiguing expedition I ever undertook," Wilson wrote to Bartram. On February 28 he was on the outskirts of Savannah, and shot two rail, his last ornithological note from the southland. The future mayor of Savannah, thirty-two-year-old William Bulloch, subscribed to the *Ornithology*—indeed, Wilson collected thirty-five subscriptions with little effort, at no expense beyond an outrageous charge for an advertisement in the Savannah *Republic*—but he was dazed with his commercial success and the wealth of bird lore he had acquired, and wanted only to rest. His ship was due to sail for New York on March 1, but complications delayed it for two weeks. A southwest wind blew steadily, bringing on heat more oppressive than that of Philadelphia midsummer, and starting up little whirlwinds of dust on the sandy Savannah streets. Eventually one learned, Wilson wrote grimly, to transverse them with both eyes and mouth shut. Cold as was the social chill that had descended in Charleston, it was still worse in Savannah, where he was invited to great houses, but where the reception was formal and stiff. The women had nothing to say. "Even in their own houses," he wrote, "they scarcely utter anything to a stranger but yes and no, and one is perpetually puzzled to know whether it proceeds from awkwardness or dislike."

He was drenched on an outing, developed a cold, and ran a fever every day. The heat soared to 82°. He lived out the delay, hoping that the salt breezes and his expected bout of seasickness would restore him to health. When he wrote to Bartram before setting sail he was bemused by his own struggles on behalf of "this bantling book of mine." It had taken him into every town from Maine to Georgia, set him wandering among strangers, exposed him to discomfort, fatigue, insults and impositions of a thousand kinds. "I have, however, gained my point in securing 250 subscribers. . . ." He could barely keep the note of triumph out of his account.

CHAPTER TWO

Listen to the Mockingbird

≫≫≫≫ • ≪≪≪≪

ICE TWO FEET THICK covered the rivers when Wilson reached New York on March 22, 1809; the city was frozen under deep drifts in the streets. Soon after Wilson returned to Philadelphia from the South he visited John Finlayson, the signer of his indenture of apprenticeship as a weaver thirty years before. He had a purpose in doing so, for he wished to write to his own father, and wanted news of his contemporaries to communicate to him. John lived on his farm near the city, in a charming valley, sheltered with apple trees, with a clear brook wimpling by the yard, and plenty of chickens and ducks. He had a fine family, a hive of bees, a ewe with three lambs, four looms, and many comforts, besides the esteem of his neighbors. In the midst of notes of family and friends, and requests to be remembered to Tom and Jean Witherspoon, Wilson reported guardedly to his father that work had become trying because he had too much to do. He added, "William Mitchell, formerly of Williamsburgh, who had been supposed dead these several years, is living and in good health at New Orleans—as a common soldier."

In Wilson's absence on his travels an important change had taken place. His printer, Robert Carr, on March 15, 1809, married Ann Bartram, the heiress to Bartram's Garden. Carr became the effective head of the household, and preserved the Garden against the encroachment of the city around it, a task that was becoming beyond William Bartram's powers. Carr also placed all American botanists in his debt by preserving, and later making available for publication, the correspondence of John Bartram with Mark Catesby, Peter Collinson, Alexander Garden, Humphry Marshall, and virtually all the pioneers of American natural history. Wilson reported the news of the marriage of Robert and Ann in a footnote in the next volume of the *Ornithology.*

While Wilson was traveling, Samuel Bradford began a program of expanding the firm of Bradford and Inskeep. He bought *The Port Folio* from Joseph Dennie, its founder and editor, and *The Mirror of Taste,* the leading theatrical publication of the country. Dennie was a Federalist, and Bradford, as the son-in-law of Philadelphia's Democratic mayor, was a Democrat, but Dennie continued as editor of *The Port Folio* for some time after the sale, and continued the aloof, nonpartisan, intellectual character of the magazine. It also continued to make money, for Dennie had achieved the feat, never duplicated in the history of the United States, of turning out a literary magazine that always showed a profit. *The Port Folio* made a profit of $6,000 a year. Dennie was in his last illness, but he was still an editorial genius, pushing along his volunteer assistants, Nicholas Biddle and Dr. Charles Caldwell, and forcing them to keep up the high standard he had established. Wilson became their leading contributor. He was introduced in a long account of the first volume of the *Ornithology,* and immediately after, serial publication of his poem *The Foresters* began, with illustrations made by the artist Barralet from Wilson's own rough sketches of wilderness scenes.

Bradford and Inskeep was now known as Bradford and Inskeep and Inskeep and Bradford, all four names being used. More of the Inskeep fortune was going into the firm, which had a printing business, a book-publishing house, magazines, and retail bookstores, as well as a New York branch; each Inskeep son, as he came of age, became a partner. Bradford was an enthusiast, but his enthusiasms were often short-lived, and the expanded outlook for the *Ornithology* because of Wilson's new subscriptions also involved a considerable capital outlay by Bradford—a heavy responsibility when he was also expanding in other enterprises. The books were not paid for by the subscribers until the end of the year in which they were received. Even printing another 200 copies of the first edition meant that Bradford paid out at least $750 to colorists before any return came in. When it did, the additional return would be $2,400, yet increased investment before payment was made pointed out the essential difficulty—with hand-colored plates there was no substantial reduction in unit costs, as there was in large editions of printed works—and Bradford was developing reservations about the bargain he had made. He had agreed (on Wilson's recommendation) to print an American edition of Michaux's volume on American trees, which had been published in France with colored plates, and Wilson publicized this fact; but Bradford delayed and stalled until Wilson felt himself to have been placed in an impossible position with Michaux. Bradford also agreed to print Meriwether Lewis' projected volume on the Lewis and Clark expedition, which was also to have colored plates, but his enthusiasm cooled, nothing more was heard of the book, and Kimber and Conrad, rival Philadelphia publishers, were now scheduled to bring out William Clark's account of the expedition, for which Peale was to make the illustrations. Bradford clearly had lost something of his appetite for expensive books in color.

Wilson set up the *Ornithology* as a separate department of the publishing firm. He made individual agreements with engravers, colorists and artists, as well as with printing specialists, like those who made the impressions from the engravings. Special craftsmen were also required for each detail, like cutting into the copper plates the neat lettering that carried the name of each bird—the engravers could not do this. When the organization for turning out the additional copies was functioning, Wilson worked steadily on his second volume. Forty-two birds were to be painted for this, even more vivid than the first—the hummingbird, with a stomach no larger than the globe of a human eye; the cardinal gros-beak, which would fight its own image in a looking glass; the scarlet tanager, greatly esteemed by the Cubans, who paid $10 for caged specimens, and once bought a shipment for $18,000; the red-eyed flycatcher, whose song consisted of a chant that sounded like *tom kelly! whip tom kelly!* repeated very distinctly; the unfortunate marsh wren, whose song was a low crackling sound, like air bubbles in mud; the ingenious brown thrush, which carefully removed the poison from wasps before swallowing them; the golden ground thrush, which, when alarmed, escaped from its nest with great silence and speed and scurried along the ground like a mouse. In June Wilson was studying hummingbirds, noting that despite the slow migration Abbot had seen, they were reported in great numbers on the Peace River just below the Arctic Circle, a fact to provoke thought in view of the delicate structure of the creature, covering such distances despite enemies superior in strength and magnitude—still more remarkable because the hummingbird laid but two eggs, compared to fifteen by the European wren, yet the hummingbird "is abundantly more numerous in America than the wren is in Europe...."

Wilson suggested that sunlight, rather than weather, might be a factor in its migration. He was given a caged hummingbird, which he happened to place in a shaded part of his room at Jones's house; he found it insensible, with no motion of the lungs apparent, the eyes closed, and the bird giving no sign of life when touched. "I carried it out into the open air," Wilson wrote, "and placed it directly in the rays of the sun, in a sheltered situation. In a few seconds, respiration became very apparent; the bird breathed faster and faster, opened its eyes, and began to look about, with as much seeming vivacity as ever. After it had completely recovered I restored it to liberty, and it flew off to the withered top of a pear tree, where it sat for some time dressing its disordered plumage, and then shot off like a meteor."

These were the matters that engaged Wilson while much of the nation was concerned with another of the great scandals of the time. At the publishing house of Hall and Pierce, a short distance down Market Street in Philadelphia from Wilson's office, there appeared in 1809 a book called *Proofs of the Corruption of General James Wilkinson,* by Daniel Clark. One of the boldest works of the sort ever published, the book stated without qualification that the general in command of the armies of the United States was a spy who had long operated as a paid agent for a foreign power. The author, Daniel Clark, was a gritty little Irishman, educated at Eton, who had become an American citizen and a wealthy merchant in New Orleans, a close friend and associate of Andrew Ellicott, on whose investigation of Wilkinson the book was to a great measure based. Now, Wilkinson, after testifying for the government at the trial of Aaron Burr, demanded that the administration show its confidence in him by restoring him to his command in New Orleans, and this was done, but his command was not quite the same as it had been before. In March, 1809, an entire new army was sent to New Orleans. It consisted of 2,000 well-equipped and well-trained men, staffed by such officers as Winfield Scott, then a young captain of artillery. This was nearly a quarter of the total armed force of the government, the Federal troops then being regarded as the nucleus of larger armies that the states would supply in the event of war. Wilkinson quartered these newcomers from the North in the pestilential, fever-laden swamps of Terre aux Boeufs below New Orleans. He ignored the protests of citizens of the city, and when the War Department ordered him to move his army to high ground, he replied that the site was essential to the defense of the Mississippi Valley. Captain Winfield Scott openly denounced Wilkinson as a traitor in public places throughout New Orleans, expecting to be court-martialed and thus have an opportunity to bring into the open the suffering in camp, but Wilkinson merely had him arrested as a thief, charged with stealing money from other officers, and effectively silenced him by keeping him in jail awaiting trial.

In June the new President, James Madison, bluntly commanded Wilkinson to get his army out of the infected area. He was told to move the troops clear out of Louisiana, to the hilly ground above Natchez, and a fleet under Commodore David Porter raced to the scene to provide transport. By that time it was too late: 795 of the 2,000 men were dead of fever. Another 166 had deserted. Half the remainder were ill or dying. Ten officers died of fever. Six were court-martialed and dismissed. Fifty-one resigned their commissions. The army that was intended to guard the Mississippi was finished before a shot was fired, and its casualty lists were longer than those of the major battles of the Revolution.

The catastrophe of Terre aux Boeufs, coming at a time when the yellow fever plagues were living memories, sent a thrill of horror through the nation, and the War Department suppressed all news from New Orleans. Wilson had long hoped to explore the Ohio and the Mississippi for the birds along their banks before he got far into the *Ornithology*—indeed, he felt he should have made the trip before he began—and he became increasingly anxious to set out after the disquieting reports came through, to be followed by ominous silence. At the very time that Madison was giving his final orders to Wilkinson—that is, in June, 1809—Wilson was trying to finish his hummingbird essay, and finding it hard going.

While he was at work on it a man came by William Jones's house carrying 29 caged mockingbirds. These birds, if they were good singers, sold for $50 or even $100, and an average one brought $7 to $15. The bird man found that about 9 of every 10 lived in captivity, and these, which he had carried 30 miles from the woods where he caught them, he expected to carry 96 miles to New York to market with no further loss. Wilson decided that it was time for him to prepare his essay on the mockingbird, the engraving of which was already prepared, and on the Fourth of July he remained at his desk rather than join in the celebrations, not because his patriotic ardor had diminished, but because he was still at work on mockingbirds.

If the truth were admitted, he said, the eagle, grand and noble as he seemed to be, was not a good symbol of the nation, presenting a fierce and warlike image of the country which its inhabitants might feel called upon to live up to despite their own peaceful inclinations. But nothing could be asserted against the mockingbird. There was no more gallant creature in the wilderness in defense of its own, hurling itself on intruders with a fury that terrified snakes, dogs, cats, hawks, rodents, yes, and even men and eagles. And yet there was no bird so peaceable and industrious, or one that seemed to enjoy life more. A mockingbird cocking its head to one side, listening intently, and suddenly whistling like a man calling his dog, imitating a baby chick, and then puffing out its throat and croaking like a bullfrog, was a truly marvelous woodland entertainer, a role it seemed to relish. Wilson had known a tame mockingbird to imitate the barking of a dog, the mewing of a cat, and the creaking of a passing wheelbarrow, then whistle a tune it had been taught, and also run through the quivering notes of a canary and the clear whistle of a redbird. Its love of music was thrilling, for a mockingbird in an ecstasy of music literally danced, its wings outspread, while it warbled like a bluebird, trilled like a robin, scolded like a blue jay, or sang the song of the wood thrush more beautifully than the thrush itself. When it did so, other birds grew quiet. The strangeness of its memory perhaps threw light on the mental processes of other birds: if a thrush's song at dawn had been interrupted by the crowing of a cock, the mockingbird, a long time later, might interpolate into its imitation of the thrush the cock crow, at exactly the time it had sounded in the original song.

Sometimes in the top of a tall bush, or a half-grown tree, in a dewy morning when the woods were already vocal with hundreds of warblers, the mockingbird's own song rose so beautifully that all the others seemed only to be accompanying him. "His own native notes are bold and full and varied seemingly beyond all limits," Wilson wrote. "They consist of short expressions of two, three, or, at the most, five or six syllables, generally interspersed with imitations and uttered with great emphasis and rapidity, and continued with undiminished ardor for half an hour or an hour at a time. His expanded wings and tail, glistening with white, and the buoyant gaiety of his action, arresting the eye as his song most irresistibly does the ear, he sweeps round with enthusiastic ecstasy—he mounts or descends as his song swells or dies away." As William Bartram beautifully said, when the mockingbird finished the last mounting strains of its song, it flew upward like an arrow, as if to recover its very soul.

Time and patience were required to put the essay in the form Wilson wanted it to have, and he delayed himself still more when he agreed to the publication of *The Foresters* in *The Port Folio*. A lingering pride in his accomplishment as a poet was responsible, after his long silence, together with his recognition that he *had* created a remarkable work, one which blocked out a fresh and unspoiled poetic terrain, and incorporated into its casual account of a simple woodland adventure its literal social history, and its isolated passages of imaginative strangeness. *The Foresters* was too long—not merely twice too long, but ten times too long; a novel in rhymed couplets, yet dealing with too inconsequential a matter for its length had it been a work of fiction. Nothing was ever finished for Wilson; he wrote and rewrote as long as possible, and *The Foresters* was the kind of a poem that called for revision and polishing. He could not have foreseen what the cost of the delay would be to the *Ornithology* in any event, nor could he have refused to publish *The Foresters* on the grounds that all his energy was required for his essential task. Yet his story would have been different had he not been distracted at this time.

In the fall, when he had the second volume of the *Ornithology* in shape for publication, he proposed to Bartram that they make their way to St. Louis, the capital of the northern district of Louisiana Territory, where Meriwether Lewis served as territorial governor. Wilson believed they should walk, because it gave them more opportunity to study birds. If Bartram seemed an elderly man for such a journey, he had himself, when young, accompanied his own father on longer trips when the elder Bartram was past seventy. Bartram tentatively agreed. But in the meantime more mysteries were added to the shocking developments in the West. Congress was led by the Terre aux Boeufs catastrophe to order an inquiry into General Wilkinson's entire career, and the network of spies and secret agents he had woven in twenty years of frontier intrigue—a network that encompassed storekeepers, tavern-keepers, thugs, hunters, politicians, ferry operators, Indian traders—was threatened with ruin with him. Among the people who were alarmed at the defenselessness of the West in the crisis was Meriwether Lewis, who also had reason to be concerned because the War Department had refused to honor his drafts for expenses resulting from the Lewis and Clark expedition, and in paying the government's creditors himself he lost his lands in St. Louis. He set out for Washington in August, carrying with him his papers of the Lewis and Clark expedition; he intended to sail from New Orleans, but reports indicated that it would be unsafe for him to go that way, so he struck out overland from Memphis. On October 10 he was found dead on the Natchez Trace.

The War Department suppressed the news of his death, and as the Terre aux Boeufs scandal continued to grow, all sorts of rumors swept Washington. Lewis owed money to the Philadelphia firm of Bryan and Schatter, and their commercial representative in Washington, hearing the stories of Lewis' death, sent word to them so claims could be placed against Lewis' estate. On the night of November 10, 1809, Wilson visited Bartram and the discussion ranged round their projected walking journey, which would take them over the northern half of the Natchez Trace. The next morning the news broke in Philadelphia that Meriwether Lewis had killed himself in Tennessee.

As the time for departure drew near, Bartram drew back, wisely, from so arduous a journey. And then Wilson himself could not get away. The delays had prevented publication of the *Ornithology* until after the first of the year—in other words, payment for the second volume would not be received until the end of 1810. Meanwhile the mystery of Lewis' death continued to deepen. There was no official inquiry. No report was published, or filed with the War Department records. The only account was that of an Indian agent named Neelly, who found Lewis' body, and buried him. His story was that he met Lewis in Memphis, and remained with him because Lewis was not altogether in his right mind. Simultaneously, stories circulated in frontier towns, long distances apart, to the effect that

Lewis had tried to kill himself in Memphis, and had been restrained by the commander at Fort Pickering there. Only unrelated items of these stories had reached the newspapers, and they asserted that Lewis had killed himself in a wilderness cabin called Grinder's Stand, often adding lurid embellishments, such as that he had cut his throat. In the Tennessee mountains it was believed that Lewis was murdered, and a coroner's jury was summoned, but nothing came of its deliberations. Wilson's admiration for Meriwether Lewis was almost as fanatical as his admiration for Jefferson, but he was shaken by these stories, and the fear grew in his mind that perhaps Lewis, like Wilkinson, had been involved in treasonable projects, and had killed himself rather than face the inquiry that Wilkinson now faced. The projected trip to St. Louis that he had discussed so lightheartedly with Bartram now appeared in so dark a light that it might well have been abandoned.

The omens were not favorable. Wilson signed the Introduction to Volume Two of *American Ornithology* on January 1, 1810, the date itself a major defeat of his hopes. In February Robert Carr presented him with the first finished copies, and with a few sample books of both the first and second volume, Wilson began alone the long journey he had thought to make in company with Bartram. He went first to Lancaster, where the Pennsylvania legislature was in session. Governor Simon Snyder, a storekeeper and mill operator, had just swept the state by 68,000 votes to 40,000 for the Federalist candidate. Snyder was of Pennsylvania Dutch stock, "an active man of plain good sense and little ceremony," Wilson described him, who took one look at Wilson's books and gladly subscribed. The Pennsylvania legislature bought three sets of the *Ornithology*. A Lancaster liquor dealer bought another. A learned Judge Hustetter, however, reproached Wilson with being undemocratic. He said Wilson's book was beyond the reach of the people, and consequently inconsistent with republican institutions. Wilson was stung; he replied hotly that Judge Hustetter's three-story brick residence was beyond the reach of the commonality; was it undemocratic too? His work was a contribution to science, and science, especially natural history, was of profound importance to every citizen in a democratic country. The good judge then calmed him down, admitting there was truth in what he said. But Wilson was a little disturbed and he finally decided that when he had finished the book he would prepare a popular edition, with good engravings, like Bewick's wonderful book on British birds, which would be within the reach of poor students.

He sold a subscription to Dickinson College in Carlisle, but Shippenburg gave him nothing, and after Chambersburg likewise turned up no subscribers he caught the stagecoach to Pittsburgh. He left the stage as soon as it passed out of Chambersburg, and, letting his trunk go on to Pittsburgh, walked the rest of the way. He spent four days on the snow-covered roads over the Alleghenies. He saw no one, and there were no birds in these midwinter mountains. The cold did not affect him; he wrote of the eerie pleasure of night travel, of the moonlight shining in deathlike stillness over the icy plain.

Within two miles of Pittsburgh the road descended a long steep hill, with the Allegheny

1. Louisiana Tanager. 2. Clarks Crow. 3. Lewis's Woodpecker.

Drawn from Nature by A. Wilson.

Engraved by A.Lawson.

20

Louisiana tanager (now the western tanager), Clark's crow, and Lewis' woodpecker, found on the Lewis and Clark Expedition, were among the many birds first pictured or described by Wilson.

River, still ice-locked, visible on the right. Wilson arrived a little after four, sunset at this season. Great columns of smoke were rising from the glassworks, forges and furnaces. The ice had gone out on the Monongahela, whose banks were lined with flatboats waiting to start down the Ohio to the Mississippi. Wilson thought that a view of the city from the hills, its great rivers, the pillars of smoke in the sunset—this would make a noble picture. When he exhibited his books, he was promptly shown a local wonder. A resident had recently shot a huge, perfectly formed snow owl, but had only winged it, and the bird was kept a captive. Snow owls, as he had noted before, were not uncommon, yet people always seemed surprised and excited by them, as if they were very rare, and when Wilson examined the powerful wings and the deep-seated, motionless yellow eyes of the bird, he felt the same sense of its strangeness.

Wilson lined up nineteen subscribers in four days. General O'Hara, the founder of Pittsburgh, James Mountain, an Irish immigrant who started as a schoolteacher and became a prominent lawyer, and Thomas Baird, one of the builders of the first bridge over the Monongahela, were typical of Wilson's backers in Pittsburgh. Many of them were connected with the Episcopal Old Round Church in Pittsburgh, like Dr. Nathaniel Bedford, and Presley Neville. Among the others were lawyers like Thomas Collins and Henry Baldwin, who told Wilson that Pittsburgh was so prosperous there had not been a single lawsuit against a merchant for three years. Baldwin was newly married to Sally Ellicott, the daughter of Wilkinson's enemy Andrew Ellicott.

In view of the prosperity of the merchants, Wilson decided to concentrate on them, and soon got an order from Thomas Cromwell, who owned big warehouses along the Monongahela, and another from Nathaniel Richardson, a prosperous drygoods merchant who went into the music business. Richardson was born in Ireland and brought to Pittsburgh in his youth. He operated a store while his father traded up and down the Ohio and the Mississippi. He married well, prospered, and was beginning to raise his large family, while his father continued to wander and eventually landed in New Orleans. Richardson was thirty-one years old when Wilson met him; he was well educated, a good musician, and loved botany —he built the first greenhouse in Pittsburgh. What brought him closer to Wilson, however, was that he loved to hunt, and had begun the practice of importing fine hunting dogs from England.

The Pittsburgh resident who had most to say to Wilson was another subscriber, Zadock Cramer, who knew more than anyone else about travel through the region that lay ahead of him. In 1801 Cramer published *The Navigator* in Pittsburgh, a landmark-to-landmark guide for travelers floating down the Ohio and the Mississippi to New Orleans. It was a tough and durable volume, with a water-resistant binding so it would not be ruined if the boat overturned, and it was packed with minutely detailed instructions the mere reading of which would dissuade all but the stoutest spirits from venturing near the river. Cramer knew almost every rock on which a boat had lost its bottom planking, and he sprinkled his guidebook with disquieting warnings against dishonest boatbuilders who used rotten timber as well. He was convinced that most losses occurred when travelers were landing, or trying to land, and believed that if it were possible they should drift with the current through the night: the middle of the river was the safest place. With all his candid accounts of stumps, rapids, mud, eddies, currents and constant hazards, Cramer loved the rivers and expressed the feeling of the frontiersmen for them with matter-of-fact eloquence. The French name for the Ohio was the beautiful river, and to Cramer its original name was right; he believed it to be the most beautiful stream in the American West, which meant anywhere in the world.

At the time Wilson called on him, Cramer was preparing the eighth edition of *The Navigator,* for he brought it up to date year by year, adding details, notes of water conditions, items about the growth of settlements, from the material that boatmen brought to his office when they returned from New Orleans. He also added, as the thought struck him, occasional recollections of his boyhood in New Jersey, and additional reports of lost shipments, and because he was an engaging as well as an accurate writer *The Navigator* had become an essential item in the pack of anyone going to New Orleans. Now for the first time he was adding maps to the work. The perplexities were great, because the channels changed rapidly. The best maps were still those drawn by Ellicott and published in his journal, but Ellicott had made the trip in a summer of phenomenally low water, when the boats had to be dragged over great stretches that were now many fathoms deep.

Guided by Cramer's instructions, Wilson bought a rowboat suitable for long-distance river travel. He painted a name, *The Ornithologist,* on the stern. On February 22, 1810, the ice broke on the Allegheny. At dawn on the 23rd Wilson placed his trunk, greatcoat, gun, biscuits, cheese and a bottle of cordial in the stern, and started down the river. He dropped a note to Lawson: "My baggage is on board—I have just to despatch this and be off. The weather is fine, and I have no doubt of piloting my skiff in safety to Cincinnati. Farewell, God bless you!"

CHAPTER THREE

Beautiful Ohio

THE SURFACE of the river was as smooth as a mirror. Wilson rowed cautiously to avoid the occasional masses of ice that were still drifting down from the Allegheny. Almost at once the river curved out of sight of the city and into its narrow valley, three or four miles wide, steep, tree-covered mountains on both sides beyond the mile-wide stretch of bottom land. Smoke from the maple sugar camps rose lazily from the mountains. There were little clearings around remote log cabins visible from the river, dwarfed by the immense heights beyond them.

A redbird whistled on the banks, a strong and sonorous whistle, thrilling with its promise of summer. He felt his heart expand with joy; he could visualize the bird in the trees, rich vermilion and dusky brown, one of the most beautiful of all the creatures of the wilderness, rare this early in the year. The current was carrying his boat downstream at the rate of two and a half miles an hour; he took up his oars, and, rowing steadily, added three or more miles every hour. The ice masses melted during the day. About an hour after dark, having covered fifty-two miles, he put into shore at an abandoned cabin, and slept on a heap of cornstalks.

Long before daylight he set out again. The riverbanks on both sides lay in intense darkness, but the bold projecting headlands, or the lines of perspective joining at the vanishing point, were mirrored on the smooth glassy surface of the river. He could only tell where he was when he passed a clearing, by the crowing of cocks. Now and then, in more solitary places, he heard the big horned owl making its hideous hollowing that echoed among the mountains. Its cry was a loud and sudden *Waugh O! Waugh O!* but it had another nocturnal cry, strikingly suggesting the half-suppressed screams of a person being throttled, unnerving to the toughest traveler. He told himself that the bird was so recluse, solitary and mysterious, its cry so discordant in the silence and gloom, that it always aroused sensations of awe and abhorrence, and always must do so.

His hands bothered him somewhat, sore at first, and later so rough he felt weeks would pass before he could draw well. He found he could easily average thirty-five miles a day, and often traveled much farther. The freedom of the river travel delighted him. He could rise in the darkness after he had slept a while and row on silently with a confidence that forest trails never permitted. On an early March day, in a snowstorm, he saw a flock of bright yellow birds flying for shelter, and tried to shoot one. He rowed into shore where they vanished among the trees. He was near the mouth of a stream, opposite the village of Portsmouth, Ohio. But the storm grew violent, the rain changing to hail and snow. A tree crashed down nearby. He could not remain near land, and steered out into the river, which rolled and foamed like the sea. His boat was half full of water and all his strength was needed to make the least headway. The snow continued violently until dark, Wilson moving downstream without knowing where he was. When it was quite dark he saw a light on the Kentucky shore, and rowed toward it. An old hunter took him in, fed him and let him dry his clothes by the fire. Wilson spent the evening in learning the art and mystery of bear-treeing, wolf-trapping, and wildcat-hunting.

Throughout his passage down the river, he watched passenger pigeons. All he had seen since he arrived in America were mere straggling parties compared with the congregating millions now overhead. He rested on his oars every day to watch their aerial maneuvers. A column eight or ten miles in length would appear from Kentucky, high in the air, steering for Indiana. As these vast bodies passed over the river the surface of the water would be marked by droppings, like the commencement of a shower. Sometimes a hawk would make a sweep on a particular part of a column from a great height. Almost as quick as lightning that part shot out of the common track, then rising again to advance at the same height as before. The leaders sometimes gradually varied their course, until it formed a large bend, of more than a mile in diameter, those behind tracing the exact route of their predecessors. This continued sometimes long after both extremities were out of sight. The whole flock, with its glittering undulations, marked a space in the heavens resembling the windings of a vast and majestic river. When this bend became very great, the birds, as if sensible of the unnecessary circuitous route they were taking, suddenly changed their direction, so that what was in column before became an immense front, straightening all its indentures, until it swept the heavens in one vast and infinitely extended line.

His loneliness became oppressive, with his need to discuss these wonders. In the warm spring days, he took every excuse to stop and talk. Once he rowed to shore to purchase some milk at a house that stood near the river. Invited inside, he was visiting pleasantly when a loud rushing roar, succeeded by instant darkness, swept the house. He thought a tornado had struck. His host said, "It is only the pigeons." Running out into the yard, Wilson saw a flock thirty or forty yards in width, sweeping along very low, between the house and the height that formed the bank of the river. These continued to pass for more than a quarter of an hour, and at length varied their bearing so as to pass over the mountain behind which they disappeared before the rear came up.

When he reached the Great Miami River, pouring into the Ohio from the north, he tied his boat and walked upstream along the Miami. It was a pure and powerful river, so strong that for many miles below its mouth there were two distinct streams, the discolored Ohio on one side and the blue Miami on the other. Wilson ran into a herd of deer, but they were too light-heeled for him. Coming back empty-handed he shot a turkey, and found it good eating. The next day he rowed up Big Bone Creek, which had enough water for his boat for a quarter of a mile, left his boat in the keeping of a farm family, and walked five miles to Big Bone Lick. This was the great deposit of fossils, then believed to be the prehistoric elephant burying ground. The bones of mammoths and buffalo lay everywhere about in a deep quagmire about an acre in extent at the middle of a craterlike valley in the hills.

On a windy, bright afternoon he looked over the morass where the bones were found, the loneliest figure in the loneliest spot in America. A flock of large, beautiful ducks was disturbed by him, and he shot two. Each was about twenty inches long, brownish black, with a head like a mallard, with large concentric circles of red on the breast and broad bands of reddish chestnut, black and white, across the wings. He recognized the gadwall or gray duck, rare in the North, though he had seen some on the way to Niagara years before. He had only wounded one bird, and in chasing it he fell into the quagmire, sinking up to his waist. The peril, as well as the loneliness of his method of travel, depressed him; he shivered at the thought of his bones among the grand congregation of mammoth tusks below.

Now weary, he started back to the creek. A big flock of green and yellow Carolina parrots swept past him. They were good-sized birds, about fourteen inches long when fully grown, with a wingspread of nearly two feet. They were unafraid of men, had a quizzical air, marvelous powers of flight, and a lame and crippled gait on the ground. Their heads and necks were bright scarlet, their bodies brilliant yellow, and they traveled in flocks that flew at low levels with great speed, seeming to graze the trunks of trees, yet easily killed when they alighted. Wilson shot one. The whole flock rose, flew about, and alighted again. Wilson had killed the one he shot. He wanted to capture one alive. But he shot about a dozen before he wounded two, proof of his weariness, for at his best he captured uninjured even small birds. One parrot was barely wounded, stunned and uninjured. Wilson walked with it five miles back to his rowboat. He built a cage of branches in the stern of the boat, and fed the parrot cockleburs, which it freely ate within an hour of captivity.

He spent the night at the home of the owner of the quagmire, leaving instructions with him as to the care of the fragments of the mastodons, so a complete skeleton could be recovered for Peale's Museum. The day following he rowed back to the Ohio, but he was weary with his excursion, and let his boat drift downstream while he rested and began training his captive parrot. He drifted twenty miles during the day, and in the late afternoon saw a small settlement on the riverbank, rowed ashore, and discovered himself in a colony of Swiss immigrants. They were experienced makers of wine, and had put in twenty acres of grapes to start their vineyard. Because Wilson spoke German he could converse with these hardy people, who made him welcome. They had imported the vines from the Cape of Good Hope, and their young colony was already thriving, producing 700 gallons of wine their first year, and the orchards of pears, apples, peaches, figs and cherries astonished them by their abundance.

When he left the next morning Wilson bought a bottle of their wine, fortifying himself with it on his way down the river. He and his parrot passed the mouth of the Kentucky River, which poured out with impressive power when seen from the middle of the Ohio. Rowing close to the bank, Wilson saw wild turkeys. He tied his boat, and scrambled through the woods, trying to shoot one. They led him further inland, and he wasted so much time, getting nothing, that it was dark when he came to the falls of the Ohio at Louisville. He had heard so much about these falls that he expected something like Niagara. At each bend of the river he peered anxiously for the lights of the town, fearing to be swept over the brink. When he could hear the falls plainly he rowed into Bear Creek in the darkness, tied his boat, wrapped the parrot in a handkerchief, and groped his way into town. There he found the Indian Queen Tavern, and gladly sat down to rest. There was a barroom adjoining the lobby, the bartender acting as room clerk and assigning the travelers their rooms; Wilson secured one at a little more than a dollar a day and was soon asleep.

CHAPTER FOUR

For the Good of the World

THE FIRST BREAKFAST BELL at the Indian Queen rang at seven-thirty. After washing in the courtyard in the rear of the hotel, where Negro slaves with hot water and towels attended them, the guests crowded the corridors leading to the dining room. The second bell rang at eight o'clock; the doors of the dining room were unlocked; everyone rushed to a table and began to eat. Everyone hurried because there was no second chance, for platters of chicken, fish and meat were placed on the tables and guests selected their own portions. Moreover, the door was locked as soon as it appeared that all the boarders had had time enough to reach the dining room—though latecomers were apt to find very little left even if they arrived before the doors were locked—and the only waiter was a boy who went from table to table taking down the names, to add twenty-five cents, the charge for breakfast, to the cost of a room.

Most of the 140 boarders at the Indian Queen were men, and after breakfast they lounged in the news room, as the lobby was called. Half a dozen monopolized the space in front of the fire. Most of the others silently paced the room like strollers on the deck of a ship. Almost everyone smoked cigars, and there was almost no conversation. No liquor was served in the dining room, but the bar opened at sunrise. A drink cost about ten cents, a glass and a bottle being given the customer, who poured as much as he wanted. At one end of the bar there was a tub of cold water, with a dipper in it, and as whisky was never taken straight, the patrons carried their drinks to the tub and mixed the amount of water according to their taste. For many of the guests, life after breakfast consisted of waiting for the luncheon bell at one-thirty, and for the supper bell after that, and it was said that no more comfortless and senseless existence was known to man than that of a permanent boarder in a frontier hotel.

Wilson left soon after breakfast and walked to the river. It was Monday morning, March 18, 1810, or twenty-three days since he left Pittsburgh. He wanted to see by daylight the falls of the Ohio whose noise had alarmed him, and was astonished to find them little more than a stretch of fast water, pouring the whole expanse of the mile-wide river. While he watched, two huge flatboats bound for New Orleans came down and dropped over the falls without difficulty. And he reflected that they were less dangerous than the rapids in the Oswego that he had run with Duncan years before.

Two miles below Louisville was the settlement of Shippingport, the head of navigation bound upstream. Wilson idled down the river below the falls, looking over the ropewalks and warehouses of Shippingport, and its huge stores, largely the creation of French-speaking merchants, stocked with imported machinery and instruments. These merchants had built fine brick homes, surrounded by wooded grounds, along the Ohio, and befriended French immigrants, including young Audubon: they planned that Shippingport should become the great port of the Ohio, and their aspiration for it included a degree of elegance that was lacking in Louisville itself.

There were no customers for Wilson's book there, and he made no attempt to interest people in it. He had four letters to prominent citizens of Louisville, and these he left in the course of the day, then walking to the foot of Third Street, where Bear Creek emptied into the Ohio, and where he had tied his rowboat the night before. It was an interesting coincidence that an uncle of Margaret Carman, his friend in Milestown days, had settled at the mouth of Bear Creek before Louisville was founded. But Wilson was not then interested in history—he wanted to sell the rowboat that had carried him down the river. The 22 days required for the journey was not fast time as river travel was measured—the flatboats drifted the 720 miles in 10 days—but Wilson had developed a kind of affection for his craft, and was disappointed that he was able to get only half what it had cost him. This was to be expected: Louisville's major industry, apart from whisky distilling, was the building of river craft. The buyer of Wilson's rowboat, noting the name, *The Ornithologist,* that Wilson had painted on it, asked if Wilson had named it for an Indian chief.

There was still no answer to Wilson's letters of introduction. At six-thirty the evening meal at the Indian Queen was hurried through, and the guests resumed their silent pacing of the lobby, and crowded the bar. Wilson was bored and restless, with no occupation beyond reading the papers and observing the social customs of the place. The Louisville paper carried an advertisement that J. J. Audubon was prepared to give lessons in drawing, and would also paint portraits that would be good likenesses; and early on Tuesday morning, a pleasant day, Wilson made his way to the store of Audubon and Rozier.

Audubon was at work at a desk when Wilson entered. There were no customers, and the Audubon and Rozier establishment was not an imposing one. Wilson introduced himself, and Audubon looked him over with interest, noting his long, hooked nose, his keen eyes and high cheekbones. Audubon was not favorably impressed by Wilson's appearance, but he was not prejudiced against him, particularly noting that his clothing, with his short coat and gray waistcoat, was unusual on the frontier.

Wilson had the first and second volumes of the *Ornithology* with him, and these Audubon examined. Wilson explained the terms on which the books were sold. Audubon took his pen, and was at the point of writing his name on the contract for a subscription, when his partner, Ferdinand Rozier, called to him in French from the back of the store.

Audubon paused. Still speaking French, Rozier asked Audubon why he wanted to subscribe. Audubon was a little confused, and embarrassed at his partner's speaking in a foreign language before a stranger, and Rozier added meaningfully in French: "Your drawings are certainly far better!"

Audubon admitted that his vanity was appealed to—he knew he was a better artist than Wilson, though he admired a rugged wholesome honesty in Wilson's work. Rozier went on, again speaking French, "You must know as much of the habits of American birds as this gentleman." This was certainly untrue, and Audubon knew it, but he was made uncomfortable by a suspicion that Wilson understood French, and saw that Wilson was displeased by something in any event. He thought that perhaps Wilson's displeasure came because he, Audubon, had reacted so quickly when Rozier called to him. But he decided not to subscribe at the moment.

Wilson politely asked Audubon if he had many drawings of birds. Without saying how many he had, Audubon produced a portfolio, laid it on the table, and let Wilson examine his work. Audubon said later that he had drawn birds occasionally since 1804, but even by his own account had few, though he was a prolific artist dealing with other subjects. Wilson examined Audubon's paintings with care, his friendliness indicated by his arranging to meet Audubon later at the Indian Queen Hotel. Audubon, his wife, and their first child, still an infant, also lived at the Indian Queen.

Wilson left no concrete references to Audubon in his many letters on his journey. As a result of Audubon's quarrel with George Ord, many years after Wilson's death, Audubon wrote his own recollections of the meeting, and in this he pictured Wilson as discouraged because he—Audubon—had even then finished so much of his great folio of American birds that Wilson saw his own work was surpassed. This part of Audubon's recollections was subsequently proven to be false, and was obviously motivated by Audubon's desire, in the face of Ord's attacks, to set himself up as having preceded Wilson. In any event, it could not have had the effect that Audubon claimed for it, for Wilson had already spent much time with John Abbot, also a superior artist, and one who had unquestionably concentrated on bird paintings.

The conclusion of Dr. Elsa Guerdrum Allen, the most objective and scrupulous student of American ornithology, was that Audubon's career as a painter of bird pictures had its origin at the moment he first examined Wilson's two sumptuous volumes. His own tremendous and still unfocused artistic gift, the quick perception of Rozier that Audubon himself could exploit the field, combined to turn Audubon from a drawing teacher and storekeeper in a frontier town into a naturalist, though many years were to pass before Audubon concentrated all his efforts in that direction. The field was so large that under ordinary circumstances there should have been no struggle for exclusive possession of it, a more normal development unquestionably calling for Wilson to be recognized as the predecessor and Audubon, in following him, as refining and popularizing his work, with bold showmanship as well as with artistic skill.

Audubon and Wilson were both associated with Miers Fisher in Philadelphia, and in Audubon's case the connection was close and important. Then twenty-five years old, Audubon had, by his own account, mentioned above, been a rebellious ward in Miers Fisher's care, sometimes living in his house; he had been on close terms with Fisher's children, and these were also among Wilson's friends in Philadelphia. They were, in fact, almost all subscribers to the *Ornithology* that Audubon had refused to subscribe to. In the account that Audubon gave of Wilson in Louisville, he did not mention the people in Philadelphia they knew in common. He said that Wilson was plunged into melancholy after seeing Audubon's paintings, and sat in his room, playing mournful airs on his flute, until Audubon took pity on him, introduced him to his wife and friends, and took him on bird-hunting expeditions to try to better his spirits. The remainder of Audubon's account of Wilson in Louisville has been proven to have no basis in fact. It dealt with technical ornithological matters. George Ord accused Audubon of having copied some of Wilson's paintings, and in at least two cases provided proof that he had done so. Audubon's reply was that they had been stolen from him—that in this Louisville meeting Wilson borrowed Audubon's paintings and copied them without Audubon's knowledge and printed them as his own, a reply that was easily proven to be false. Audubon was then still a portrait painter, and Wilson's neglect in mentioning his work in the *Ornithology* had its source in the simple fact that Audubon had not then painted birds.

Wilson was irritated by Louisville, principally because he received no answers to his letters of introduction, saying in a letter that literature and science did not have a single friend in the place. The opportunism of the citizens was exceptional, he wrote; each man thought only of what he himself could gain. One example that he thought striking lay in the location of the town—it could easily be made healthy, but it was surrounded by marshy ground, and while only a short canal would be required to drain the marshes, for the city stood above the Ohio River, yet the citizens would not dig the canal because each man asked what he himself would get out of it. And as a result there was an uncommon degree of fever.

Wilson spent part of two days exploring these marshes. He found no new birds. But he saw with a thrill of recognition pintail ducks that he had hunted on the Delaware in his schoolteaching days, the most elegantly formed and graceful of all ducks. On the borders of the ponds there were many snipe, shy and agile, perhaps the hardest hunting of all the game birds. As he watched them he reflected that only the most dexterous and eager of all sportsmen would hunt snipe. They were fine eating, of course, which made them sought after, but they were the most difficult to shoot because of their wild zigzag flight at terrific speed. While Wilson watched on the shores of the ponds, a flight of whooping cranes appeared, winging low over the water, in single file, a rare and beautiful sight, last seen by him almost exactly one year before on the Waccamaw River in North Carolina.

He was pleased with these natural wonders, which compensated for his disappointment in Louisville, and reported himself to his friends in Philadelphia as in good health and spirits. He occupied his leisure by teaching his parrot tricks, and it now crawled into his pocket of its own accord when he went out, perched on his shoulder, and ate from his hand. Wilson made arrangements with a Louisville merchant—never identified—to ship his trunk ahead by the next freight wagon that was bound for Nashville, and prepared for the next stage of his journey with a leisureliness rarely met with during his travels. He set out on Friday morning, March 23, 1810, the residents of the Indian Queen Hotel gathering on the veranda to say good-by to him and his parrot, a sign of friendliness he had not anticipated. He wrote lightheartedly enough that he and his parrot both parted with regret from the gentlemen on the veranda.

He was certainly in good spirits as he walked through the rolling gentle hills, tree-covered, each valley carrying a clear pure brook splashing over loose flags of limestone. Parklike forests, abounding in pigs, pigeons, squirrels and woodpeckers, immense fields of Indian corn around log cabins, the richest soil he had ever seen, and sunlight checkering the grass under the trees, gave him a glimpse of the country he had never dreamed of, so wealthy he barely hinted at it, lest the avarice of possible invaders be increased.

He had heard that a great roosting place of passenger pigeons ran through a stretch of woods not far from Shelbyville. He left the road to search for it, though the birds had abandoned it a few years before. These roosts were dead woods. The branches of the trees were broken with the weight of the birds, the trees killed as if girdled with an ax, and the ground for thousands of acres covered with dung. When a roost was discovered, the natives visited it at night with guns, clubs, poles and rocks, loading their horses with birds. When the young were fully grown, before they had left the nest, another great harvest took place, the whole countryside gathering with wagons, axes, beds, and cooking utensils, camping for days near these immense nurseries.

Wilson found the abandoned roost, like a slashing of dead wood three miles wide through a forest of beech trees. Checking it repeatedly as he walked southward, he found that it ran roughly forty miles, with as many as ninety nests to the tree.

He did not return to the road, but continued to traverse the woods running parallel with it. Early in the morning he watched the pigeons flying north. They had exhausted the food near at hand, and flew each day to the Indiana prairies. About one o'clock in the afternoon they began to return in such immense numbers as he never before had witnessed. Coming to an opening, by the side of Benson Creek, he had an uninterrupted view, and was astonished at their appearance. They were flying with great steadiness and rapidity, at a height beyond gunshot, several strata deep, and so close together that could shot have reached them, one discharge could not have failed of bringing down several birds. From right to left, far as the eye could reach, the breadth of this vast procession extended, everywhere equally crowded. He took out his watch to note the time, and sat down to observe them. It was then half past one. He sat for more than an hour, but, instead of a diminution of this prodigious procession, it seemed rather to increase both in numbers and rapidity. Anxious to reach Frankfort before night, he rose and went on. About four o'clock in the afternoon he crossed the Kentucky River, at the town of Frankfort. At that time the living torrent above his head seemed as numerous and extensive as ever. Long after this he observed them, in large bodies that continued to pass for six or eight minutes, and these again were followed by other detached bodies, all moving in the same southeast direction till after six in the evening. This one flight was at least 240 miles long. The birds were moving about a mile a minute. There were at least 3 pigeons to the square yard, which meant that this flock contained more than 2,000,000,000 birds.

Aside from the passenger pigeons—and another snow owl that startled the inhabitants of Bardstown—there were only familiar birds of the eastern seaboard to be found here, though more rusty grackles than were common. On the banks of the Kentucky near Frankfort Wilson found a kingfisher's nest, with the female on the nest. The birds had dug into the steep dry bank, penetrating in about a foot, and then running a corridor parallel with the face of the cliff. The dirt they had excavated formed a platform before the nest, and commanded a view of the river. A young Kentuckian saw Wilson's interest in the kingfisher's nest, and told him that the birds built permanent residences. He had seen them coming back to the same nests year after year, and once took out eggs to see what the birds would do, though always leaving one egg in the nest. He found that the female laid again, even though he repeatedly stole her eggs.

Spring was late, no further advanced than in southern Pennsylvania. There were no flowers in Kentucky when Wilson set out from Louisville, and he could see no difference between the Kentucky woods and those of Pennsylvania but in the magnitude of the timber, and superior richness of the soil. The trees were greening every day, and suddenly the blossoms of the sassafras, the dogwood and redbud were everywhere. Birds were everywhere, too, some with songs totally unknown to him, some, like the quail and the martin, surprising by their numbers. The orchards around cabins and neat farmhouses were glowing purple and white, wonderful in their contrast to the deep green of the woods, a relief when he emerged from the dusky solitude. He traveled very slowly, taking a week to cover the short distance between Louisville and Lexington.

The forest came within half a mile of the town itself. Snipe were remarkably numerous, a strange fact, since they were so shy. Dawdling and watching them, Wilson reached Lexington half an hour before sunset. There was a quarry outside town, neat fenced farmlands, a stream that drove several mills, and then the small white spire of the church, and good brick or painted frame houses. It was exhilarating to walk the streets—the only place on earth Wilson said as much for. He spent four days in Lexington, pleased with the pavements constructed of stones from the quarry, the well-dressed girls on the streets, the shops filled with goods, the wonderful horses, the hardiest in the world, and the fact that many citizens subscribed to his books. He was displeased with Lexington only because the architects, infatuated with the modern admiration for somber Gothic, had transformed the interior of a good square courthouse into a place of melancholy and reverential gloom, shadowy, damp and chillling.

William Morton, known as Lord Morton, the younger son of a titled English family, lived in luxury on Fifth Street in Lexington, the president of an insurance company, a founder of Transylvania College, and one of the most prominent of the 2,000 inhabitants. He subscribed to the *American Ornithology,* as did Thomas January, who ran the general store, and William Barry, a young lawyer, only three years out of William and Mary, who was on his way to Congress, the governorship, and—later on—a post in the Cabinet of his friend Andrew Jackson. A dozen lawyers, merchants and medical men in Lexington subscribed, an extraordinary response for a small frontier community.

The first recognized artist to settle west of the Allegheny Mountains was an acquaintance, George Beck, a landscape artist who had lived near Wilson in Philadelphia. Beck became the art teacher in a girls' school in Kentucky, his young wife, who was a very clever artist in her own right, accompanying him to the frontier. Their friends in Philadelphia heard nothing from them. Barralet, the closest friend of the couple, had asked Wilson to look them up when he reached Lexington. Wilson wrote that he had the most melancholy news to send to Barralet. Beck's wife had become deranged, and was closely confined—she had been confined for two months. Beck himself was in despair, with no work, no prospects, and owing $300 in rent alone. Wilson did not send word to Barralet that he himself had seen Beck, nor give the source of his news, but he believed what he was told. His view of their future, however, was gloomier than was warranted, for Mrs. Beck recovered, became a well-known artist herself, and lived to great age, dying in 1848, while Beck himself successfully established himself as the first artist of Kentucky.

Except for Beck's misfortune, however, the picture of Lexington was bright, and Wilson's feeling for the place was increased because he bought a horse there, and the animal turned out to be a responsive and intelligent mount that he came to love. At every occasion thereafter he asserted that the finest horses in the world were bred in Kentucky. He rode out of the city on April 8, 1810, in high spirits, to discover that travel had become easy and interesting. Nineteen miles out of town the road descended rocky cliffs to the Kentucky River, here winding between perpendicular heights of limestone. Wilson shot a brown lark, and jotted down the date and the place. He had seen these birds in South Carolina in February, and in Maine in October. The country delighted him. Flatboats were passing down the river, the sound of their boat horns melodious and thrilling in the wild. Plants and flowers he had never seen before grew high among the rocks, bank swallows skimmed over the surface of the river, reminding him that he had seen no barn swallows for a long time, and reawakening his wonder as to where they had nested before barns were built. He rode only a few miles a day.

Beyond the Kentucky he climbed steep cliffs, and in a few miles climbed down again, a height equally imposing, to Dicks River. It was nearly dark, but fossils on the riverbank absorbed him, and some beautiful specimens of mother-of-pearl. There was a mill at the ferry crossing, and the roaring of the mill dam and rattling of the mill prevented the ferryman from hearing him. Consequently it was dark before he reached the other shore. Waiting in the twilight, he heard a whippoorwill, the first he had heard, and wrote in his notebook the place, Danville, Kentucky, and the date, April 14, 1810.

The mill owner at length heard his shout, and ferried him across the river. His horse carried him the rest of the way to Danville in the darkness. Danville was a town of eighty houses, two ropewalks, one woolen mill, nine shops, three taverns, one Catholic church, standing in rocky country abounding in springs, surrounded by excellent pasture grazing many sheep. Here Wilson learned that he was 180 miles from Nashville, without a town or village on the way. He set out as soon as possible. The next morning, at the base of a high mountain beyond Danville called Mulders Hill, he heard the mingled music of bells and the shouting of drivers echoing in the mountains, and came upon a family going west. A four-horse wagon loaded with farm equipment went first, followed by a six-horse wagon, a column of horses, steers, cows, sheep, hogs and belled calves, then eight boys, riding double on four horses, a Negro girl and white child riding another, the mother with one child riding behind her, and an infant at her breast, and ten or twelve colts following. This was one family on its way to the Cumberland. The father, a fresh, good-looking man, walked on one side of the wagon, and his eldest son on the other, each holding ropes to prevent its turning over. They interested Wilson, and he kept company with them for some time, to lend any assistance necessary.

The warblers were pouring into Kentucky from the south. He saw a warbler he had never known before, olive-green and bright glowing yellow, an active, sprightly little bird, with a loud, rapid, *tweedle tweedle, tweedle* call; he shot one to draw and paint, and realized he had discovered a new species, to which he gave the name of the Kentucky warbler. When the family to which he was attached turned south, he continued on across the Barrens alone, and now new birds were everywhere. The trees ended; there were only a few saplings, and isolated groves of hardwood, the remainder of the land so open he could see for miles ahead. The ground was covered with grass and flowers, or low brushy thickets and berry patches, wild strawberries so abundant that in places the whole prairie was covered with their blossoms. The distant groves of oaks, little islands in the dry rolling landscape, harbored birds of all kinds, and as Wilson set off across the Barrens he found in one of these groves another new bird, which he called the prairie warbler, yellow and black, spotted on the back with reddish chestnut, a tiny bird, only four and a half inches long, with a single feeble *chirr* note. The birds in the groves were almost tame, not alarmed by men, who rarely intruded on them; for half an hour Wilson watched prairie warblers sitting silently on the low branch of a tree, and the birds permitted him to approach the trunk of the tree without becoming disturbed.

During the daylight hours, the whippoorwills sat in silence in the deepest shadows of the groves. If Wilson disturbed them by walking near, they flew low and slowly, a few yards at a time, settling again on low branches, their sight plainly weak in daylight. They were now everywhere, more numerous than Wilson had ever seen them. He bedded in one of the groves, where great oaks rose majestically over a tiny stream. As twilight fell and the branches were outlined against the purple sky, the whipporwills began to call in incredible numbers from the brushy banks of the stream. Considering how rarely met with they were in the eastern states, this was plainly their native land, the most congenial climate and terrain for them. With darkness their shrill and confused clamor became incessant. Two males, calling at the same time near each other, sounded in a volume that was really surprising: *whip-poor-will,* the first and last syllables uttered with great emphasis, with about a second to each repetition. Even in woods where they were rare, as in Pennsylvania, they made so much noise, as if each tried to overpower or silence the others, that strangers to the sound could not sleep. Here in the Barrens the birds were so numerous that Wilson was surprised at the volume, and it kept him awake because of his interest in it; then the clamor became agreeable and familiar, with its own rhythm, like the sound of the sea to seashore dwellers. About midnight, when the birds grew quiet, the silence awakened him. At the first light of dawn their song arose with the same strength and liveliness, and the full-throated call of the grouse added a bass tone to the concert.

He shot grouse, which were more plentiful than he would have believed possible had he not seen them himself. They kept out of the timber, hiding in the dry plains where trees were rare and low thickets provided shelter and wild berries provided food. They were pinnated grouse, different from the ruffed grouse of the eastern woodlands, too clumsy and laborious in their flight to swerve and turn through branches as woodland birds ordinarily did. This was the mating season, and the orange-colored bags of skin on both sides of the neck of the male birds were inflated, enabling them to produce a sound that resembled that of a horn blown a long distance away. There were three notes, of the same tone, each strongly accented, the last held twice as long as the others, but what made the sound perplexing and often disagreeable was that many birds sounded at the same time, the triple notes running together, producing a loud humming effect, so that it was impossible to tell from what direction the sound came, or from what distance. And now and then the repetition of the triple notes was broken with a rapid cackle, like that of a person giving a shriek of laughter on being unexpectedly tickled.

Scattered farms lay at great distance apart over the Barrens, with luxuriant fields of corn and wheat. Much of the land was dry, sometimes so dry it was uncomfortable searching for water, though it ran everywhere under the surface. Subterranean rivers laced the whole region together, flowing through limestone caverns and channels, and deep caves opened into the earth. Prowling into one of these, Wilson came to the dark water of a stream wholly underground, where fish sported on the surface. All these matters interested him intensely; he never traveled so slowly as when riding alone across the Kentucky spring. Beyond Bowling Green he put up at the house of a worthy Presbyterian and spent four days loafing and exploring, the only time in his travels he recorded such a thing of himself. He was made welcome because he gave drawing lessons to two daughters of the household. An immense and mysterious cave, reaching miles underground, opened not far beyond, and was said to be the scene of a murder, the owner having killed a neighbor and hidden his body inside. Wilson passed the owner's house and called. He expressed an interest in the cavern. The owner was a mulatto, corpulent and lame. He looked capable of any deed of darkness. Another man, apparently a passing traveler also, was present. The owner invited both him and Wilson to examine the cavern.

He had a wooden door, with a lock on it, on the perpendicular front of rock. The stream that ran through the cave was used for cooling milk. Carrying a light, the owner led the way inside. Wilson followed, and the third man came after him, but gradually dropping back. Forty or fifty yards inside, Wilson became alarmed, fearing his horse would be stolen while he was led deeper. He drew his pistol.

Presently the owner stopped, saying his rheumatism prevented his going further. The third man had disappeared. Wilson said that his host could not be ignorant of the reports that circulated about this cave. "I suppose," he said, "that you know what I mean."

"Yes, I understand you," the owner replied. He seemed unembarrassed. "That I killed somebody and threw them into this cave—I can tell you the whole begininng of that damned lie."

He told a long and involved story that Wilson felt did not inspire much confidence in him. Wilson asked him why he did not call together a group of reputable neighbors and ask them to examine the cave. The owner said it would be well to do so, but he did not think it would be worth while. Wilson regretted the impulse that had led him to explore the cave; as he started back the third man appeared bearing a light. Now seriously alarmed, Wilson made his way out of the cave with his hand on his pistol. He found his horse was tied where he had left it; he mounted and rode away with no further inquiries. He told himself that he had no right to assume any guilt on the part of the man who had shown him the cave, and that his alarm was illogical; nevertheless, the cave owner's conduct was strange for a person who wished to be on good terms with his neighbors, and not likely to allay suspicion.

As was so often the case in Wilson's wilderness experience, he found himself in a harvest period of new and unusual birds at the moment he emerged from a human melodrama. Near the Cumberland River he saw a plain little bird, with a cream-colored breast and greenish, olive-green, silky wings, deep in the thickets of cane, extremely shy, and very silent. It attracted his attention for that very reason, the prairie warblers and Kentucky warblers having been so unsuspicious. He spent more time hunting for it in the lowlands, and thus found another species, which he named the Tennessee warbler. Where the cover was thickest he found the hermit thrush hidden also, a bird he had seen occasionally in Pennsylvania, and in the evening he heard the chuck-will's-widow. He was now nearing Nashville, and the end of the journey before he entered the Natchez Trace—the end, that is, of its pleasant and comfortable phase. He hated to have it end. He loafed and lazily explored the few remaining miles, and in the evening of April 16, 1810, camped again, though he could have ridden in.

Early in the morning he started reluctantly on the last leg, but thirteen miles from Nashville came to a structure like a big farmhouse, facing a pleasant expanse of level ground. Behind the house was a wooded hill, and a clear creek poured through a charming hollow beside the dwelling. It was an inn, with its long veranda across the front, characteristic of such places, and Wilson arrived as breakfast was being served. He stopped to eat, and came into conversation with the landlord, whose name was Isaac Walton, a thoughtful and observant man. Wilson decided to rest a day before going on; he hunted a little in the nearby hills, finding nothing, though he saw a flock of Carolina parrots. The day passed so pleasantly that he remained another day, merely from his pleasure with this agreeable spot and its hospitable company. On the third day, as he went to pay his bill, Walton refused to take any money for his board and room and the care of his horse. "You seem to be traveling for the good of the world," he said, "and I cannot and will not take your money."

The words were so unusual that Wilson recorded them. A marker on the highway later

1. Mocking Bird. 2. Egg. 3 & 4. Male and Female Humming Bird, nest and eggs. 5. Touhe Bunting. 6. Egg.

Mockingbird (top), with male and female hummingbirds, and towhee bunting.

indicated the spot where these words were exchanged; it remained a pleasant countryside. Riding on to Nashville, Wilson locked himself in his quiet room at Salter White's tavern, which was not so agreeable. For eight days he worked steadily, painting the birds he had found, rarely leaving the room. He sent the drawings to Lawson, expressing profound satisfaction with his progress. To Sarah Miller he wrote affectionately: "To have forgot my friends, in the midst of strangers . . . and to forget *you,* of all people, would be impossible." But he had no cheerful news interesting enough to send her, and he would not send her anything else. The fashion notes of Kentucky and Tennessee were not to be compared with those from Paris and London—a Kentucky fashion for girls was a blanket riding dress and a straw sidesaddle, and a mule with ears so long they looked like reins. The beau of one of these girls might be unshaven for three months, unbathed, and reeking of whisky, with three yards of cloth wrapped around his legs, and wearing a ragged greatcoat. One amusement of the ladies was flogging the slaves and Negro wenches, which they carried through with coolness and satisfaction, and which gave them an air of great dignity. The landlady at Salter White's tavern was particularly adept at it, producing more screams from beatings on shins, elbows, and knuckles than her slave-owning friends could produce by merely flogging slaves on the back. These barbaric scenes were what Wilson meant when he said he had no news worth sending to Sarah Miller, and wanted to discover something both interesting and pleasant.

He wrote her agreeable nonsense about his parrot, which was very nearly tame. It was learning to talk, knew its name, and came when he called. When Wilson left his room, he wrapped his parrot in a handkerchief and put it in his pocket—"although," he said, "we generally have a quarrel about this." He was nearly out of handkerchiefs. Now he told Sarah (more seriously), he was at the point of setting out on a 780-mile trip through Indian country, alone except for his parrot, but in good spirits and confident of finding all sorts of previously unknown birds in the wilderness.

CHAPTER FIVE

The Natchez Trace

WILSON WROTE HIS farewell letter to Sarah on Tuesday night, May 1, 1810, and as she loved ghost stories he concluded by saying he would write at once if he observed any hobgoblins on the way to Natchez. This was a standing joke between them, the matter of ghosts and spooks, for she enjoyed the current fashion in Gothic novels, with their mysteries, coincidences, and wild improbabilities and wonders. Wilson disliked the fashion because he believed in reason and the ending of superstitions—indeed, he disliked the Gothic generally, as shown in his criticism of the Lexington architect who altered a good square building to conform to the current Gothic rage.

But the Gothic novelists were themselves responding to the mysteries and the horrors of a time too melodramatic to be interpreted by the followers of the age of reason, just as Charles Brockden Brown in Philadelphia could write a Gothic novel about the yellow fever plague merely by describing realistically some of the things that happened there. Wilson opposed the Gothic novelists—or the ghosts that he ridiculed to Sarah—like a reformed drunkard opposing alcohol: he had lived in the coldest of old castles in Scotland, and ghosts, apparitions, and contrived coincidences were old enemies of his. Yet he knew realities as strange as the wildest fantasies in the Gothic novels. On May 2, 1810, the day after his letter, for instance, William M'Dowell, his former patron, committed suicide at Castle Semple in Scotland. It could not have escaped Wilson that no romance by Charles Brockden Brown was so strange as the story of the M'Dowells that he himself knew. And was there a more Gothic novel than the tragedy of his friend, fellow poet, and fellow weaver Robert Tannahill? On May 17, 1810, Tannahill committed suicide by drowning in a pond near Paisley, mourning for his lost sweetheart Janet Tennant, dispirited because his poems were rejected, and broken by the terrible riots sweeping Paisley. And surely the story of Meriwether Lewis was mysterious as the tales of the Gothic novelists, for this was still, eight months after Lewis' death, a subject of discussions, whispers and rumors throughout the frontier. And elsewhere, as well—for people were now beginning to speak of Lewis' potentialities, and Dr. Samuel Mitchill, the scientist and Wilson's friend, in running for Congress said that Lewis could have filled the highest office in the land. The rumors about Grinder's Stand could not have been stranger had the place been haunted. The flatboatmen, traveling in groups from New Orleans for safety, would not stay there. Another stand had been built six miles nearer Nashville.

To Lawson, Wilson wrote that he had been warned not to go over the Natchez Trace. But he reasoned that he had a good horse, two loaded pistols in his pockets, a loaded fowling piece across his shoulders, a pound of gunpowder in his flask, and five pounds of shot in his belt. He had learned also that town dwellers always exaggerated wilderness terrors.

But they could not exaggerate the mystery of the death of Meriwether Lewis. In the warm May sunlight and the blossoming woods, the horrors of the Natchez Trace appeared and disappeared in the shadows, like the glint of a rifle barrel in the forest, or a snake in the path. It was not known when Meriwether Lewis began his fatal journey, nor was it then known how it ended, for Wilson alone uncovered the story of Lewis' last hours. Some facts, however, were on record: As governor of Louisiana Territory, Lewis was placed in an awkward situation when, as recounted above, the War Department returned unpaid some of his drafts; he was in debt for land he had bought, and the rejection of his official vouchers alarmed his local creditors, who descended on him with demands for immediate payment. Moreover the rejection—though the sums were not large, one only $18—was couched in terms that Lewis thought reflected on his loyalty. He wrote to the Secretary of War that he would leave St. Louis for Washington on August 25, 1809, bringing papers which proved his firm and steady devotion to his country: "Be assured, Sir," he concluded, "that my country can never make a Burr of me—she may reduce me to poverty, but she can never sever my attachment for her."

He vanished from St. Louis near the end of August or the first of September, saying he would travel by way of New Orleans, but midway he changed his route, so it was not known exactly when he left or which way he had gone. If Lewis had any enemies determined to prevent his reaching Washington, they would not know either. Some time in the third week in September, Lewis was in Memphis, at Fort Pickering, though under ordinary circumstances this was only a week or ten days' travel from St. Louis. On September 16, 1809, Lewis wrote to President Madison that he had changed his plans, and would proceed overland to Washington from Memphis, for fear of his papers falling into British hands if he sailed from New Orleans, then shaken by the Terre aux Boeufs scandal. Five days later, Lewis wrote from Memphis to Major Amos Stoddard, an old friend stationed at Fort Adams near Natchez, saying that he could not visit him in Fort Adams, ill health forcing him to travel overland rather than down the Mississippi.

Both these letters were perfectly rational and composed, yet it was at this time that Lewis was reported to be out of his mind, and the story circulated in Nashville that he had been locked up by the commanding officer in Fort Pickering to prevent his suicide. Nothing more was positively known of Meriwether Lewis until his death was reported at Grinder's Stand on October 11, eighteen days after his last communication.

The time of travel from Memphis to Grinder's Stand was eight or nine days. October was the best month for wilderness travel, for the streams and rivers were low, the days warm and the nights cool. When James Neelly, the Indian agent for the region, wrote to Jefferson about the death of Meriwether Lewis he did not say when Lewis left Memphis. He reported that he found Lewis there in bad health: "I furnished him with a horse to pack his trunk & on, and a man to attend to them; having recovered his health to some degree, we set out [from Memphis] together." There was a minor mystery here, for Lewis was accompanied by his own servant, John Pernia, and a slave, Captain Tom, belonging to his brother, Reuben Lewis—not a servant of James Neelly. But there were darker mysteries. As the party proceeded eastward from Memphis, Neelly reported to Jefferson, it seemed to him at times that Lewis was deranged. They rested two days when they reached the Chickasaw country—Neelly was agent to the Chickasaws. This was at a place which the Indians called the Big Town, an ancient Indian village, located where the trail from Memphis intersected with the Natchez Trace. It was not far from where the Civil War battle of Shiloh was later to be fought, and near the mythical town of Frenchman's Bend in William Faulkner's cycle of Mississippi novels. Big Town was a collection of twenty log hunts, with a few peach and plum trees growing around them.

After two days of rest—continuing with Neelly's letter to Jefferson—Meriwether Lewis and his party went on. "One day's journey after crossing Tennessee River & where we encamped we lost two of our horses. I remained behind to hunt them and the Governor proceeded on, with a promise to wait for me at the first house he came to that was inhabited by white people; he reached the house of a Mr. Grinder about Sun Set, the man of the house being from home, and no person there but a woman who discovering the governor to be deranged gave up the house and slept herself in one near it, his servant and mine slept in the stable loft some distance from the other houses, the woman reports that about three O Clock She heard two pistols fire off in the Governors Room; the Servants being awakened by her, came in but too late to save him, he had shot himself in the head with one pistol & a little below the breast with the other—When his Servant came in he says: I have done the business my good Servant give me Some water. he gave him water. he survived but a short time."

It was impossible to prove or disprove Neelly's story, because there were no settlers along the Natchez Trace to report on the time when the Lewis party passed. And John Pernia and Captain Tom were sent on to Lewis' family in Virginia, where they gradually vanished from sight. But it was possible to retrace Lewis' journey as Neelly reported it, and Wilson did so, though he traveled in the opposite direction. Neelly gave the average rate of travel of the party as twenty-four miles a day. It was ninety-six miles from Memphis to Big Town—four days—and seventy-two miles from Big Town to the Tennessee, three days away. From the Tennessee to Grinder's Stand was forty-eight miles, and Neelly allotted two days to this part of the trip.

When one figured back from Grinder's Stand, which Lewis reached at sunset on October 10, the average rate of travel made it possible to see roughly where the horses had strayed. And this point, Neely wrote to Jefferson, was one day's travel after the crossing of the Tennessee—the night of October 9 was spent at some indeterminate point around twenty-four miles north of the Tennessee (which presumably they reached on October 8) and some twenty-four miles south of Grinder's Stand, granting a few miles in either direction. Neely's account indicated that the night of October 8 was spent at the Tennessee itself, but this led to contradictions which were only evident on the scene. If the night of October 8 was spent on the river, the night of October 7 was spent approximately twenty-four miles nearer Big Town, and the night of October 6 approximately twenty-four miles before that. But this only added to the mystery, for while it worked out arithmetically that Grinder's Stand was five days' travel, at twenty-four miles a day, from the Indian village of Big Town, the stopping places were not so evenly placed along the trail, and twenty-four miles from Big Town would place one almost in the exact center of an enormous swamp.

Therefore the party must have traveled more than twenty-four miles on the first day after leaving Big Town. It appeared that the distance must have been nearer thirty-six miles that first day, if the night of October 6 was to be spent beyond the swamp. But in that event, the night of October 7, at the average rate, would be spent only a few miles from the Tennessee, the night of October 8 would be spent well beyond the river, and thus the party would have been well beyond Grinder's Stand by October 10. Even if the party had traveled only half a day on October 8 to reach the Tennessee, and rest there before crossing the next morning, still the mystery remained, for one day's travel north of the river was through easy country, a magnificent woodland of huge chestnuts and hickory trees, but the second day was into wild mountain regions where the going would necessarily be slower.

Wilson left Nashville at daylight on Friday, May 4, 1810. He traveled very fast. He kept an exact account of his times of arrival and departure, the only period of his travels in which he did so. And he kept a careful account of the condition of the Natchez Trace. Eleven miles from Nashville he found the Great Harpath River flooded, flowing with great violence, and so high he could not find the entrance of the ford. He plunged in, and almost immediately his horse was swimming. Wilson set its head aslant the current and soon landed on the other side, but almost at once he came to another flooded stream, this one more dangerous as his horse became entangled in driftwood sweeping down. The country was almost uninhabited—completely uninhabited after the first day. He rode up and down steep hills, crossed low bottom country, and put up at night at a miner's cabin.

At this point the Natchez Trace itself began. A marvel of prehistoric engineering, a trade route of the Indians, the road followed the crest of ridges between rivers for nearly 500 miles. The infinite number of streams and creeks, with floods like those Wilson had already met, made cross-country travel impossible; the Trace was designed to eliminate river crossings, and to minimize as much as possible up and down climbs by heavily laden Indian carriers. It was as nearly level as such a road could be, at almost exactly a thousand feet above sea level for hundreds of miles.

In its first stretch beyond Nashville the Natchez Trace followed unerringly along the very crest of the great divide between the Cumberland and Tennessee Rivers. Travelers were like people moving along the ridgepole of a roof. Rain that fell on one side of the road drained into the Tennessee, and on the other side into the Cumberland. The trail climbed steadily, up shale hills where Wilson dismounted and led his horse. He noted nothing of birds in this region, except that he saw no crows, while hawks and ravens were numerous. At Duck River he saw magnificent white and purple-black swallow-tailed hawks, but travel was too dangerous to permit any search for birds. The road descended steeply from Duck River Ridge, rough and gravelly soil, where he had to dismount and slide. The river rolled in silent majesty in the depth. On the opposite side a sheer cliff rose 250 feet. The trail led along the edge of this chasm, up a slow incline to the thousand-foot crest again.

Wilson met several parties of flatboatmen homeward bound from New Orleans. They were dirty, sunburnt, their clothes in tatters, each carrying his belongings wrapped in a blanket, and each wearing the eighteen-day beard grown on the Trace. Their stories of what lay ahead of him stiffened his resolution to be prepared for everything. Above the Duck Creek chasm, the road turned sharply south. It was again following the highest point of land. Between the trees he looked out over an endless expanse of hilltops on both sides, an aerial view of wooded crests and deeply dissected valleys, each creek cutting deep ravines a hundred or two hundred feet deep. The Trace began a slow descent of a couple of hundred feet to Swan Creek, with high hills on both sides of the trail, climbed again on the other side, and brought him to Dobbins' Stand at nightfall.

He was nearly seventy miles from Nashville, five miles from the border of the Indian territory where Meriwether Lewis' body was found. When General Wilkinson first improved the Natchez Trace, he made treaties with the Indians providing that only Indians could operate the taverns and ferryboats in the Indian territory through which the road passed. In practice, these resting places, about one day's journey apart, and called "stands," were operated by halfbreeds. Dobbins' Stand, a new stand that had been started since Lewis' death, was outside the Indian territory, and was owned by a white man. A dozen flatboatmen were spending the night at Dobbins', stretched out on the floor. In the morning they complained of feeling unwell, saying it was because they had slept indoors for the first time in two weeks.

It was now Sunday morning, and Wilson rode the six miles to Grinder's. Leaving Dobbins' Stand, he followed the trail winding along the crest of a bony, narrow ridge that projected like a rock trestle over the hills. On the north side, within a mile, twenty small creeks began their descent to Little Swan Creek. The land dropped steeply away, 250 feet within a quarter of a mile. On the south side of the ridge there was a maze of creeks, so there was no way to go except along the ridge, some times only wide enough for the trail itself. Elsewhere a traveler might go along one side of the trail or the other, but all traffic funneled through this narrow space.

After crossing a branch of Little Swan Creek, Wilson climbed to the spot where the land leveled (and where the Meriwether Lewis National Monument was later erected). Here lay a high tableland, exactly 1,000 feet above sea level, a famous expanse known as the Flat Woods. The plain rose above the surrounding country as if the top of a high mountain had been sheared off level at that point.

When Wilson came out of the woods to the Flat Lands, he saw two new, roughly built cabins and a barn. This was Grinder's Stand. The two cabins stood at right angles to each other, forming two sides of a rough enclosure. The ground was only partially cleared. There was a tree in the yard, and a stump stood in the doorway between the entrances of the two cabins.

Wilson rode to the cabins and dismounted. He told the man who appeared that he was a friend of Meriwether Lewis, and wanted to locate Lewis' grave and leave some money for its care. Grinder was a taciturn individual, unfriendly, uncommunicative, and resentful of the rumors regarding Lewis' death. He said he had not been at home at the time; he was helping with the harvest at a farm sixteen miles on toward Nashville. But he responded favorably to Wilson's suggestion that he pay him to care for Lewis' grave. He led Wilson back the way he had come. At the point where the trail joined the flatland, there was a mound of earth, with a few loose fence rails piled over the grave. To the east the morning sunlight came through the trees over a bold projecting bluff on the opposite side of a chasm, the rocks stained red with iron ore. Wilson thought in future times men would come by and experience a start of surprise that the great explorer had died in this spot.

He paid Grinder, who gave him a written promise to put a strong fence around the grave, and was pleased with the bargain. Wilson then asked if he might be told the circumstances of his friend's last hours, that he might carry word back to his sorrowing friends in Philadelphia. Grinder led him back to the main cabin, and left him alone in the room while he spoke to his wife. The room held a large fireplace, and a bed along the opposite wall. Wilson understood that Lewis had died in the bed by the wall, and had shot himself at this place before the fireplace where he was sitting.

Mrs. Grinder came into the room. She was an intense, embittered, imaginative and observant woman. Wilson was prepared to ask her questions about Lewis' death, but found it unnecessary. The terror of the night she had lived through, and the rumors that were spreading about Lewis' death, had preyed on her mind, and she poured out her story with torrential eloquence, with graphic power that amounted to genius.

Wilson took out his notebook, and sat at the table taking down Mrs. Grinder's account. She said Lewis had appeared alone from the woods in the west at sunset. In the wilderness, the woods became dark while the sky was still light. Remaining on his horse, Lewis asked if he could stay the night. He dismounted, and brought his saddle into the house. There were the three young Grinder children with Mrs. Grinder, a girl named Polly Spencer, and a little Negro boy, a slave.

Lewis asked Mrs. Grinder for a drink. She placed the spirits before him, noting that he drank "a very little."

She asked, "Do you come alone?"

Lewis replied there were two servants behind, and that they would soon be along.

Twilight had fallen by the time his servant, John Pernia, and Captain Tom, his brother's Negro slave, appeared. Mrs. Grinder heard Lewis ask the Negro where the gunpowder was, saying he was sure he had powder in his canister. The Negro made an indistinct reply that she could not hear. Lewis became agitated and began to pace back and forth before the door. As Mrs. Grinder prepared supper, it seemed to her at times that Lewis intended to speak to her, but he approached and turned away again, to continue pacing.

At supper Lewis sat down to eat, but had eaten only a little before he leaped up, with a suppressed exclamation, his face flushed, speaking to himself in a violent manner. He settled down again, finished his dinner quietly, and then drew a chair into the doorway, where he sat facing the west, smoking his pipe. He spoke gently to Mrs. Grinder, saying, "Madam, this is a very pleasant evening."

He smoked for some time in peace. Then again paced restlessly about the yard. He sat down, apparently composed, looked wistfully at the sunset, and said again that it was a sweet evening. As Mrs. Grinder began to prepare his bed, Lewis said he would sleep on the floor of the cabin. Captain Tom spread bearskins and a buffalo robe on the floor. John Pernia and the Negro then went to the barn.

Mrs. Grinder was alarmed. She retired to the small cabin adjoining the main cabin, which served as a kitchen, and bolted the door. With her were the children, Polly Spencer, and the small Negro boy. Through the night she heard Lewis pacing the floor in the adjoining cabin. She said he continued to talk to himself "like a lawyer."

Two hours before dawn she heard a pistol shot. There was the sound of a heavy fall, and the words, "Oh, Lord." Immediately after came the sound of another shot.

Through the gaps in the cabin wall, Mrs. Grinder could see someone moving in the shadows. Several minutes passed. To her horror, she realized that Lewis was trying to open the door to her cabin. He made a gasping cry for help, saying he was wounded. She was afraid to open the door.

Lewis staggered out into the open. He fell against the stump of the tree that stood between the two cabins. Then he crawled to the trunk of a tree at the edge of the yard. Grasping the trunk, he pulled himself erect, and leaned against the tree in plain view for some time. Then he vanished again into the shadows.

She could no longer see him. When she next became aware of him, he was again at the door of her cabin. This time he did not speak.

Presently she heard a crawling and shuffling movement outside. Through the chink in the logs she saw Lewis make his way to the water bucket and fall beside it. With terrific exertion he managed to get the dipper lowered into the bucket. There was a scraping sound. The bucket was empty.

Silence settled again. As soon as the sky became light, Mrs. Grinder sent the two older children to the barn to rouse the servants. When they arrived, Lewis was nowhere in sight. They found him in the bed he had refused to sleep in the night before. There was a frightful wound in his forehead, which was blown open, and the frontal lobe of the brain exposed. The wound had bled very little. He was conscious, and drew back the bedclothing, showing another fearful wound in his side. His wrist and throat were lacerated. He was fitfully conscious, begging them to kill him and end his agony, promising them money to do so. He said, "I am so strong, so hard to die." Mrs. Grinder said Lewis died as the sun came over the top of the trees on the spur of the rock to the east.

This narrative was not what Wilson had expected—or feared—to hear. He could not have missed the intensity of Mrs. Grinder's emotion, or the fitful illumination of her account, like something seen by flashes of lightning. Nor could he have missed the sinister and hysterical contradictions that were intermixed with the convincing and bloody details of her story, with the plain revelation that Lewis was murdered emerging from the report of his suicide. Wilson's own report of Lewis' death became the only historical source on one of the most enigmatic episodes in American history. Wilson was the only American citizen to inquire as to the circumstances of the death of one of the greatest American heroes, and to publish his findings.

But at the moment Wilson was startled and frightened at the tragedy and the mystery he had uncovered. Something of his own intense feeling was indicated when he left. He thanked Mrs. Grinder, paid his respects to the landlord, gave no outward sign of his feelings, and rode out into the Flat Woods. Then, out of sight of the cabins, he buried his face in his arms and wept. In his confused emotions there was a sense of shame and relief, mingled with his grief: he had feared that Lewis, too, might be revealed as a traitor to his country, and his shame came because he had doubted Lewis' honor, as his relief came from a vindication of Lewis that he now saw in Mrs. Grinder's account.

Wilson grew calmer, and, as he often did to organize his thoughts, expressed them poetically. He stopped in the forest, rested, and wrote a brief elegy on the death of Captain Meriwether Lewis, summing up

> The anguish that his soul assailed,
> The dark despair that round him blew,
> No eye, save that of Heaven beheld,
> None but unfeeling strangers knew.

The dark lesson of the poem was that Lewis' death was the death of Intelligence itself:

> Poor reason perished in the storm.
> And Desperation triumphed here!
>
> For hence be each accusing thought!
> With him my kindred tears shall flow;
> Pale Pity consecrate the spot,
> Where poor, lost Lewis now lies low.
>
> Lone as these solitudes appear,
> Wide as this wilderness is spread,
> Affection's steps shall linger here,
> To breathe her sorrows o'er the dead.

Folding his poem among his papers, Wilson rode on into the vale of mystery that Lewis had crossed before him. He was aroused from his melancholy by the roaring of Buffalo River. Leaving the Flat Woods, Wilson followed the trail over a ridge only a few feet wide, with sheer drops on both sides. A massive escarpment, the base of the Flat Woods itself, lay in an east-and-west ridge like a wall, the trail winding down 400 feet to the Buffalo, now flooded and hard to ford. Beyond the river crossing, Wilson passed between gigantic spurs of red rock on both sides of the trail. Then the trail climbed steeply again, a hundred feet over a narrow ridge, descending a hundred feet again to another branch of Chief Creek, within a quarter of a mile of the branch he had just crossed. Then in dim and secluded country he came to Chief Creek itself, really a considerable river.

All this land was deserted. There was not a house, or an Indian hut, or one of the wild wilderness farms found elsewhere along the trail. Again the trail climbed and descended, and in three miles reached the crossing of the Little Buffalo River. The ford of the Little Buffalo was not clear, and for a mile and a half up and down the stream travelers picked their own way across the swift and noisy river. Directly beyond, another heartbreaking climb of 250 feet led through rocks into thickets.

Whatever happened to Lewis, he was not insane. Only a man in full possession of his faculties, and in reasonably good health, could get through this country as fast as Lewis had traveled. Wilson now followed the Natchez Trace into less rugged terrain, deep woods, a straight, narrow, ascending road, in enveloping thickets that kept it in semi-darkness. It remained gloomy, mysterious and uninhabited country a century and a half later.

Between the headwaters of Forty-eight Creek, which flowed north, and Cypress Creek, which flowed west, lay another stretch of deeply dissected Tennessee mountain country, the Trace following the ridges between a labyrinth of creeks. The wild headwaters of Green River and Chalk Creek on the west, and Double Branch, Sweetwater Creek, Pinhook Creek, Sheep Neck Branch, and the many branches of Factory Creek, poured on either side of the Trace. A place called Dogwood Mudhole (south of the later village of Ovilla, Tennessee) was a camp ground where Neelly said the Lewis party spent the night, and where the horses strayed. Wilson now gave evidence of the only fright he revealed in his travels. Neelly's story was demonstrably false. Wilson's own progress revealed that the party could not have made the progress that Neelly said it had made. Had Lewis traveled as Neelly said, he would not have reached Grinder's cabin at sunset. He would have been far beyond there. Wilson whipped his horse out of this gloomy portion of the road. He rode fast down the branches of Cypress Creek, which the Natchez Trace followed to the Tennessee. A hint in his letters suggested he feared the theft of his horse at night. There were a few Indian huts nearer the Tennessee River, where the rough mountain country gave way to magnificent woods, and where deer and turkeys were plentiful. Wilson passed the first cabins, and stopped for the night at the third. The Indian spread a deerskin on the floor for his bed. Wilson put his portmanteau under his head for a pillow and "slept tolerably well," an old Indian stretched out on the floor near him.

In the morning he rode fifteen miles, stopped at another Indian hut to feed his horse, and entertained the savages by taking his parrot from his pocket and putting it through its tricks. Two army officers rode up, giving him a grim account of the road that lay ahead of him. At five in the evening, still light in the spring weather, he reached the Tennessee. "A growth of canes of twenty and thirty feet high covers the low bottoms, and these cane swamps are the gloomiest and most desolate-looking places imaginable. I hailed for the boat as long as it was light, without success."

The Tennessee here was a quarter of a mile wide, flowing swift and silently below Muscle Shoals. Beyond lay George Colbert's Ferry, and, another six miles on, the stand operated by his brother Levi Colbert, called Buzzard's Roost. Levi and George Colbert were the sons of a mysterious Scottish refugee who settled in the woods and married an Indian girl. George Colbert collected $2,000 a year in ferry fees from the flatboatmen alone, charging a dollar to ferry them across the Tennessee. Morose and uncommunicative, he became a great chief of the Chickasaws, and one of the large landowners and slaveowners of the South.

He did not answer Wilson's call. The reconstruction of Lewis' journey that Wilson was making demonstrated that Meriwether Lewis' last hours could not have been what Neelly said they were. By Neelly's account the horses strayed after one day's travel north of the Tennessee. But again Wilson's rate of travel indicated that such an occurrence must have taken place far beyond where Neelly reported it.

"I sought out a place to encamp," Wilson wrote, "kindled a large fire, stript the canes for my horse, ate a bit of supper, and lay down to sleep—listening to the owls, and the chuck-will's-widow, a kind of whip-poor-will that is very numerous here. I got up several times during the night to recruit my fire, and see how my horse did, and but for the gnats, could have slept tolerably well. These gigantic woods have a singular effect by the light of a large fire—the whole scene being circumscribed by impenetrable darkness except that in front, where every leaf is strongly defined and shaded."

His parrot dozed by his side, or watched the fire unblinkingly. The night passed, and at dawn Wilson hunted for game.

At six he began calling for the ferry. At eleven the boatman appeared. Wilson upbraided him fiercely, threatening to publish an account of him in the newspapers. "This man charges one dollar for a man and a horse," he wrote, "and thinks because he is a chief he may do in this way what he pleases."

Beyond Buzzard's Roost the extraordinary change in the country restored his good nature. "One could see a mile through the woods, which were covered with high grass fit for mowing. These woods are burnt every spring, and thus are kept so remarkably clean they look like the most elegant noblemen's parks." The ground was also covered with red and crimson sweet william, orange and carmine sunflowers, and superb thistles in flower, all species he had never seen before. At Bear Creek (where Bishop, Alabama, was later built) he came upon a group of Indian boys shooting blowguns made of cane, the arrows covered with thistledown spiraled around them. With these they could kill partridges at twenty paces. Wilson tried them, "but generally found them defective in straightness."

He shot a turkey near a small brook, where he had made camp. Returning to his camp, he found four boatmen had joined him. The turkey made a god meal for them all. In the morning Wilson heard more turkeys, but he was afraid to leave his horse with his companions, and rode on alone.

This was his fifth day on the road, Wednesday, May 9, 1810. Between Bear Creek and Big Town, the main Indian village, thirty-odd miles ahead of him, the Natchez Trace entered a vast swamp, covered with enormous canes, and cut with deep black streams, the woods so dense they shut out the light for miles. Steep clay banks dropped into the stream, his horse sliding into deep mire up to its belly. Struggling out of the worst of these, Wilson met another party, a soldier and two servants, leading a pack horse.

They stopped and discussed the road. The officer was General Wade Hampton, who had succeeded General Wilkinson as commander of the army. Wilkinson had been removed from his command and ordered to Washington to stand trial. Hampton, who had been ill, was on his way to Nashville, an indication that the crisis in the Southwest was over. "I told him of the mud campaign immediately before him," Wilson wrote. "I was covered with mire and wet, and I thought he looked somewhat serious at the difficulties he was about to engage."

One of the strangest experiences, in retracing Wilson's journeys, is to note the unerring accuracy of his descriptions. The stands on the Natchez were unmarked. A kind of shorthand system developed for identifying the stands that were reliable. Thus, Dobbins' was a safe place to spend a night, Grinder's was not. Just beyond the swamp, and outside the Big Town itself, was a stand called Old Factor's, recommended to travelers as honest and easy to locate because a dead tree stood before the door of the cabin. Wilson knew nothing of this Natchez Trace lore, yet he described the place unmistakably:

About half an hour before sunset, being within sight of the Indians, where I intended to lodge, the evening being perfectly clear and calm, I laid the reins on my horse's neck to listen to a mocking-bird, the first I had heard in the Western country, which, perched on a dead tree before the door, was pouring out a torrent of melody. . . . I had alighted, and was fastening my horse, when, hearing the report of a rifle immediately beside me, I looked up, and saw the poor mocking-bird fluttering to the ground. One of the savages had marked his elevation, and barbarously shot him.

I hastened over into the yard, and walking up to him, told him that was bad, very bad! that this poor bird had come from a far country to sing to him, and that, in return, he had cruelly killed him. I told him the Great Spirit was offended at such cruelty, and that he would lose many a deer. . . . The old Indian, father-in-law to the bird-killer . . . replied that when these birds come singing and making a noise, somebody will surely die. . . .

Wilson passed through the Big Town the next day, a collection of twenty cabins on a plain red with wild strawberries. More than the Indian trail from Memphis joined the Natchez Trace at this point; from here ancient trails ran south to Mobile and east to Charleston. Another night, in the cabin of a white man with two Indian wives and a host of savage children, another meeting with an army officer, this time a young lieutenant anxiously inquiring after General Hampton, and Wilson was over the worst of his journey. Then, however, he suddenly fell desperately ill. He was attacked by something like dysentery, half paralyzed, unable to sit on his horse, and parched with fever, his mouth and throat so dry he could barely restrain himself from drinking the poisonous swamp water. He bought raw eggs at an Indian cabin, and found they helped him. Thereafter, for seven days, he ate only raw eggs, until he reached Natchez.

He arrived late in the afternoon of May 20, a flawless spring day. Seven warships were drawn up in the Mississippi, anchored at equal distances along the stream, their flags flying. They were part of Porter's fleet summoned to defend the Mississippi. Wilson climbed to the old Spanish fort on the south side of town, and looked over the river, Natchez on his right, green trees, and white and red houses, the majestic river two hundred feet below the fort, hundreds of flatboats tied up along the shore, noisy with their produce and the continual crowing of the poultry that filled many of them. The whole country beyond the Mississippi from south to west and north was one universal ocean of forest, bounded only by the horizon. The sounds of industry from the enormous number of flatboats, sounds that were softened by distance and evening, made the scene cheering and exhilarating in a more profound way than he had ever known before. The most cheering part of the scene, he wrote, were the flags flying from the masts of the warships, their red, white and blue alive and radiant in the golden light on the gray Mississippi and the green forest beyond.

He sat alone on the bluff over the water, watching until the sun descended in the west, the river still glowing smoothly in the twilight, bright in the darkening shadows, as though giving back slowly the light stored in daylight hours. In his time there was still a simple emotion known to the sailor returning to his home port, or to the wilderness traveler coming back to civilization, a thrill of relief at the first sight of the flag still flying as proudly as when the journey began—a deep strain in the national inheritance, a recurring affirmation of faith over treachery, the emotion known when the first light of dawn revealed to the beleaguered fort that the flag was still there.

VII

The Last Months

When the population of this immense western Republic will have diffused itself over every acre of ground fit for the comfortable habitation of man—when farms, villages and glittering cities, thick as the stars in a winter's evening—overspread the face of our beloved country. . .

—Alexander Wilson, February 12, 1812

CHAPTER ONE

The Forest

❧❧❧❧ ● ❧❧❧❧

FOR TWO DAYS Wilson remained in his room in a Natchez hotel, writing out his report on his trip from Nashville, including the detailed account of Meriwether Lewis' death as Mrs. Grinder had told it to him. Near the end of the second day, as he was completing it, a Negro appeared at the hotel, leading two horses, and asked for him. He gave Wilson a letter from William Dunbar, whose plantation stood south of Natchez. Dunbar wrote:

Forest, 20th May, 1810

Sir:

It is unfortunate that I should be so much indisposed as to be confined to my bedroom; nevertheless, I cannot give up the idea of having the pleasure of seeing you as soon as you find it convenient. The perusal of your first volume of *Ornithology,* lent me by General Wilkinson, has produced in me a very great desire of making your acquaintance.

I understand from my boy that you propose going in a few days to New Orleans. . . . But, as I presume it is your intention to prosecute your inquiries into the interior of our country, this cannot be better done than from my house as your headquarters, where everything will be convenient to your wishes. My house stands literally in the forest, and your beautiful orioles, with other elegant birds, are our courtyard companions.

The bearer attends you with a couple of horses, on the supposition that it may be convenient for you to visit us today; otherwise, he shall wait upon you any other day that you shall appoint.

I am, respectfully,
WILLIAM DUNBAR

Wilson rode to the Forest, a big square white plantation house deep in the oak woods nine miles south of Natchez and four miles inland from the east bank of the Mississippi. He knew Dunbar by reputation as one of the great scientific figures of the country, but he was totally unprepared for the deep respect with which he himself was welcomed, and the awe with which the Dunbar children regarded him. He was taken to the sickroom of the master of the Forest, who greeted him with forthright praise, with expressions of his satisfaction on finding that Wilson in person lived up to the impression created by his work, and with insistence that he live at the plantation.

Dunbar was sixty-one years old, with pronounced Scottish features, and the air of the old country lingering in his phrases. He had the blunt friendliness of the Scot to a kindred spirit; still more, he had the uncalculating candor of a man of action who finds himself unable to act. After almost forty years of tireless activity in the wilderness, Dunbar had been felled by illness whose seriousness he recognized, like some unwelcome associate of his youth returned to haunt his old age.

Wilson agreed to stay at the Forest; he could not have done otherwise in view of the pleasure his presence gave to the Scottish nobleman, even had the plantation been less hospitable than it was. His visit, and the effort that Dunbar had made to welcome him, however, had tired his host and Wilson left him, promising to bring his goods from the hotel. He was now taken to a neat and comfortable room, which Dunbar's wife Dinah told him was his.

Dunbar was born near Elgin, Scotland, in an immense and gloomy castle that looked like a dozen Towers of Auchinbathie haphazardly joined together. He was a mathematical genius, educated at Glasgow and at London, where his calculations, at the age of twenty, interested the astronomer Sir William Herschel. His father, Sir Archibald Dunbar, died and William's half-brother Alexander became Sir Alexander, but there were confusions in the family, his father never having claimed the title, and William was known as Sir William Dunbar. His own health failed so seriously that he was not expected to live. He left for America in 1771, aged twenty-one, with no clear purpose in mind, but with every likelihood of dying in the wilderness. However, he not only grew strong, but prospered greatly as an Indian trader.

Wilson finished his report at the hotel, mailed it to Lawson (who gave it to Nicholas Biddle at *The Port Folio*), and moved to the Forest on the day following his first meeting with Dunbar, to begin the visit that he described in the *Ornithology* as giving him some of the happiest days of his life. The plantation was not elaborate, but it was spacious, far more than comfortable, and uniquely interesting. The Forest was an experimental plantation: Dunbar had improved the cotton gin, was the first to see the value of cottonseed oil, and was the inventor of the press by which cotton was, for the first time, packed efficiently into square bales for economical shipment. The Forest was his second plantation venture. In his earliest years in America he became a partner of John Ross, a Scottish-born shipowner and merchant of Philadelphia, a great patriot—Ross paid £20,000 of his own money for supplies for Washington's army—who was entrusted by Witherspoon with secret missions in Europe. With Ross's capital, Dunbar created a plantation near Baton Rouge, but a slave insurrection and raids by Spanish soldiers and American irregulars forced its abandonment. Sir William, as the Mississippians continued to call him (though he made no claim to the title and was a fervent supporter of the American government), then carved the Forest out of the uninhabited Natchez countryside, and was soon wealthy enough to buy Ross's share of the property.

Each evening Wilson visited with Dunbar, whose strength would not permit any real social life—only six months of life remained to him, and he died in October, 1810. The planter was the first to have kept daily weather reports of the Mississippi Valley, and he had built on his plantation an elaborate observatory, with expensive equipment imported from Europe, his observations from this point keeping him in touch with the astronomers in Europe, as his was the extreme western point from which celestial phenomena were scientifically reported. Dunbar was one of Jefferson's favorite correspondents, the President having personally recommended him for membership in the American Philosophical Society, and appointed him to lead exploring expeditions up the Ouachita and the Red Rivers, on which Dunbar tried to carry out studies of natural history on his own.

The Port Folio, bearing the illustrated installments of Wilson's *The Foresters,* was in the plantation library; it was the favorite magazine of the Dunbar family. In the chaotic situation produced by Wilkinson's disgrace, Dunbar was a central figure, though a passive one. He was a very close friend of Daniel Clark, who was more responsible than anyone else for giving publicity to the stories of Wilkinson's treason, and it was Dunbar whom Clark picked to handle his property, under his power of attorney, when the crisis forced Clark's absence from New Orleans. Yet Clark also died suddenly in early middle age, soon after his denunciation of Wilkinson, and soon after Dunbar's death.

Dunbar's closest friend, however, and his most trusted advisor, was Andrew Ellicott; and as Congress' inquiry into Wilkinson's past got under way, and Wilkinson demanded that Clark substantiate his charges, Ellicott was ordered to produce his reports on Wilkinson, which were unanswerable. These reports were based on Ellicott's investigation of Wilkinson, at the time that Dunbar and Ellicott were working together on boundary surveys in the Natchez area. Dunbar was consequently deeply involved in the whole Wilkinson story, but he was personally indifferent to politics, and the excitement and elation that now swept through the West, as Wilkinson's dominance ended, came too late to have meaning to him.

He was rather pleased and refreshed to have as his guest a man of science, a fellow Scot, with whom he could discuss such subjects as the mastodon bones he had found in Louisiana, or ways of determining longitude in the wilderness where thick woods prevented unobstructed views, with only one observer, and no knowledge of the exact time. A good deal of Indian lore crept into the *Ornithology,* plainly revealing the influence of Dunbar's talks with Wilson. For example, Wilson learned that the peaceful Chickasaws called the parrot the kelinky, and were amused by the bird. The warlike Choctaws and the gentle Chickasaws both built bird houses for purple martins. What was stranger to Dunbar was that his Negro slaves, newly arrived from Africa, also made bird houses exactly as the Indians did.

Wilson had now carried his parrot a thousand miles, but the bird tore up so many handkerchiefs, and escaped from his pocket so often, forcing him to dismount and chase it through the woods, that he was tempted to let it go. When he arrived at the Forest, the Dunbars gave him a bird cage. He placed the parrot, which called itself Polly, on the veranda of the plantation house which stood one floor above the ground, and thus level with the lower branches of the trees. Pleased at being in the open, the bird began to call and screech happily, and an extraordinary thing happened: Carolina parrots were quite numerous in that area, and flocks of these big yellow birds assembled on the trees beside the porch, attracted by the sound, to carry on a constant animated conversation with the prisoner.

The seven Dunbar children—seven-year-old Robert, on up through Archibald, Thomas and Margaret to Eliza, who was a young lady—found Wilson the most interesting visitor who had ever appeared at the plantation. He gave Eliza drawing lessons, and he so interested the Dunbar boys in his work that of their own accord they sent valuable specimens to him after he returned to Philadelphia. Moreover he had arrived at the moment of the spring when the flowering woods were changing daily and the great feathered migration was approaching its peak.

The painted bunting had just begun to arrive from the south, the little bird that the French settlers called *le pépe,* and the Americans called the nonpareil, a sociable and winning little creature, as easily domesticated as a canary, as colorful as a flower, purplish blue about the head, giving way to rich vermilion, glossy yellow over the back, stained with deep dark green, dusky red on the wings, except for green at the edges, purplish brown on the forked tail, and the breast and body deep glossy red that shaded to carmine. The nonpareil was a fairly rare bird even as far south as Natchez, but other birds that Wilson had found further north were now abundant, prairie warblers, Tennessee and Kentucky warblers, and the little flock of yellow warblers that his friend Charles Willson Peale had first discovered years before. The prothonotary warbler, one of the rarest and shyest to be found in the North, was numerous also, but only along the river itself, rarely seen in the higher ground inland, a brilliant yellow, olive and lead-blue bird that haunted the deepest shadows.

Wilson's visit stimulated Dunbar, whose health seemed for a time really to be bettered. But there could be no permanent recovery, and one morning after his talk with the planter, Wilson rode out to the cleared ground at the edge of the plantation in a grave and thoughtful mood. His own illness on the Natchez Trace had left him weak; he needed the long rest that his visit had given him, and his plans were in a confused and uncertain state. Aside from his responsibility for his book, he was under no obligation to return soon to Philadelphia, and he could find nowhere in America a richer ornithological hunting ground than that which lay before him, nor a better place from which to study. Hawks were sailing in easy circles at great height in the cloudless sky. Near them were turkey buzzards, and Wilson watched them, wondering, as he always did on seeing them together, why birds so dissimilar were often flying this way in company. Wilson was the finest poet in the America of his time, and these images of the hawk and the vulture, coinciding with his somber thoughts on Dunbar's illness, were characteristic of the elliptical way he revealed his own preoccupations in his nature writing. The hawk and the vulture were known to fly together to immense heights before storms; in this benign weather, Wilson believed they must be hunting their food, the buzzards looking for carrion, and the hawks feeding on winged insects that were carried high on the air stream.

He shot at a hawk, and to his surprise, because it was so high, hit it, and the bird was precipitated from vast height in an instant. He rushed to pick up the hawk where it lay stunned on the ground, but it wheeled around on its rump, unable to rise, its dark red eyes venomous with rage as it struck with its claws. Wilson seized it, but as he did so the hawk struck its hind claw so deeply into his hand that it penetrated to the bone; he could not disengage it, for the claw only contracted more powerfully with spasmodic strength when Wilson touched the leg. The man and the hawk were now pinned together, both bleeding and lacerated, Wilson suffering excruciating pain with each movement as he tried to free himself. Still determined to save the life of the bird, he secured his penknife and cut the sinew of its heel.

He had found another new specimen, the Mississippi kite—an imperious, clean white, gray, ash, black and reddish sorrel hawk of unquenchable spirit and courage. His captive gave him perhaps the most spectacular plate in the *Ornithology,* the most vivid proof of Wilson's curious ability to capture the wildness of living creatures. He returned to the Forest with the hawk, kept it alive, and, when his hand was bandaged, drew it from life. Whenever he came into view the kite started with recognition of him as its enemy, watching Wilson's every movement, its eyes fierce, the feathers of its head erect, and plainly considering Wilson, as he wrote, "a greater savage than himself."

If Dunbar could not give Wilson much help with material on birds, he could assist him by telling his friends of Wilson's worth. Now, as Daniel Clark wrote to Jefferson, there was no man in the West more esteemed for "Science, Probity and general information" than William Dunbar, and his standing, combined with the general concern felt at his illness, made it almost obligatory for anyone he notified to welcome Wilson. Dunbar had only to approach Benjamin Farrar, who pioneered with him in starting the first scientific society in Mississippi, and Farrar took over the responsibility of carrying out Dunbar's wishes, and introducing Wilson to men with an interest in science. Dunbar had only to express his regret that he could not entertain Wilson himself, and his son-in-law saw to it that Wilson was received into the homes of his friends in Natchez. Wilson thus became an honored guest, the plantation owners like George Overacker or Burwell Vick, whose father founded Vicksburg, deeming it an honor to be asked to subscribe to Wilson's books. Wilson could now talk of education with Lyman Harding, a Natchez lawyer and Dunbar's attorney, whose son was in Clermont Academy in Philadelphia with one of Dunbar's boys. He could discuss Western exploration with Colonel Thomas Freeman of Natchez, who had been on surveys with Dunbar and Ellicott, or the development of the West with James Wilkins, a young Natchez merchant, or Silas Dinsmore, a former Indian agent, or Winthrop Sargeant, the first territorial governor of Mississippi, living in retirement on his plantation nearby. Subscribers were secured with no labor on Wilson's part—twenty-three in all from the neighborhood of the small town of Natchez.

In the light of this wonderful reception, with "the sweet society," as he called it, of Dunbar's family, why should Wilson move on at all? True, he had a minor financial problem to face—he had spent nearly $300 on his trip and his passage home would cost him more than $100, yet he had already succeeded beyond all expectations in terms of new material for his book, new subscribers and new friends. He had only to state his wish to Dunbar, and he could make his home in the South, with a friendly beginning he had never known in his career.

When he left, he did not have the courage to tell Dunbar that he was going home from New Orleans, and in truth he was undecided. As Thomas Crichton had written long before, no one was so deeply moved by the calamities of existence as Wilson, and Dunbar's illness unnerved him. It was understood that Wilson was to visit along the Mississippi and in New Orleans, with every likelihood of returning to the Forest. He therefore was spared a farewell from his host that both would have known was final. Wilson rode some thirty-five miles down the river to the plantation of Dr. Samuel Brown at Fort Adams, set on a bayou amid lofty fragrant-breathing magnolias.

Brown was another pioneer whose energies were released by the challenge of the wilderness: at forty-one his accomplishments were well-nigh incredible. He was the son of a Presbyterian minister from Virginia, educated under Dr. Nisbet at Carlisle, then studying medicine under Dr. Rush, and showing such promise that he was sent to Edinburgh. Brown had begun practice at Lexington, Kentucky, twelve years before, launching his career by persuading 500 people to be inoculated against smallpox at a time when inoculation was all but unknown. As insatiably curious as Wilson himself, Dr. Brown explored the Kentucky caves as a source of niter (from bat droppings), for the manufacture of gunpowder, and he invented the process for using steam power in the distillation of Kentucky whisky. After his marriage to Katherine Percy, whose family owned plantations which extended down the east bank of the Mississipi, Dr. Brown practiced medicine only rarely, spending most of his time on his plantation, writing scientific papers, and organizing medical societies to enforce professional standards on the frontier.

He knew nothing of birds, but he was altogether willing to learn, and with Wilson rode into the country and sailed with him down the bayous. Subsequently Dr. Brown sent to Wilson in Philadelphia fine mounted specimens of rare hawks he shot. Now he was absorbed in watching Wilson as he shot a red-tailed hawk and dissected it to discover the contents of its stomach—in this case, fragments of frogs and lizards. Wilson also shot and dissected Mississippi kites, as many as he could, to determine their food, finding in each the insects that convinced him the bird must feed in the air, though he suspected that it also fed, like other hawks, on mice and other small birds.

Dunbar had sent Wilson to Dr. Brown, and Brown now introduced him to other planters. Wilson had wandered into the middle of a political conspiracy, for the planters were preparing to seize the land west of the Mississippi that was owned by Spain. In September—three months in the future—they captured Baton Rouge, the Spanish provincial capital, in a bold and well-organized move which took the Spaniards by surprise. They then declared the independence of the region, and asked that it be annexed to the United States, which was promptly done. In the way that his poaching expeditions in his boyhood led him into smugglers' trails, Wilson's bird hunts now brought him into the ranks of political adventurers. However, the actual execution of their plot was still distant, and in the meantime they were concerned to give the impression that they had only peaceful and gentle interests. In this objective, Wilson was, for the moment, an ideal assistant, for he was really thrilled by the magnificent scenery, the endlessly blossoming woods, wild tropical flowers, the dark silent flooded streams. The bayous were flowing backwards, pouring out of the Mississippi into the swamps, and creating a turbulent inundated world of shallow reedy ponds. On the shores of these, visible from a great distance, were many snowy herons, glossy white, plumed and stately, and an occasional wood ibis, with its blue head and queer toucan-like bill. The water was dark and sullen, lizards and reptiles abounding in it, and here Wilson found the fish crow, the same bird he had seen at Stephen Elliot's in Georgia, flying low over the oily surface, and rising with a lizard in its claws. The grackles and the water thrush, the warblers and the common birds of the north were here, but with this difference: there were now thousands for every migrating bird he had seen in the North. The painted bunting that was scarce even in Natchez sang from every fence along the road. Mockingbirds were so many he regretted he had written about them before seeing them here. As he rode, he realized that the stories he had heard of mockingbirds alone in these past few weeks would make a wonderful book.

The great wilderness pattern remained constant as he threaded his way down the east bank of the Mississippi—the west bank was Spanish territory—from one plantation house to the next. He left subscriptions to his book, and took away more bird lore, but he found no more new species. Only the cranes were new to him, a great many blue cranes, along the river below Baton Rouge, blue, brown and slate-colored birds, night herons and yellow-crowned herons—all birds he was determined not to consider until he completed the land birds.

His progress became a triumphant procession. He was lionized. In New Orleans he was warmly received by Daniel Clark, now returned to the city; by Dominick Hall, the Federal judge who alone had dared to oppose Wilkinson openly; by Dr. Brown's brother, James

Brown, the United States Attorney. Commodore David Porter, commanding the naval force that had been rushed to New Orleans after the Terre aux Boeufs debacle, subscribed to Wilson's books, as did Dr. Samuel Heap, a twenty-nine-year-old naval surgeon from Carlisle, Pennsylvania, serving in New Orleans, who had just married Porter's sister Margaret.

Sometimes Wilson wandered along the streets of the French Quarter, finding a subscriber at almost every house. Jean Blanques, a leader of the French-American legislature, who lived at 24 rue St. Louis, signed up for the set of books, as did Beverly Chew at 23 rue St. Louis across the narrow street. At 9 rue Royale, where one J. Pitot lived with six slaves, Wilson found a subscriber, and another at 33 rue Royale in Joseph Tricou, who had ten household slaves to attend his wants. Dr. William Rogers on rue de Chartres was a subscriber, and along the same street David Urquhart, who had six slaves, and Thomas Urquhart as well.

Judge Moreau, who was preparing a digest of French laws to be adapted to the American legal system, was a subscriber, as was Pierre Sauve, who carried to Congress petitions from New Orleans at the time of the Louisiana Purchase, and Pierre Auguste Charles Bourguignon Derbigny, the official translator and unofficial ambassador between the Creoles and Americans, famous because he delivered the first French Fourth of July speech in New Orleans. Thomas Williams, the most intimate friend of William Dunbar—they were David and Jonathan, in the language of the time—was a subscriber; he had just been appointed Collector of the Port, and was so diffident he could not believe the appointment had been meant for him. Bolling Robertson, the Secretary of State for Louisiana, and another subscriber, was a friend of Meriwether Lewis—in his financial straits when he left St. Louis before his death, Lewis had drawn on Robertson to pay his most pressing debts. Many of the Americans and the Creoles were at odds, but Wilson's subscribers were drawn from the leaders of both sides, Derbigny and Robertson, who became rival candidates for the governorship, both buying his books. Hostilities within each group were spanned as well: Daniel Clark subscribed, and so did Governor Claiborne, who had been wounded by Clark in a duel arising from the Burr and Wilkinson conspiracy. Stephen Henderson, the obscure Scottish financial genius who was then building up one of the largest fortunes in the South— he left his money to buy the freedom of slaves—bought a set of the *Ornithology*.

At dawn Wilson haunted the French Market, ranged along the crescent of the Mississippi beyond the bare Place des Armes. The Indians arrived with game birds—herons, gray owls and the young of the wood ibis, all esteemed as good eating by the French. Indian peddlers appeared with plumes that both the savages and French women valued as ornaments. Then Wilson visited the planters below New Orleans, admiring their magnificent gardens, and secured another subscription from Kilty Smith, one of the first American merchants, who lived in grandeur on Bayou St. John. He rode on at dawn to Lake Ponchartrain, to watch the white ibis stalking with Egyptian dignity along the gray shore.

It was not until June 24, 1810, half an hour before his ship sailed for New York, that

Wilson wrote to Dunbar to say that he was going back north and not returning to Natchez. He had with him specimens of a dozen new birds, completed paintings of others, two tame parrots, and six painted buntings in a cage. After squaring his accounts, selling his horse, and paying for his passage home, he found that his trip had cost him $455, for which he had traveled 3,000 miles and spent nearly 6 months in the wilderness. Now he wrote that he could never forget the pleasure with Dunbar's charming family, nor the kindness of his wife. He was pleased by a report of improvement in Dunbar's health, and added incoherently: "May Heaven prosper for (I would almost say) a thousand years the health and happiness of so worthy a family." He had expected to travel by land to Florida—"but the season is too far advanced, the birds either young or losing their plumage in this and the next month would supply me with very bad specimens and might lead me into error—I do intend in a year or two to sail for this country in January and stay until April for the sole purpose of making a complete collection of all the Aquatic tribes of birds found in your rivers and Bayous—I have made many excursions round this place and have found a few curious and new to me. . . . I have succeeded here in obtaining 64 subscribers to my Book. . . ."

CHAPTER TWO

The Spontaneity of the Wild

THE SHIP carrying Wilson from New Orleans to New York sailed down the Mississippi out into the Gulf, and lay becalmed. His parrot flew overboard and was drowned. In the listless days, Wilson rowed to islands off the Florida coast and studied their birds. The ship drifted to the southernmost tip of Cuba before the winds rose; then they came as storms. Entering the Gulf Stream, great numbers of stormy petrels appeared around the ship, to provide the only ornithological observations of the voyage. They often came up immediately under the stern, where Wilson could examine them with as much accuracy as if they were at hand. He watched them fly with their wings forming an almost straight horizontal line with the body, the feet partly seen stretching beyond the tail. In calm weather they seemed to stand, or even to run across the surface, collecting around any refuse thrown overboard, facing to windward, their long wings extended and their webbed feet patting the water.

The weather grew stormier. He remained on deck to watch the petrels in a gale, coursing over the waves, down the declivities and up the ascents of the surf threatening to burst over them, sweeping into the troughs as into a sheltered valley, and mounting with the billows again, occasionally striking the water with their feet and bounding high in the air. They swept from side to side of the ship's wake, or flew far ahead, and suddenly shot back at tremendous speed. He remained on deck during the whole of a dark, wet and boisterous night. The petrels flew about the after-rigging, making a singular hoarse chattering. Now and then it seemed that they alighted on the rigging, making a low noise.

Eighty or ninety miles off the Carolina coast, when calm succeeded the storm, Wilson shot fourteen stormy petrels to get a perfect specimen to draw, thereby arousing the superstitious fears of the sailors. But they put down a boat and collected the birds. Wilson dissected the petrels patiently, cataloguing the stomach contents of each, and adding another drawing to those he was taking home.

The slow voyage upset his schedule and deepened his impatience. He reached Philadelphia on August 2, 1810, but secluded himself for several weeks. He sent drawing paper and colored plates to Eliza Dunbar, advanced Lawson $140 for still-to-be cut engravings of the kingfisher and grouse, and paid young Hopkins $59.50 to tie up his services in coloring an additional 238 plates; then he locked himself in to work on his drawings. A full month passed before he notified Bartram of his return.

In the tragedy of Wilson's last months, a tragedy that began at the high point in his fortunes, the old obscurity and mystery in his past was the central agent of his destruction. "I have sacrificed everything to print my *Ornithology*," Wilson wrote to the French botanist Michaux, soon after he returned to Philadelphia, at a time when his work, on the surface at least, was succeeding. He could only have meant that he had refused a new life, a new career, for the sake of the great book he was completing. Any remaining mechanical or commercial obstacles to it had been removed by his success in New Orleans, yet new problems arose from the increased magnitude of the work, and these were of such nature that his inflexible reserve made it difficult for him to meet them. The subscriptions to the *Ornithology*, which amounted to $60,000, had been gained through his work alone; what was more immediately important was that the orders he had taken on his Western trip were to begin with both Volume One and Volume Two, or a first payment of $24, a total of more than $2,000 in working capital, the first surplus Wilson had had to work with.

He was thus in a strong position insofar as his work was concerned. But he had reached an age when reserve about himself, and a caution about revealing his past, had become second nature. He was now a public figure. The second volume of the *Ornithology* had been admiringly noticed throughout the country. *The Port Folio* in the fall carried his long account of his solitary voyage down the Ohio and across Kentucky. Wilson was, however, the son of a smuggler and a convicted blackmailer who had learned that there were episodes in his past he could not hope to have understood, and his instinctive reaction was to blot out all his past from all public discussion.

Among the people who became interested in Alexander Wilson as he began to be widely known, the most influential was George Ord. He was thirty years old in 1810, a tall, spare, stoop-shouldered young man with a shock of light hair and heavy, good-looking features, and a slow, deliberate way of speaking. He was the son of a wealthy Swedish woman who had married a Philadelphia ship chandler; inheriting wealth, Ord was also the head of G. Ord and Son, 99 South Wharves, though not active as a businessman. He lived in a mansion on South Front Street near the river, only a few blocks from the home of William Jones where Wilson lived.

Ord was a sportsman and hunter, whose favorite hunting ground (in common with many Philadelphia sportsmen) was Duck Island on the Delaware. His housekeeper was Margaret Carman, whose brother owned Duck Island, and who had lived across the river when Wilson taught school at Milestown. When Wilson left Milestown on his mysterious flight eight years before, Margaret Carman was twenty years old. She had grown into a reserved and self-possessed young woman, and remained unmarried, though in the intervening years her brothers had established their families and her sister was soon to be married in Philadelphia.

The last person to have known Wilson intimately—the last survivor, that is, when all the friends of his generation were dead—was Margaret Carman. In his memoir of Alexander Wilson, Ord wrote that when Wilson and Duncan arrived in the United States on the *Swift* they were given a small amount of money by a benevolent fellow passenger named Oliver, who discovered they had no money at all. Ord did not give his source for the story, which no other writer on Wilson mentioned, but what gave it interest was that the Carmans and the Olivers had been linked for generations to the wild country along the New Jersey coast. Margaret Carman's great-great-grandfather was the first settler at Cape May. His land grants and purchases from the Indians gave him title to enormous acreage. Marriages between the Carman and Oliver sons and daughters increased their dominance of the area. Margaret's mother was one of the Oliver clan, and Margaret's brother Joseph married his cousin Elizabeth Oliver. The branch of the family into which Margaret was born had moved north to Bordentown and Duck Island, but her kinspeople were the pioneers in the land south from Little Egg Harbor to Cape May, and this was also a favorite hunting ground of George Ord.

In the beginning the interest that Ord felt in Alexander Wilson was almost supercilious. Ord pictured himself as both an outdoorsman and a scholar. He was well educated, well read, with considerable knowledge of Latin; he belonged, moreover, in the category of the nineteenth-century elegant, fashionable and sophisticated young men who had adopted the pose of being philosophers, men of cultivation and learning, or even of science, but whose attainments were ornaments of leisure, the graces of civilized existence, rather than practical accomplishments for the generality of mankind. Ord's reaction on reading Wilson's work was to ask by what authority Wilson spoke. By no means so crude as to question Wilson's education or his background, Ord rather wondered at Wilson's motive in believing he could catalogue the birds of the air, and at what seemed to him to be Wilson's boundless egotism. In his first dealing with Wilson, he probed to find out, not only what Wilson knew about birds, but what critical and skeptical faculties he possessed with regard to the world in general.

Wilson's passionate conviction that the study of American wild life was of practical significance to everyone, an integral part of the culture of the new nation, was incomprehensible to George Ord. "The contemplative hours," he wrote, quoting the amiable Cicero to his friend Varro, "alone deserve to be called life." To Ord the study of natural history was of value because it offered a "calm retirement from the cares and sorrows of life." The lover of nature was superior to accident; the clamor of party dissension could never reach him; he lived "where oblivion may be found of the injustice and wickedness of mankind. . . ." Such was George Ord's credo of natural history. Anyone who held such convictions, of course, had no notion of what Wilson was writing about, and in truth Ord at no time shared Wilson's crusader's belief that human injustice could be corrected. At the beginning of his relations with Wilson, George Ord was not concerned with ornithology, but with Wilson as an intruder in the calm of academic detachment that he believed the study of natural history should be.

The melodrama that surrounded Wilson all his life, the smuggling of his father, his own arrest and imprisonment, the mystification with which he concealed himself, his interest in matters like the mystery of Meriwether Lewis' death, all combined to make it fitting that some equally dark and sinister matter should be involved in his end, that some mastermind of iniquity as skilled as Callender, or an enemy as dangerous as Wilkinson, should accomplish his destruction. But in an age when society was less closely organized, disharmonies of existence were frequently met with, and Wilson's tragedy came about, not as the result of the machinations of such bold and unscrupulous opponents, but because of the action of a critic of his use of Latin. Before he took up the study of natural history, George Ord's occupation had been to prepare (or rather to plan for some future date) a great dictionary of obsolete words. It was his intention to become the world's great authority on obsolete words of all kinds. In this enterprise, in some fashion that never became clear, he was frustrated by the obtuseness of Noah Webster, the lexicographer, who failed to take advantage of Ord's generous offer to turn over to him the obsolete words that he had collected, or hoped to collect in the future. Ord never forgave Webster for refusing his assistance, and with Ord there was no distinction between someone with whom he disagreed, and an enemy. It was his misfortune to be unable to understand any relationship except one in which he was alone dominant in whatever issue was raised. One of his life-long associates in Philadelphia said that Ord had no knowledge of friendship, "having been denied that blessing by nature herself." He did not flare up when opposed or contradicted, but deposited the disputed question in the depth of his rather exceptional mind, thereafter ceaselessly depositing facts, evidence, and opinions, until he constructed an answer which bore less resemblance to a logical argument than to a dangerous coral reef. It was not the rightness of his argument that convinced opponents, but the awesome effort that had gone into his creation of it, often when the person he was convincing had altogether forgotten the matter. Withal, Ord was soft-spoken and kindly. His daughter died in infancy, and his wife, after bearing a son, was in an asylum for the remainder of her life, and Ord gave a fortune to the institution where she was confined.

Such was the individual who, from the seclusion of his quiet mansion, began to study Alexander Wilson and his work. At no time in the history of the *Ornithology* did Wilson appear to less advantage than in the fall of 1810 and the subsequent period when Ord observed him. The drawings Wilson had sent from Nashville never arrived. These were of the new warblers and other birds found in the Kentucky Barrens that he had painted in the first enthusiasm of his discovery. Proof existed that he had sent them—he wrote to Lawson at the time—yet anyone unfamiliar with his work (or with birds) might question whether he had really found the new species he claimed. He now made new paintings to replace the lost shipment, but he had to draw from the dead specimens he had brought home with him.

The circumstances that led George Ord to communicate with him were ludicrous in their complexity. In his first two volumes, Wilson wrote of robins, jays and all manner of familiar birds, so familiar, indeed, that the deepest resources of his ability were tapped to make his comments interesting and fresh. He feared his books might be criticized because anyone around any American town could have learned as much. But with the third volume, Wilson announced proudly, "Nearly half of the whole number of birds are such as have never before been taken notice of by naturalists. . . ."

Now in November, 1810, he made the first of many trips to Great Egg Harbor on the New Jersey coast, to secure specimens to complete the fourth volume. Great Egg Harbor was almost Ord's private domain, the ancestral home of the Carman family, and a factor in the disaster of Wilson's last volumes. About the time that Wilson's expeditions there began, he learned that his third volume, after all, was proceeding so slowly that printing could not begin until after the first of the year. Payment would not come in until the *end* of 1811. How serious the financial result was could hardly be suspected by anyone unfamiliar with the paradoxical situation of Wilson's enterprise. In broad terms, the *Ornithology* could not be bettered as an investment. The total of $60,000 in orders from citizens of first-rate credit standing was an amazing commercial feat. Bradford and Inskeep invested in the neighborhood of $3,000 for each volume, and received $6,000, minus Wilson's own share—this last, however, never paid. As accounts were settled yearly, and the booksellers were often sluggish in forwarding payments, considerable amounts were tied up in producing the books before substantial returns came in. The publishing schedule of the *Ornithology* was as follows:

Volume I. September 21, 1808. Two hundred copies printed, at $12, or a total of $2,400 due at the end of 1808. However, an additional 200 copies were printed after Wilson's first Southern trip, making $2,400 due in 1808 and $2,400 due in 1809.

Volume II. Not published until after January, 1810, in an edition of 400 copies, or a total of $4,800, due during the year, subsequently increased to 500 copies, or $6,000. However, approximately a hundred orders secured on Wilson's trip to New Orleans began with $24 for Volume I *and* Volume II, or a total of $7,200.

Now, had Wilson been able to bring out the third volume and collect for it in 1810, the return in that year would have been adequate to finance the *Ornithology* in the hard period that lay ahead; more importantly, the books would have been spaced evenly, with both costs and returns roughly proportionate. But what was the result of the revised schedule? One volume was published in 1808, none in 1809, and one in 1810, the second volume that Wilson hoped to published in that year appearing in February, 1811. Accumulated material would have made it possible to publish three volumes in 1811, though this was impractical because subscribers were reluctant to put more than $24 a year into the books. Therefore only two books could appear in 1811, while those which could be published in 1812 were being prepared. The time was approaching when this remarkable financial impasse would be reached: 1) two volumes published the previous year had not been paid for; 2) two volumes of the current year were being printed; 3) Wilson had nearly completed two additional volumes for the next year.

The problem first presented itself in a negative sense, as the mounting overhead tied up increasing amounts of capital before any return was in. Yet when the situation described above was reached, work worth $36,000 had been done. Wilson once wrote of himself that he knew no more of money and how to make it than a moorland maid who had never seen any cottage but her own; and this was true in the sense that he lacked cunning, foresight, the art of trade, and the knowledge of the way shillings were made into pounds. Nevertheless, he had created a commercial enterprise that many a hard-headed Scottish merchant might have envied, and he was literally in the position of a man to whom a fortune was due. He had earned his fortune, moreover, with no sacrifice of standards. "No other work in ornithology of equal extent," wrote Dr. Elliot Coues, "is equally free of error." Baron Cuvier wrote of Wilson: "He has treated of American birds better than those of Europe have yet been treated." *Blackwood's Magazine* said truly of Wilson's prose: "By the mere force of native genius and of delight in nature he became, without knowing it, a great and good writer." And the earlier editions of the Encyclopædia Britannica, in their account of the *Ornithology,* stated a truth that was dropped after the Eighth Edition: "Passages occur in the prefaces and descriptions which, for elegance of language, graceful ease, and graphic power, can scarcely be surpassed."

Wilson was thus a literary and scientific figure on the edge of very great eminence, and an impoverished artist with very substantial sums due him, when George Ord interested himself in Wilson's work. So long as Wilson was an obscure schoolteacher, his isolation was relatively unimportant, however lonely he himself was. But now his life-long habits of reserve made him a mysterious figure. Ord knew nothing of him. He was never in Wilson's living quarters. Because Wilson had acquired a reputation, and the *Ornithology* was successful, Ord assumed that Wilson had means. Because Wilson had read widely, and almost every work on ornithology was quoted in his essays, Ord assumed that Wilson possessed his own library. Because Wilson kept a meticulous record of the birds he shot, and the new or unfamiliar birds he saw on his travels, Ord assumed that Wilson had gathered a great store of material in his notebooks. Because Wilson had written long and detailed travel letters to his friends, to Sarah Miller and to Alexander Lawson, and these letters, suitably edited, were printed in *The Port Folio,* Ord assumed that similar journals had been kept for all Wilson's travels.

But all these assumptions were wrong. Wilson's life was almost wholly concentrated on work. He arose each morning before dawn, walked to his office, organized the work of his colorists, prepared his own material for the printer, and sometimes varied his routine by an early-morning bird-hunting expedition to secure some specimen to give his colorists a model to copy. The social life he enjoyed consisted of an occasional evening with the family of William Jones, or with their allied Miller kindred, and at rare intervals a Sunday expedition to Bartram's Garden or a visit to the family of Alexander Lawson. As swiftly as his fame was growing, Wilson was not a member of the Columbian Society, the organization of Philadelphia artists, nor of the American Philosophical Society, whose Thursday night meetings, with the accompanying open house given by Caspar Wistar, were almost obligatory for scientific figures in the city. Though Wilson was now a literary personage, he was not part of Philadelphia's literary society either. Yet, according to Nicholas Biddle, his account of the death of Meriwether Lewis was at that time circulating from hand to hand in manuscript and "excited much interest in the private circles to which it was confined, and for which alone it was originally intended." Biddle tried to get Wilson to let him publish it in *The Port Folio,* but Wilson was reluctant to do so. Insofar as Wilson was known in any of these groups, it was as a member of some other group—the literary men thought of him as a scientist, the artists as a poet, the scientists as a schoolteacher. Even in the matter of his means Ord was greatly mistaken, for Wilson existed only on his salary as assistant editor of *Rees's Cyclopaedia,* and he could not collect this if he spent all his time on his *Ornithology.*

Samuel Bradford was far more critical of the publishing arrangement of Wilson's books than he had been before. He was selling property as fast as he had previously purchased it, disposing of *The Mirror of Taste* outright, and selling a half-interest in *The Port*

Folio to Nicholas Biddle for $9,000, quite a remarkable price for a magazine that earned $6,000 profits yearly. The social contacts between Bradford and Wilson had virtually ended, and Bradford, in fact, knew nothing of Wilson either. Dr. Charles Caldwell, who was on close terms with both Bradford and Ord, and who wrote of Wilson in terms of the deepest admiration, knew nothing of him personally. On one occasion Wilson was persuaded to repeat the song of a bird, and to Dr. Caldwell's astonishment Wilson whistled it exactly. Then he imitated one bird after another, whistling and chirruping so perfectly that the sounds he made could not be distinguished from those of the birds. Dr. Caldwell had never heard anything like it, and he recorded that "it would scarcely be a deviation from the letter of the truth to say that he could converse with any of the birds in their own language."

But these glimpses of Wilson hardly added up to a concrete impression of him as a human being, and in the ambiguities of his career the misunderstandings and confusions took root and grew, permitting the obscuring of his accomplishment. The amount of work that Wilson performed in the months after his return from New Orleans was almost without parallel in natural history. In the opinion of Dr. Elsa Allen, writing a century and a half later, Wilson sensed that his future was dark, and was now racing against time. Professor Francis Herrick, who, as the author of the definitive biography of Audubon, was not biased in Wilson's favor, wrote that Wilson's accomplishment was phenomenal: "When we consider that Wilson's entire working period on the *Ornithology* was not over ten years," Professor Herrick wrote, "and that at the age of forty-seven he was called to lay down his pen and brush forever; that he produced in this brief space a work of great originality and charm, which did inestimable service in promoting the cause of natural history in both America and England, and which is likely to be read and prized for centuries to come, the achievement of this man is little short of marvelous."

As striking as this tribute was, it did not exaggerate the essential facts. Malvina Lawson, for example, wrote that Wilson spent only seven years on the *Ornithology*. But Wilson was teaching school in the first of these years, and for five he was an assistant editor of the encyclopedia; he gave his full time to the work only near the end of his life. Nearly a full year was given to his three great trips, through New England in 1808, the Southern states to Savannah in 1809, and the West to New Orleans in 1810. Really only five years were spent on the *Ornithology* itself, and in this period between thirty-six and forty-eight months of uninterrupted labor. In comparison, Mark Catesby spent thirty-five years on his *Natural History of the Carolinas*. If Audubon's own account of his career is accepted, he spent twenty-five years on his *Birds of America* before he began publication.

Dr. Allen's interpretation of Wilson's driving speed as goaded by necessity is unquestionably warranted, yet there was a factor apart from it implied by the evident happiness and high spirits of the work itself.

The extent of Wilson's achievement in so brief a period was explicable only as a sustained creative inspiration. Catesby and Audubon were artists, often very great artists, whose

1. Belted Kingfisher. 2. Black and yellow Warbler.
3. Blackburnian W. 4. Autumnal W. 5. Water Thrush.

Belted kingfisher (shown with warblers, above and right, and water thrush, at bottom of page) provided
Wilson with a bold subject, and much folklore.

purpose was instinctively the creation of superb paintings of which birds were a part—great art, rather than great birds. The greater fidelity of Wilson's work was an aspect of his deeper purpose, a purpose obscurely connected with his faith in democracy, and his vision of its promise, and related, also, to his political thought, whose practical consequences led him to investigate the death of a Meriwether Lewis, or to urge rural industry to avoid the creation of industrial slums. Wilson's aim was to discover the design of the world of birds as a link to an unspoiled past of nature. The bird life of America was so much richer and more varied than that of Europe that it hinted at the existence of a natural pattern of life on this continent, something persisting from the time when there were no white men here, to which the habits and migrations and interwoven economy of the birds provided a fabric for study. The millions flying into Pennsylvania in the spring, the amazing numbers he had seen in Carolina in the winter, and the billions he had watched in the Western forests, seemed to Wilson a surviving fragment of some primitive order of natural existence, native to America, the study of which might enlighten Americans to the habits of life on the immense and unknown continent they had inherited.

Wilson's purpose made elaboration or decoration all but impossible. The wild life of America provided a clue to a terrestrial pattern from which men had become separated, and the labor of presenting it involved at the outset an act of humility, and recognition of an aspect of nature that "even the lords of creation," he wrote, "might study with profit." His purpose was not to use birds as part of man-made design, but to find, as he said, the underlying natural design in the amazing diversity of their habits, economy, form, disposition and faculties—"so uniformly hereditary in each species and so completely adequate to their own wants and conveniences."

Catesby's wonderful bird paintings, challenging those of Audubon in their delicacy and freshness, were elements of floral patterns. Catesby was primarily a botanist, a kind of press-agent of unearthly genius, who wanted the ruling class of Queen Anne's day, or even Queen Anne herself, to concentrate on the incalculable wealth of the New World. Audubon came into prominence in the early period of self-conscious American nationalism; he wore his coonskin cap and his fringed buckskin frontier garb in London society, an artistic exponent of Jacksonian democracy, strident and self-assertive, a woodsman, a hunter, a theatrical figure living up to the Daniel Boone image of the native American naturalness pitted against exhausted European affectation.

As honest and ingenious as Mark Catesby was, he had no hesitancy in drawing his buffalo from a calf imported to London, and claiming he had seen it in Carolina. Audubon's devotion to his work was profound, but he had no hesitancy in making melodramas of his bird scenes—snakes climbing trees to attack birds' nests, for example—and his huge folios, selling for $1,000 apiece, with each bird painted life-size, turned often into such spectacular views that one forgot birds were the subject, or that these were supposed to be the familiar birds visible to everyone in trees and fields. As Audubon painted them they were so much more glowing that the real birds appeared tame and drab by contrast. Wilson's paintings were less caressing and flattering. His birds were wild, and it was their wildness that absorbed his genius, the mysterious difference from whatever is domesticated, a wildness of eye and manner, and of wild woodland habits and songs and actions that the most vivid tame imagination could not anticipate. The wilderness lived not only in the expanse of forest, but in these wild messengers, filtering through the gray streets of rough frontier towns with colors and melodies that made them an art in themselves, or the living equivalent of what art could contribute to civilized life.

CHAPTER THREE

The Eyes of the Owl

THE POPULATION of the New Jersey coast increased at the time Wilson first visited Egg Harbor in the fall of 1810, for canvasback, pintail, mallard, snow geese and Canada geese attracted Philadelphia hunters there. When Wilson hunted along the Neshaminy at Milestown years before he was on the fringes of vast flocks of migrating birds whose main gathering place was in Chesapeake Bay and along the wild shore. The postponement of the third volume had startled him to intensified work, however, and of this expedition, at the height of the duck season, he reported that he shot a little owl, the smallest, neatest and most shapely American owl, very numerous in the pine trees that grew in the sandy ground along the Jersey coast. A short time later he secured a beautiful snow owl from Egg Harbor. It provided him with one of his finest paintings. The great northern hunter, as he called it, had won his admiration ever since he first watched its powerful flight on the moonlit nights of winter, skimming low over the icy wastes, spotting any movement on the snow, and striking in an instant. He wondered at its vision, and as he dissected the owl he had shot, he found that its eyes were fixed immovably in their sockets by a hard elastic cartilaginous case, which was cone-shaped. The case, being covered with skin, appeared to be one piece, but as Wilson removed the membrane, he found the case to be made up of fifteen separate pieces that were fitted like the staves of a barrel. These overlapped at the narrow end of the cone, apparently capable of being enlarged or contracted by the muscular membrane enclosing them, and thus focusing like a lens, widening or concentrating over a considerable range. It was evident that the owl's eye could focus like a telescope. The eye being always fixed, the owl had to turn its head to bring into view any object not directly before it, but the neck of the snow owl was almost a pivot, and the bird could turn its head nearly a complete circle without moving its body. In January, 1811, Wilson secured from the woods near Egg Harbor a magnificent bald eagle, so much superior to the one he had drawn before that he scrapped his old drawing and made a new one.

These three notes—on the little owl, the eye of the snow owl, and the new eagle—were all that Wilson wrote of Egg Harbor at that time. Yet his life was becoming involved with the lives of Margaret Carman and George Ord in ways he did not understand. He was perplexed to find that Samuel Bradford was less friendly. Bradford was increasingly critical of the costs and delays of the *Ornithology,* and not so disposed as in the past to pay Wilson's salary as editor of *Rees's Cyclopaedia* while he actually worked only on his book. The reasons for the delays Bradford knew, and Wilson wrote: "Complaints and regrets for what is irrecoverable, as unavailing as apologies for what could not be prevented, would be improper." He added that there was not likely to be a recurrence of similar obstacles. The plates for the fourth volume were in the hands of the engravers, and "every effort will be made, consistent with the correct execution of the work, to atone for past delays. . . ."

He was stung by a comment that he had written at great length about such familiar birds as the blue jay, but printed only perfunctory notes about the new species he had found. He replied hotly that he had "traced the wilds of our western forest alone, for upwards of seven months; and traversed, in that time more than three thousand miles, a solitary exploring pilgrim. As nearly half of the whole number of birds [in Volume Three] are such as have never before been taken notice of by naturalists, a complete details of their habitude and manners cannot reasonably be expected." Years of observation would be required to establish the facts of their migration and habits. Wilson was therefore led to request that "gentlemen of leisure" who were interested in natural history send him information about birds he had not yet pictured. It was apparently in reply to this invitation that Ord began his communications to him.

There was now a general belief that war with England was imminent, and to add to the commercial disorder produced by the threat of war, the banking system of the country was thrown into confusion when Congress, in January, 1811, refused to recharter the Bank of the United States. With no central banking agency, the problem of payments from one part of the country to another became doubly difficult, and early in February Wilson wrote to Duncan that he could not think of anything else because of the harassment of publishing his book. He quit as editor of *Rees's Cyclopaedia* to give his whole time to the *Ornithology* (and to better his relations with Bradford and Inskeep). He parted company with unreliable engravers, and gave Lawson a share in the royalties of the *Ornithology* in return for cutting the remaining plates. These emergency measures could not help the situation at the moment, however, for the plates for the fourth volume were done before printing of the third began.

That printing finally got under way on March 12, 1811. The book might reach subscribers by fall, three full years after the first volume appeared. The next volume Wilson opened with an exultant essay on the fish hawk and the wonders of Duck Island where Margaret had lived. He began by describing the arrival of the fish hawks as it seemed to the fishermen. His essay became a hymn of praise to spring: the first birds awaited as the happy signal of the shad run; the hawks flying in the bright spring weather, calmly reconnoitering, sailing in easy curving lines, turning sometimes as if on a pivot, easily moving their wings, their legs extended in a straight line behind them and their great length and curvature of wing easily distinguishing them from all other hawks. A kind of cheer went up along the coast when the first fish hawk was sighted. Wilson had seen one of these birds dive for a fish, but shoot off before reaching the water, as if ashamed that it had lost its intended prey, then mount to vast height, to descend again like a perpendicular torrent, plunging under the surface with a loud rushing sound and with the certainty of a rifle shot. It emerged with a fish, shaking itself like a water spaniel. Then the bird flew its heavy and laborious course toward land—slowly, for ospreys seized the big fish, some weighing six pounds or more.

The New Jersey coastal wilderness that was Margaret Carman's ancestral homeland figured in the fifth volume of the *Ornithology* in almost every essay. South of what became Atlantic City, all the way to the tip of Cape May at the extreme point of Delaware Bay, lay a stretch of almost uninhabited sandy ground, covered with dwarf cedars, myrtle, and occasional pine growths. On the Atlantic side of the peninsula, which lay between the ocean and the river and the bay, long narrow islands cut with tidal inlets were great breeding places for snowy herons, whooping cranes, night herons, blue cranes, skimmers, terns, oyster catchers, plovers, turnstones, sandpipers, bitterns, and coots. It was almost as thinly settled as it had been when Great Egg Harbor was the smugglers' capital of America. If Wilson's previous books evoked the wild life of the New World in general, his new volume became a tribute to this part of it in precise, spring-scented particulars. Even more the exultant tone of the book testified to the revolution that had taken place in his emotional life. He wrote of the birds in the joyous train of the season, hailing spring with their melodies, and fulfilling their sexual attachments—attachments, he wrote obscurely, sometimes formed before the birds came north with spring, arrived at before by some mysterious understanding now fulfilled, and destined to continue for years. "Is it possible for a rational and intelligent being to contemplate these scenes without interest and without admiration?" Wilson asked. "Can we survey the sportive and endearing manners of these with indifference?"

It had been many years since any such note had been sounded in Wilson's writing. And he now broke up the pattern of his daily routine, as he had earlier when he desired privacy, still making his home with William Jones's family on Spruce Street, but at the first good weather moving to Bartram's Garden to spend the summer in expeditions to hunt birds. In May he let it be known that he was on a trip to Albany, and in June he was again on the New Jersey coast. On the winding northern shore of Great Egg Harbor, on the edge of narrow passages of blue sea water, bordered by rushes or silver white sand, there was an old tavern, Beasley's Tavern, still in existence a century and a half later, and it became one of his refuges. Inland were slow-moving rivers that poured from swamps through large stands of dwarf pines, the air fragrant with their resinous scent mingled with the odor of the white sand and salt sea. Near Cape May and along the short Tuckahoe River that flowed into Egg Harbor were groves of swamp oaks and deep-shaded cedar swamps, where herons, egrets and bitterns nested. In the early twilight the night herons flew toward the marshes, uttering their hoarse and hollow cries, and the bird life of the region, once the migrating geese departed, was not so much beautiful as it was eccentric, a florid example of rococo nature, long-legged creatures pacing endlessly along the shore, and shovel-mouthed sea birds scooping up their food over the waves.

Wilson was surely a happy individual when he wrote these pages, something that could confidently be said of him at few times in his life. When Biddle asked him again to permit *The Port Folio* to publish his report on Meriwether Lewis, Wilson good-naturedly gave his permission; he had freed his own mind of this tragic mystery, and was concerned with happier matters. Soon after he moved to Bartram's Garden he saw a Baltimore oriole, arriving in advance of the female, sauntering in a bored fashion about the part of the grounds where the nest was to be built. Several days later the female flew in, and the male became sprightly and vigorous, singing so constantly that his voice became as well known to Wilson as the voice of his most familiar friend. Watching this pair in the nesting season led Wilson to try to compute the number of migratory birds. Bartram's Garden covered eight acres, or roughly one-four-hundred-thousandth of the Pennsylvania woodland. In periods of rest from his drawing Wilson counted birds and birds' nests. In Bartram's eight acres he found one more Baltimore oriole nest, ten of barn swallows, five nests of catbirds, five of house wrens, four of purple grosbeaks, three of yellow warblers, three of chipping sparrows, ten of orchard orioles, two of chimney swallows, ten of warbling flycatchers, and one nest each of indigo buntings, yellow-breasted chats, purple martins, white-eyed flycatchers, swamp sparrows, and robins—in all, fifty-one pairs of birds, not counting those merely passing through and the hummingbirds and tanagers whose nests he could not find. Assuming only the same number in more remote woods meant a bird migration of a hundred million birds into Pennsylvania alone.

While he was engaged in these midsummer tasks, a letter came to him early in July, 1811, from Tom Smith, a Great Egg Harbor resident whom Wilson had met on an earlier trip. Smith wrote excitedly that he had a full-grown fish hawk in captivity—something everyone agreed was impossible. Smith was hunting with Beasley, the tavern owner, when they found a nest. Smith climbed to it, only to have the hawk drop on him with such fury he thought it had put a hole through the crown of his hat. Before descending in haste, Smith noted there were three young birds the size of pullets in the nest. No adult fish hawk could be taken, but Smith decided to capture a young one and raise it until it was old enough for Wilson to draw. He climbed the tree again the next morning, with a length of string to set as a snare and a stick for protection. As he pulled the young bird from the nest the hawk dropped on him but he swung the stick, hitting the right wing, and the bird fell to the ground, where his companion seized it.

Wilson decided to go to Egg Harbor himself. He made it a leisurely trip, reaching Beasley's Tavern on July 17, and climbed to the hawk's nest, where he found the young birds remaining were now of full size. "They made no attempt to fly," he wrote, "though they both placed themselves in a stern posture of defense. . . . The female had procured a *second* helpmate; but he did not seem to inherit the spirit of his predecessor, for, like a true stepfather, he left the nest at my approach, and sailed about at a safe distance with his mate, who showed great anxiety and distress. . . ."

Back in Philadelphia Wilson saw the forms locked on Volume Four by mid-September, 1811—perhaps in time this year to permit the books to reach subscribers before Christmas. However the *President* had fought a battle with the *Little Belt* only a few miles offshore in September: war with England had begun, even though the declaration of war would not come until the next year. What could be said of the value of a book devoted to birds in the midst of such events? Wilson believed that in times of general embarrassment, dispute and perplexity, there was still a contribution to be made, and that the violence of partisan political feeling might be lessened by his work. To this end the unassuming pages of his book, "with little to recommend them to them but the simplicity of truth" might make their modest contribution.

In October his half-brother, David Wilson, arrived in Philadelphia from Paisley. He was impetuous, well-meaning, awkward, and wanted to become a writer. He moved in with Wilson at William Jones's home and he brought over with him all of Wilson's early poems —the tragicomic story of Meg Duncan and old Craig, the satire on the rake who died of syphilis, the lampoon on prominent Paisley citizens who were so frightened of revolution they lost control of their bowels, the funny story in "The Insulted Peddler" about the peddler who answered a call of nature in the woods of a nobleman's estate. David thought these poems were fine, and doubtless would have read them to everyone, had Wilson not burned them.

David brought word that the rest of the family wished to come to America. Wilson wrote a letter addressed "To my Brothers and Sisters." If they had the heart to endure the initial period of sadness and hardship, he thought they should come over. From what they wrote him of conditions in Scotland, he did not see how they could be asked to stay; he could not think of remaining any more than of living in a house that was falling down.

He did not doubt but that they could make a living here. In his years in America the population had grown from four million to seven million, and in general the newcomers did well. "I have, however, determined with myself never to entice or persuade a man from his native country to a foreign land," he wrote. "Should you determine on coming here, I will render you every assistance in my power; but difficulties must be met with everywhere in this world."

A letter was brought also from Thomas Crichton. Wilson replied that he could not recall his previous social views without a smile. He had been an enthusiastic young man pursuing what he thought right without considering its expediency, "and frequently suffering (and that feelingly, too) for my temerity." He now felt the same ardor in pursuit of his objective, but the objective was chosen with more discretion.

A little later, as the war clouds darkened, Wilson wrote to Crichton:

> I love the arts of peace. Everybody here hopes for a good understanding with Great Britain. Of the sentiments of many in the government, I can say nothing, being little conversant with the matter, and having long ago quitted the turbulent field of politics.

He recognized that the coming war changed the perspective for the immediate future of his books, but he had no doubt of the value of his work, and in some emotion wrote to Crichton:

November 3, 1811

> My Dear Friend,
> I was a wanderer when I was in Scotland, and I have been much more so since my arrival here. Few Americans have seen more of their country than I have done, and none love her more. Fortune has not yet paid me all her promises, after all the wild goose chases she has led me; but she begins to look a little more gracious than usual, and I am not without hope. . .

In September, the blue-winged teal swept in from the north, flying fast, and dropping down suddenly into isolated ponds and streams, the first arrival of the migrants, a hard bird to hunt, and fine eating. In the third week of September rail-hunting began, to last until the middle of October. About two hours before high tide the rail-hunters were poled in light boats through the reeds over the flooded flatlands, the hunter in the bow. The rail leaped as the boat came near, usually one at a time, the boatman poling toward the fallen bird, the gunner reloading and firing as another rail started up. The birds were flushed and fell, the gunner firing and reloading, the sport continuing for almost an hour after high water. An expert could get ten dozen rail at a tide, and the plump birds, considered as delicious as any game, sold for fifty cents a dozen in the markets.

The rail was the commonest of game birds. Wilson found that along the James River the Negroes gathered rail at night, merely rounding them up as they stared stupefied at the lights, three men in a boat collecting a thousand birds in three hours. Because hunters saw these birds, everywhere so numerous, yet never flying in great flocks like geese, they were a subject of folklore and legend. Almost anything could be asserted about the rail. "It comes, they know not whence," Wilson wrote, "and goes, they know not where. No one can detect their first moment of arrival; yet all at once the reedy shores and grassy marshes of our large rivers swarm with them, thousands being sometimes found within the space of a few acres." Wilson explained that the rail belonged to a genus of birds of which about thirty different species were known. The enormous distances in the United States, the long uninhabited stretches, and the rail's manner of flight, made it impossible to log its migration. In such a case the best procedure was to take the closest related species that could be traced—in this case the British land rail, whose migration had been logged. In any event, none of the twenty-nine species of the rail hibernated, and it was illogical to assume that the American bird did so.

This was the final word on the subject, and Wilson hurried on to other problems. The essay on the rail was destined for the sixth volume, and printing of the fifth was soon to begin. In the fall Charles Leslie, his best colorist, left for England—one of the younger Inskeep sons, newly admitted to partnership in Inskeep and Bradford and Bradford and Inskeep, began his professional duties with a long leisurely visit to London; Wilson and a group of friends bought up Leslie's apprenticeship from Bradford, and young Leslie was sent to London in young Inskeep's care. Unexpectedly, *The Port Folio* published Wilson's report: *Particulars on the Death of Captain Lewis,* almost exactly as Wilson had sent it from Natchez, but the date of his journey was changed by the editor from 1810 to 1811.

After Wilson had finished his essay on the rail, but before it was published, he received a strange communication from George Ord:

> My personal experience has made me acquainted with a fact in the history of the rail, which perhaps is not generally known. . . . Some time in the autumn of the year 1809, as I was walking in a yard, after a severe shower of rain, I perceived the feet of a bird projecting from a spout. I pulled it out, and discovered it to be a rail, very vigorous, and in perfect health. The bird was placed in a small room, and I was amusing myself with it, when, in the act of pointing my finger at it, it suddenly sprang forward, apparently much irritated, fell to the floor, and, stretching out its feet, and bending its neck until the head nearly touched the back, became to all appearances lifeless.
>
> Thinking the fall had killed the bird, I took it up, and began to lament my rashness in provoking it. In a few minutes it again breathed, and it was some time before it perfectly recovered from the fit into which, it now appeared, it had fallen. I . . . resolved that, on the succeeding day, I would endeavour to discover

whether or not the passion of anger had produced the fit. I entered the room at the appointed time, and approached the bird, which had retired, on beholding me, in a sullen humor, to a corner. On pointing my finger at it, its feathers were immediatey ruffled, and in an instant it sprang forward, as in the first instance, and fell into a similar fit. The following day the experiment was repeated with a like effect.

Wilson made no comment on Ord's letter. It was, of course, nonsensical as a scientific contribution, and Wilson (and probably Ord) knew it. "I had my doubts," Wilson wrote owlishly, "about classing this bird under the genus *Rallus.*" But Ord was a prominent and wealthy amateur, and Wilson had requested "gentlemen of leisure with an interest in natural history" to send him material. Moreover, with respect to Ord, Wilson seemed curiously submissive, and accepted from Ord the kind of material he commonly disregarded, or opposed as superstition, from others. From the point of view from which Wilson wrote, Ord's comment ridiculed his whole argument, and in printing Ord's letter, Wilson said merely that these curious particulars came from a gentleman of respectability, and merited further investigation.

The War of 1812 was now on, though the declaration of war still did not take place until June 18, 1812. Bradford led a number of businessmen holding meetings to memorialize Congress against the War. Through the first months of the year Wilson was wholly absorbed in the array of hawks and owls of his next volumes, writing to Dr. Samuel Mitchill that "the United States will exhibit such a display of noble Eagles and Hawks as I think no other country can produce." He sent Robert Carr to Mitchill (now an extremely influential Congressman) because Carr wanted help in getting a commission in the United States Army. Wilson said he knew Carr would support the honor of his country as a soldier, that he would never dishonor those who endorsed him, and that his bravery and intelligence and high sense of honor were recognized by all who knew him. This appeal was successful. Carr, who was a major in the Pennsylvania militia, received his commission. As the Army of the United States then numbered only 6,744 men, Carr's subsequent heroism in the War of 1812 made him no small part of the total military might of the nation. Under Dr. Eustis, the retired physician and the old enemy of Meriwether Lewis, the War Department had been reduced to eight clerks, the medical corps had been done away with, West Point was being sabotaged, and the adjutant-general's staff consisted of one colonel who had not left Washington in eight years. Dr. Eustis nevertheless remained as Secretary of War by virtue of his firm party regularity until shortly before the burning of Washington. As for General Wilkinson, proceedings against him were delayed, and as the approaching war became real he was hastily acquitted.

In the spring of 1812 Wilson decided that he could not spend the summer at Bartram's Garden because David was with him and there was no room for two people. He paid a visit to Bartram on April 30, before starting for Egg Harbor. It gave him a start of pleasure to find that the Baltimore oriole of the year before was back on the same tree in the same quarter of the garden, "whistling his identical old chant."

At Egg Harbor he stayed at Beasley's Tavern, whose front porch faced an inlet and the sea. George Ord accompanied him on this trip; it was the only one in which Wilson definitely described traveling with Ord. Wilson wrote much of this 1812 trip to Cape May, but only once of Ord himself. About a mile from Beasley's Tavern he found a sea eagle's nest on the top of a large yellow pine tree. Beasley wanted to fell the tree to get the nest. Ord wanted to save the eggs or the young. Ord climbed to the nest, Wilson and Beasley preparing to shoot in case the eagle attacked him. But the nest was empty. If the episode was revealing, it was because in many similar accounts in the *Ornithology* Wilson himself did the climbing. Now he was tiring and grateful for help. While Ord was tramping to the source of the Tuckahoe River to find herons, Wilson was sitting by the harbor where the river entered, watching some carpenters building a sloop. His day was not wasted, for he found the nest of a summer duck not twelve feet from where the men were working.

Ord provided him with an embarrassment of ornithological treasures. He brought in birds in quantities, sometimes better specimens than Wilson had drawn, or the females of species Wilson had neglected to picture in his first volumes. Each day Ord turned up something new. Wilson had already closed the first section of the volume he was working on. He could not get at the plates again, or change the text. He wrote of the black-capped warbler that the plumage of the female (which he had not pictured) differed little from that of the male. Now Ord presented him with a specimen of the female with dusky brown wings, altogether unlike the black and yellow wings of the male he had pictured. So Wilson conscientiously tucked the black-capped female in a corner of a page filled with hawks, and described in gritted-teeth prose in the last pages of his book a flat contradiction to what he had stated in the opening pages.

In a corner of another page jammed with pictures of hawks and owls, Wilson drew the mysterious little yellow and brown bird that he called the small-headed flycatcher. In the accompanying text he did not say that he shot it. When Wilson shot a bird, he generally said so. In this case, however, he wrote that the bird was shot "on the 24th of April, in an orchard, and was remarkably active, running, climbing and darting about the opening buds and blossoms. . . ." A last-minute addition (this was almost the final page of the book) stated that since writing the above "I have shot several of the same species." He said he knew little of the bird, which was very rare.

Twenty-six years later Audubon pictured a similar bird in the last volume of his *Ornithological Biography*. He said Wilson had stolen his picture from a drawing that he had loaned Wilson in Louisville. Ord replied that he was with Wilson when the bird was shot. Lawson added that Audubon was lying; he testified that he had engraved the bird with Wilson's or Ord's mounted specimen at hand. As the dispute grew bitter, Ord submitted positive proof that Audubon had copied the Mississippi kite from Wilson's book. The strangest part of the whole business, however, was that no small-headed flycatcher existed. It was suggested that Wilson had drawn a black-throated green warbler, thinking he had found a new bird. Now, when Audubon prepared his own folio, he had no small-headed green flycatcher to draw. He supposed Wilson had possessed one. In his desire to make his folio complete, he copied Wilson's bird which he claimed he had discovered himself.

The mysterious bird in question was never seen again. No small-headed flycatcher has ever been located anywhere except in Wilson's sixth volume in 1812 and Audubon's fifth folio in 1838. "What has become of this mysterious phantom that has been a wandering and disturbing voice among ornithologists for over a century?" asked Professor Herrick. He concluded that both Wilson and Audubon were independently mistaken. So far as Wilson was concerned, the explanation was likely correct. The bird was a mere footnote, a hurried addition, drawn at a moment when he was working in haste on sea birds, and preserved only for fear its exclusion might confuse his account of the warblers he had previously pictured. In the same spirit Wilson added, at the same time, a tiny yellow and black and olive warbler to a plate with a broad-winged hawk, making the following explanation: "The new and beautiful little species was discovered in a maple swamp, in Cape May County, not far from the coast, by Mr. George Ord of Philadelphia, who accompanied me on a shooting expedition to that quarter in the month of May last."

In the context, "May last" means May, 1812. Wilson called the bird the Cape May warbler, which name it still carries. The Cape May warbler was George Ord's one claim to ornithological fame. He discovered it, and his discovery was attested by Wilson at the time, and put into print with a date that permitted no mistake. But the section of Audubon's work that appeared in 1835 had a similar bird, so like the one Wilson had drawn that both Sir William Jardine and Charles Bonaparte thought they were identical. Audubon said he had found *his* bird in Henderson, Kentucky, in 1811. He offered no proof. His drawing was dated, in his own handwriting, May 7, 1811. With a rather pathetic haste, Ord changed the date of his Cape May trip from 1812 to 1811 in an effort to reclaim priority for his discovery. But this involved him in contradictions in the publishing dates of the books. As we have seen, *The Port Folio* had also changed the date of Wilson's trip to the West, in his article on Meriwether Lewis, from 1810 to 1811. Ord subsequently systematically changed the dates of Wilson's experiences when he took charge of Wilson's papers.

Among the ironies involved in the *Ornithology* was its amazing impact on George Ord. He began his association with Wilson in a way that appeared to be mocking, yet still with a seriousness that makes one wonder what he himself believed. As Wilson published his strange letter in the *Ornithology* itself, and their association continued, Ord gradually developed an almost fanatical absorption with birds. He devoted his whole life to them. It was almost as though he had discovered that something he meant to be a joke was too profoundly serious to be laid aside, though it cost him a fortune, and led him into circles where he was not at home, and where quarrels and bickerings were constant. It would hardly be too much to say that from this time on Ord was constantly involved in fights in which he struggled desperately over matters about which he knew little, and in which he was generally on the wrong side. An embittered anti-Jeffersonian in his politics, he now found himself among people of the opposite belief in the pursuit of his subject. A natural pedant, he could not undertake any work without pointing out the mistakes of others, but he was really not much of a student of birds, and on one occasion (after Wilson's death) he seized one sentence of Wilson's, concerning the ruddy duck, and published a 2,000-word correction, only to discover that he was in error.

Wilson took Ord with him to the informal social gatherings that Lawson now regularly held. Malvina Lawson, the young daughter of the engraver, then a little girl, was a pet of the artists of the city, and when Ord appeared she approached him with the friendliness she expected to receive. Ord drew back with a distaste so unexpected and so shocking to her that she remembered it all her life. She wrote that he detested children, in itself inexplicable in that family civilization, and (later, in her old age) she remembered George Ord as fussy and jealous, and said that he talked like a woman.

Wilson had no appetite for the daily trips into the woods from which Ord returned with more birds than he could carry. He was more than content to talk with Beasley on the veranda of the tavern. One day Ord went alone up the Tuckahoe River and returned with five great snowy herons to be skinned. He was now making the findings that Wilson once made alone.

Or many of them. Wilson could still find more bird life at his back door than most naturalists could in the jungle. He did not really need the five snowy herons Ord brought back to him, for he had already pictured the bird. Tramping along the beach alone he came upon the little bird now known as Wilson's plover. The day after Ord's heron-shooting trip up the Tuckahoe, Wilson found a big breeding place of the snowy heron among the red cedars of Summers Beach on Cape May, almost at his front door. Then in Maurice River Cove, below Egg Island, Wilson found what appeared to be a principal settlement of the turnstone, "this beautifully variegated species," that the natives called the horse-foot snipe.

Wilson was alone when he collected the birds he really needed, the least bittern, the whooping crane, the night heron, the black skimmer. He was alone also when he watched skimmers feeding in the inlets of the myrtle-covered islands. "One of these birds which I wounded in the wing, and kept in the room beside me for several days, soon became tame and even familiar," he wrote. "It refused every kind of food offered it, and I am persuaded never feeds but when on the wing." Wilson was alone also when he shot a bird he called the pied oyster catcher, "not far from a deep and rapid inlet . . . I broke the wing of one of these birds, and being without a dog, instantly pursued it toward an inlet. . . . We both plunged in at nearly the same instant, but the bird eluded my grasp, and I sank beyond my depth. On rising to the surface, I found the bird had dived, and a strong ebb current was carrying me toward the ocean. . . . I was compelled to relinquish my bird, with considerable mortification." When he reached shore, exhausted, he saw it swimming with great buoyancy among the breakers.

Wilson was back in Philadelphia by July 1, 1812, for on that date he agreed to serve as executor of the estate of John Morton, a Philadelphia merchant who was a friend of William Jones. Morton was a Quaker, whose son James Morton had been a neighbor of Wilson's at Milestown, but Wilson was not a member of the circles in which Morton lived, and the request was another tribute to his "probity, gentle manners and accomplishments." His reputation was attested to when he was called to be the guardian of Caleb Bickham's children under his will, with Miers Fisher the executor. He needed these expressions of confidence from men of standing. The war meant a degree of suspicion was attributed to exiles from Britain, especially those who, like Wilson, had not posed as political refugees. Now he was elected to the Columbian Society, the organization of Philadelphia artists, in the first gesture of community acceptance of him. He remained a mysterious figure to the common people generally, and the years of seclusion were to take a greater toll.

His tragedy and his accomplishment were alike indicated by the publishing schedule of the remaining volumes of his great work. Since each volume contained ten colored plates, with from two to four birds on each plate, Wilson was completing studies of more than a hundred birds a year, and writing the text to accompany each painting, in some periods finishing the text and the painting within three days. By the reckoning of Emerson Stringham, Wilson presented 264 of the 343 species of birds found in the United States of his time; he added 48 new species to those previously known; he prepared good life histories for 94 species; and vernacular names he employed became accepted for 40 species. He missed only 79 species in the immense wilderness, and scarcely more than a score of errors, most of them minor, have been found in the *Ornithology* in a century and a half. The amount of labor of superlative quality packed into the volumes in the brief time allotted was all but incredible:

> Volume III. Not published until February, 1811, in an edition of 500 copies at $12 each, or a return of $6,000 due in the course of the year. However, by that time

> Volume IV (eventually published in September, 1811) was ready, or a total of $12,000 due in the course of the year—yet, before the end of the year, Wilson had Volume V sufficiently in hand to permit its publication in 1811, or $12,000 plus the late accounts of 1810.

Volume V went to press on February 12, 1812, the delay partly occasioned because subscribers were reluctant to pay $36 in any one year. But Wilson had Volume VI finished by June, 1812.

Volume VI. Distributed to subscribers in November, 1812, making $12,000 due in the course of the year.

When George Ord came to describe Wilson's character, he said that he was irritable, the only person who knew Wilson to so describe him. There was doubtless much in Ord's make-up that was irritating; he had, moreover, a dangerous temper, and it was said that in his rages he literally did not know what he was doing. In any event, he and Wilson were plainly less closely associated than they had been, for Ord often did not know Wilson's whereabouts. After he returned to Philadelphia, Wilson resumed his meetings with Sarah Miller, but these now proved difficult also. On August 12, 1812, Wilson wrote to Sarah:

My dear Sarah,

I cannot be out tomorrow as I expected, Mr. Bradford and I having all our accounts to settle; but I will take the first opportunity of coming out to let you know particulars. In the meantime do not be alarmed when I tell you that I must now either run the risk of losing all or make one last and very long and expensive journey to collect what is due, and see how accounts are with the agents. There is no other choice left between this and absolute ruin. You will not therefore my dearest friend object to this as on it my whole hopes of happiness depend. Mr. B. has positively refused to advance anything until he receives it and I have as positively told him that I will proceed no further with the work until I am paid for what I have done.

It will be two or three weeks before I think of setting out. I will see you many times before then. I would ask forgiveness for all these disappointments but I know you are goodness itself and judge my suffering means more than your own— Therefore a good heart—amuse yourself with your kind friends from Montgomery— But do not forget your ever affectionate

ALEXANDER WILSON

To Miss Sarah Miller
at Jacob Miller's Esq.
near Milestown

Wilson left Philadelphia in September, sailed up the Hudson to Albany, then crossed overland to Lake Champlain. He was sometimes troubled by a violent palpitation of the heart that made traveling uncomfortable, and he remained near towns or close to woods, hunting but little, and perplexed and depressed by his physical weakness. On the shores of

Lake Champlain he discovered the semipalmated sandpiper, another unknown bird, a white and black sandpiper with a light, airy, zigzagging flight; but he was so preoccupied, and so concerned with other matters, that he barely noted the fact in his log book, where previously he had written his very descriptions in the woods, on the spot where the birds were seen.

The autumn scene in the mountains, however, stirred him to a brief renewal of the freshness and spontaneity of his best nature writing. Despite his sense of physical weakness he climbed continually. When he reached the Connecticut River that marked the border between Vermont and New Hampshire he was only about twenty miles from the Canadian border, a thickly wooded country where isolated farms and small settlements were hidden in its narrow river valleys. His destination was Dartmouth College in Hanover, where he was sure of a friendly reception, but he was unhurried, and at Haverhill, thirty miles up the Connecticut from the college, he spent a day wandering in the hills behind the town.

Haverhill lay at the point where trails and roads leading east and west intersected with those running north and south along the Connecticut River. The town had been planned to become a great wilderness center, but its strategic location involved it in such violent local conflicts that the Revolution there became civil war, and after the Revolution domestic warfare broke out again over the question of whether the loyalists who fled to Canada should be permitted to return and their property be restored to them. They were at length allowed back, but the reconciliation did not follow, and Haverhill was still split, a quarter of a century after the Revolution, into patriots and loyalists, living in an uneasy condition of mutual distrust. Even that degree of truce was broken by the start of the War of 1812, for Haverhill was the first town that an invading force from Canada would strike, and rumors were spreading that one was on its way.

The day of Wilson's visit was windless and cloudless, with the bright freshness of the New England fall in the air. The highest point of land nearby rose in a peak not far from town, and Wilson spent the day climbing to the crest. From this height he could see into Canada, with an immensity of forest spread below, extended in all directions to the farthest verge of the horizon. No sign of civilization was visible anywhere; nothing above the tops of the trees except the columns of smoke that rose straight up in the calm air from isolated burning brushlands and forest fires. These Wilson watched for some time.

When he came down the hill he was arrested as a spy. A group of Haverhill patriots had observed his strange conduct since his arrival, had seen him prowling through the woods in search of birds, and decided that he was a British agent reconnoitering the invasion route from Canada. They conducted him to the magistrate at Haverhill. Wilson explained who he was and what he was doing, and was released at once, with apologies.

The charge dismayed him, and its effect was to reduce his dwindling confidence in a period when it was most needed. He hurried on to Dartmouth, and crossed to Boston, after which, having collected enough to satisfy Bradford for the time being, he returned to

Philadelphia. There news of another disaster awaited him: his colorists had left him, and work on the *Ornithology* had stopped. He could not spend the money he had raised on colorists, even if he could secure them, and began coloring all the plates himself. He continued to draw and paint when he could on the plates of herons and flamingoes, and at night colored plate after plate of the land birds for the volumes going to press.

During the dark winter of 1812, when trenches were dug outside his old school at Gray's Ferry, he remained indoors, scarcely leaving the house for months for longer than half an hour. One duty that called him out was to begin his tasks as the executor of John Morton's will, the merchant having died in December.

There could be no further question of another trip to the South to secure the specimens he had not yet collected. But Abbot sent him beautifully preserved and mounted birds. Stephen Elliot presented him with a magnificent wood ibis. William Dunbar was now dead, but his son secured a roseate spoonbill and sent it to Wilson in time to be included in the volume.

By the spring of 1813, Wilson's enthusiasm revived and he wrote to Bartram in April, asking: "Will it be convenient for the family to accommodate me (as I shall be alone) this summer? Please let me know." He was touched to receive at this time the gift of a painting from no less an artist than Benjamin West, who had become a subscriber to the *Ornithology,* as well as the teacher of Charles Leslie, a gift delayed in reaching him from London because of the war. Wilson was deeply pleased, too, to be elected to membership in the American Philosophical Society, and told Bartram he expected to work out during the summer at Bartram's Garden the address he would be expected to deliver as a new member.

On March 1, 1813, Wilson signed the Introduction to his seventh volume, and two months later wrote to Bartram that the book would be released in another week. There were delays, however, and the book was not published until November, the month Wilson had expected his eighth volume to be in the hands of subscribers.

The financial consequences of this new delay were obvious. By July, 1813, Wilson was finished with the wild ducks that filled his next-to-the-last book with savory hunting lore. He had completed eight of the books he had contracted to produce, a total of $48,000 that should have been received from subscribers he had signed up. As he had received nothing, his share of the royalties being absorbed by current costs, his interest was a substantial one, even though the war had made all these calculations academic at the moment.

Ord's description of Wilson as often irritable was justified at this time, and doubtless the disasters to the American army, beginning with the surrender of Detroit without a battle, cast a pall over all social life, even that of Beasley's Tavern. One of the bright exceptions in the steady rush of bad news was the record of Colonel Carr. He commanded at Niagara, at Sackett's Harbor, and was placed in command at Fort Oswego, where an attack by the British fleet on the lakes was driven off; later he became an outstanding hero of the battle of Lundy's Lane, which revived American morale.

1 American Crossbill 2 Female. 3 White-winged Crossbill 4 White-crown'd Bunting 5 Bay-winged B.

Crossbills and buntings made a brilliant pattern of reds and browns.

VIII

But Wilson's actions were shrouded in deeper obscurity than at any time in his own past. His arrest in Haverhill had a catastrophic effect on him, summoning up the whole period of his ordeal in Paisley twenty years before, and he worked with obsessive concentration. Ord attributed the catastrophe to overwork. William Peabody, who wrote the first objective account of Alexander Wilson some fifteen years after his death, also wrote that Wilson took upon himself more labor than he could possibly perform. He was "too proud to suffer any part of his work to appear in an unworthy form. . . . He drew largely upon the hours that should have been given to rest, besides spending the day in unnecessary exertion." Friends remonstrated with him, but he could not be dissuaded.

It remained for Malvina Lawson, shortly before her death, to point out another meaning. In her reminiscences of Wilson, she wrote:

> I remember perfectly his brilliant eyes, and hair as black as an Indian's, and as straight. . . . I think that a great moral lesson may be drawn from his life. When a man in seven years becomes famous as a man of science and as a draughtsman whose birds live forever, without any other help than the cheering voice of friendship to aid him in his new standing, it seems almost a miracle. When we think of Wilson shouldering his gun and setting out for the wilderness, not only of nature, but of ignorance and prejudice, and after months of wearying travel, returning with his drawings and specimens, worn out with fatigue and oppressed by poverty, to sit down to the composition of a work as truthful, as beautiful and as charming to read as any romance, what a sermon on the virtues of faith and perseverance! And to all his other trials was added the fact that killed him—the dishonesty of his publisher.

Wilson made his final trip to the Cape May country in the summer, remaining about a month. The story of his death that Ord told was that Wilson was talking with a friend when he spotted a bird he had long wanted, pursued it, and was forced to swim a river to shoot it. He took cold from exposure, which brought on dysentery. Ord mysteriously set the time in May. At the time that Ord wrote, Wilson's own account of a similar happening, when he was nearly swept out to sea the year before, had not been printed. When Peabody wrote his version, fifteen years later, he placed the event in July, and stated that Wilson lived only ten days afterwards. Neither Ord's account nor that of Peabody was convincing; both echoed Wilson's own story of his swimming after a wounded plover, and both disregarded that fact that Wilson was now rarely concerned to search for new birds—at least not in such well-hunted country as that near Beasley's Tavern.

In any event, he was still well on Friday, August 13, for on that day he was in Philadelphia, preparing a list of the birds he had still to do. There were twenty-four of these—the loon, pelican, gulls, the swan, and a few, like the wild turkey, that he had somehow neglected in their proper place. He had painted, drawn and described 264 species.

On August 19, Dr. Charles Caldwell was called to William Jones's house. Caldwell knew Wilson through their work on *The Port Folio;* he admired him as a writer, and was deeply impressed at his achievement. He found Wilson extremely weak from dysentery, but calm and composed, and with a recognition of how seriously ill he was. After he left, Wilson made his will. He left everything he owned, including all rights to the *American Ornithology,* to Sarah Miller, except one set of the books to be given to William Duncan, and two sets to his father in Paisley.

Daniel Miller was named executor, Susannah Jones and Henry Coryell witnessed the document. Miller was an intelligent young businessman, and he had long been Wilson's friend, but he had no particular literary interest, and George Ord was named co-executor with him.

Dr. Caldwell called each day for four days, methodically noting the date and $3 for each visit. On August 23, 1813, he wrote after Wilson's name, *Departed.*

Wilson was buried in the family lot of William Jones in the churchyard of the Swedish Lutheran Church. As he was not a member of the church, the minister, a Reverend Mr. Clay, was perplexed as to how to enter it in the record and wrote a separate entry apart from the burials of the members:

> 1813, August 24. Alexander Wilson, native of Scotland, but resident here for many years, author of *American Ornithology,* aged about 40 years, not married. He had for a long time lived with Mr. William Jones, last in Spring Street, near Seventh Street, & was buried in his lot. The disease was flux.

CHAPTER FOUR

Conclusion

GEORGE ORD was out of the city during Wilson's illness. When he returned to Philadelphia he found that Wilson was dead and buried. The will appointing him executor with Daniel Miller was proved on September 25, 1813, and he hurriedly went through Wilson's papers and journals, expecting, he said, to find copious material.

To his dismay, he found that Wilson had nothing. Three plates of drawings were ready for the engravers. Beyond these he could not see what Wilson intended to do. His next thought was that Wilson's notebooks would contain material on the birds not yet described. But he found of some of the remaining birds only a few notes scattered throughout the journals, "and of others, no word whatsoever."

He had expected to find a travel journal like the articles that had been appearing in *The Port Folio*. What he found irritated and confused him. On his last trip to New England, Wilson had written to Ord that on Lake Champlain, "I found the little coot-footed tringa, or phalarope, that you sent to Mr. Peale." Ord looked to see what Wilson had written on the relevant date about his discovery. "I found an account of the bird," he noted, in something like disgust, "there called a *Tringa,* written with a lead pencil, but so scrawled and obscured, that parts of the writing were not legible."

It was all ludicrous, or would have been, had it not blotted out the genuine contribution that Wilson made. For with all his attacks on Audubon in Wilson's name, Ord did not collect or publish Wilson's poems or letters and incidental writings. He said he was unable to learn anything of Wilson's early life, or even the date of his birth, when he wrote his memoir of Wilson, though Wilson's sister, or William Duncan, could readily have supplied them. The editors of *The Port Folio* shortened his long memoir, softened its tone, and made it a graceful, unpretending tribute—probably Biddle's work. Ord was incensed at the liberties taken. As the article had gone to press (with a note explaining it was abbreviated), *The Port Folio* published in the same issue Ord's original version, immediately following the edited one. There were thus two complete obituaries in the magazine, identical in most respects, but with Ord's version more pretentious, less accurate, and badly written. It was plain that Ord had objected to the editing of his article, that the editor had printed a notice stating it *had* been shortened, that Ord then exaggerated the changes made, so the editor had published Ord's original as well. The confusion was symbolical of Ord's work on Wilson. Ord, too, was insistent on certain errors, and some falsehoods, asserting, for example, that Wilson had failed to secure subscribers on his Southern trip.

A full decade passed before any question was raised in Paisley about Alexander Wilson's strange career. His father, who died in 1816, had long since lived down his early reputation as a smuggler, and was known only as a citizen of good standing with his neighbors. David Brodie lived to great age. He kept his school on Old Sneddon Street, near where the Paisley railroad station was located, and not far from Crichton's home. William Sharp of the Long Mills continued to prosper. His son David Sharp, becoming a manufacturer in turn, married the daughter of the Swedish consul at Glasgow, and their son William Sharp became a famous English man of letters.

Thomas Crichton died at the age of eighty-four. He remained Governor of the Town Hospital, and was senior elder of all the Presbyterian churches of the area. Crichton wrote poetry all his life, and began his recollections of Wilson for the newly started *Weaver's Magazine* as a letter. It aroused a lot of interest, and he followed it with half a dozen others, until he had a brief biographical essay written. Crichton wrote very slowly, concerned to be absolutely fair, and followed his work on Wilson with his life of Dr. Witherspoon. He was sparing in his enthusiasm for both, but without censure, though he seemed a little irritated with Wilson for leaving Scotland. Crichton was copying one of his religious poems, and had written the word "glory," when his head sank to his desk, and he was found to be dead. "He has finished his career," said the local newspaper, "without one stain upon his character."

In the years of rioting, Sheriff Orr retired. The post of sheriff-substitute he had filled when he jailed Wilson, and ordered him to burn his poems, was taken over by William Motherwell, a young poet of ability, the son of a Glasgow ironmonger. Motherwell was largely instrumental in starting *The Paisley Magazine,* which he edited, and which first published the story of Alexander Wilson and his family in the Tower of Auchinbathie. Motherwell also made two collections of the work of local poets, *The Harp of Renfrewshire,* and emerged with an admiration for Wilson for the positive honesty of his work.

Motherwell's work had its effect, and in 1831 Thomas Crichton presided at a dinner on Wilson's birthday, gathering the people who had known Wilson. Presently a Scottish sculptor, David Anderson, who had carved a scene showing Watty and Meg, prepared a little marble tablet to be placed on Wilson's birthplace. The local Odd Fellows Lodge, which had adopted the name of the Alexander Wilson Branch, planned to march along High Street, Gauze Street and Thread Street, to Seedhill Street. It was a fine September day, and an amazingly large crowd turned out. The lanes leading to Wilson's house were spanned with arches of flowers and evergreens, and "shouts of rejoicing and numerous discharges of firearms mingled agreeably with the rush of waters tumbling over the crags in the immediate vicinity."

The occasion was so moving that Anderson felt badly that he had only made a little plaque. He began working for a monument to Wilson. A committee was formed, money raised, and the sculptor, John Mossman, selected. He began carving a statue showing Wilson in hunting garb, his rifle in his hand, head down as he examined a bird he had shot, a more sensitive piece of work than such memorials usually are. Twenty-nine years of discussion followed. Ord, visiting Paisley for the first time in 1855, gave $300 to encourage the work. By 1861 the statue was fairly well along, and the committee was discussing where it could be placed. Twelve years later it was calculated that about one month's progress had been made. By that time the committee had a sizable balance in the bank—£273—after paying Mossman. Eventually the statue was erected on the edge of the grounds of the Abbey, not far from where Wilson burned his poems, and a fine statue of Tannahill raised beside it.

Before it was dedicated a city official, MacKean, journeyed to Philadelphia, to gather material about Wilson's life in America. Ord had died, his heir a nephew, Karrick, and while Wilson's effects "were affectionately regarded, many of them from time to time disappeared." MacKean wanted particularly to see Margaret Carman, Ord's housekeeper, as he knew that she had known Wilson intimately, and that she was the only person still living who had known him. First, however, MacKean made his way to the old Swedish Lutheran Church to visit Wilson's grave. As he approached the church, he met a crowd of mourners coming out. They were the mourners from Miss Carman's funeral. MacKean returned to Paisley, where he reported that he felt it was remarkable that a fellow townsman on a pilgrimage to Wilson's grave should arrive "just at the moment when the remains of the last person who knew him were in the course of being consigned to Mother Earth close by his own."

There remain a few other careers to be mentioned. Ord became a power in the scientific organizations of Philadelphia, curator and later vice president of the Academy of Natural Science, and secretary, treasurer and president of the American Philosophical Society during forty years of active membership. He became a familiar Philadelphia character, known for his benign countenance, gray hair, slow speech, and fierce hostility to Audubon.

In his ceaseless battles with Audubon, Ord was aided by the eccentric English naturalist Charles Waterton, an authority on the poison curare, who challenged Audubon on everything from the sense of smell in the vultures to the fangs of snakes. These two pilgrims in the cause of scientific exactitude became close friends, traveling through Europe together, and carrying on a literary campaign which produced an accumulation of as dull a body of writing as can readily be found.

After Wilson's death, Sarah Miller married Nicholas Rittenhouse, of the old Pennsylvania family. He was eight years younger than Wilson, seven years older than Sarah. They had no children. Both lived to old age, Rittenhouse dying in 1858 and his wife on December 19, 1859. It was revealing of the underground reputation that Wilson possessed in these years that two young collectors purchased, after Sarah's death, a trunk that had belonged to Wilson, and whose contents were unknown. The trunk turned out to contain a few plates of the *Ornithology,* and a colored drawing of the hermit thrush.

Daniel Miller became a prosperous glass manufacturer, with his works in New Jersey, while he also flourished as a Congressman, three times representing his Philadelphia district as a Jackson Democrat. He died suddenly in 1831, aged forty-seven.

Perhaps the most remarkable career of all the people remotely connected with Wilson was that of a descendant of his old enemy William Sharp, the Mr. Shark of his unfortunate poem. The grandson of the manufacturer first established one reputation in the nineties as a critic and essayist, under the name of William Sharp. He was happily married, a friend of the young William Butler Yeats. In his middle years he suddenly decided that he was two people. One was a man, and one was a woman. The man was William Sharp. The woman was named Fiona Macleod. Sharp began to write mystical and sensuous fiction as a woman, carefully building up the pseudonym of Fiona Macleod and successfully keeping it secret. He appeared to believe that Fiona Macleod was a real person, over whose trancelike imaginative flights he had no control, and he wrote about her with detachment in his public career as William Sharp. He did well in both his literary careers, though Fiona Macleod's was more profitable, as her books were bestsellers. She also wrote nonfiction works on nature. Most remarkably of all, her lush rhapsodies on nature became extremely popular in the United States, perhaps more frequently quoted than any other in anthologies of gems of nature writing, thick, overblown prose about sunbeams slanting through glens, and mist rising from meadows.

The readers of Wilson in Scotland did not know his American life, nor did his American readers know his life in Scotland. As wonderful as Wilson's books were, they were unfinished, and perhaps they could never be finished so long as the two halves of his existence were separated. It was not only that he completed only eight of the ten books in the *Ornithology*; the individual accounts, and many of the paintings, have an unfinished air, just as many of his poems in Scotland give the impression of being the framework of great works still to be written. In the crevices of his unfinished masterpiece the extraordinary confusions of his life grew like weeds, the mixed-up dates, and the trivial distortions that led to decades of argument among the scholars and the loss of interest of the public.

The loss was some vision of American wild life that he possessed and which sustained him through his years of work. Glimpses of it appear now and then through the earlier volumes of the *Ornithology,* enough to suggest his meaning, and to reveal a vital purpose that saved him from pedantry and his work from becoming a mere catalogue. No American poet before Whitman sang of nature with the confidence of Alexander Wilson. All his work taken together, his poems, journals, and the scientific material combined with personal experience in his nature writing, form a rough, literal, unsparing photographic record of the country as he saw it—swamps along the Natchez Trace, the streets of Easton, Pennsylvania, a colony of Swiss immigrants in Ohio, a grotesque Indian cabin in the woods, a deserted mill in New Jersey, chickens roosting on the loom. But there was a line of color woven in this gray fabric of life, and it was exemplified for Wilson in the variety and ceaseless activity of the birds—something elusive and brilliant, diffusing a peculiar radiance through fields and orchards and forests, an intangible, constantly shifting pattern of vivid and vibrant life, of little practical value to man in any immediate sense, and yet so highly organized within itself, with each part so completely adequate to its own wants and conveniences, that the lords of creation might derive some useful hints from its study. Wilson believed that the beauty of poetry must lie in its recording of the beauty of God's creation, if we could but see it, not in the creations of the poet's imagination surrounding hard familiar truth with the shadows and highlights of poetic allusion; and if the injudicious following of that credo got him in trouble with the law of Scotland, it also led him as faithfully to picture the colors of flamingoes and the wings of swallows and hawks. His creation in the *American Ornithology* was so rare, strange, and hauntingly beautiful, that it transformed a work of science into a work of art, the vindication of his faith that the wonder of nature was sufficiently evident to warrant our finding in it proof of the wisdom and goodness of its Creator.

Appendices

I

The Shark;
or Lang Mills Detected

"Yes, while I live, no rude or sordid knave
Shall walk the world in credit to his grave."
—Pope.

Ye weaver blades! ye noble chiels!
  Wha fill our land wi' plenty,
And mak our vera barest fiels
  To wave with ilka dainty;
Defend yoursels, tak sicker heed,
  I warn you as a brither;
Or Shark's resolved, wi' hellish greed,
  To gorge us a'thegither,
      At ance this day.

In Gude's-name will we ne'er get free
  O' thieves and persecution!
Will Satan never let abee
  To plot our dissolution!
Ae scoun'rel sinks us to the pit,
  Wi' his eternal curses,
Anither granes,—and prays,—and yet
  Contrives to toom our purses,
      Maist every day.

A higher aim gars Willie think,
  And deeper schemes he's brewin';
Ten thousan' fouk at ance to sink
  To poverty and ruin!
Hail mighty patriot! Noble soul!
  Sae generous, and sae civil,
Sic vast designs deserve the whole
  Applauses of the devil
      On ony day.

In vain we've toiled wi' head and heart,
  And constant deep inspection,
For years on years, to bring this art
  So nearly to perfection;
The mair that art and skill deserve,
  The greedier Will advances;

And saws and barrels only serve
  To heighten our expenses
      And wrath this day.

But know, to thy immortal shame,
  While stands a paper-spot,
So long, great Squeeze-the-poor! thy fame,
  Thy blasted fame shall rot;
And as a brick or limestone kiln
  Wi' sooty reek advances;
So grateful shall thy mem'ry still
  Be to our bitter senses,
      By night or day.

Lang Willy Shark wi' greedy snout
  Had sneaked about the C-n-l,
To eat his beef and booze about,
  Nor proved at drinking punch ill;
Till, Judas-like, he got the bag,
  And squeezed it to a jelly;
Thae war the days for Will to brag,
  And blest times for the belly
      Ilk ither day.

The mair we get by heuk and cruk
  We aften grow the greedier;
Shark raiket now through every neuk
  To harl till his speedier;
His ghastly conscience, pale and spent,
  Was summoned up, right clever;
Syne, wi' an execration sent
  Aff, henceforth and for ever,
      Frae him that day.

This done, trade snoovt awa wi' skill
  And wonderfu' extention;

[265]

And widen't soon was every mill,
  (A dexterous invention!)
Groat after groat was clippet aff
  Frae ae thing and anither;
Till fouk began to think on draff,
  To help to haud thegither
      Their banes that day.

Now round from cork to cork he trots
  Wi' eagerness and rigour,
And "Rump the petticoats and spots!"
  His Sharkship roared wi' vigour;
But, whan his harnishes cam in
  In dizens in a morning;
Ans a' grew desolate and grim,
  His rapture changed to mourning,
      And rage that day.

Thus Haman, in the days of yore,
  Pufft up wi' spitefu' evil,
Amang his blackguard, wicked core,
  Contrived to play the devil;
High stood the gibbet's dismal cape,
  But little thought the sinner
That he had caft the vera rape
  Wad rax his neck, e'er dinner
      Was owre that day.

Wha cou'd believe a chiel sae trig
  Wad cheat us o' a bodle?
Or that saw fair a gowden wig
  Contained saw black a noddle?
But Shark beneath a sleekit smile
  Conceals his fiercest girning;
And, like his neighbors of the Nile,
  Devours wi' little warning
      By night or day.

O happy is that man and blest
  Wha in the C-n-l gets him!
Soon may he cram his greedy kist
  And dare a soul to touch him.
But should some poor auld wife, by force
  O' poortith scrimp her measure,

Her cursed reels at P——y Corse,
  Wad bleeze wi' meikle pleasure
      To them that day.

Whiles, in my sleep, methinks I see
  The marching through the city,
And Hangman Jock, wi' girnan glee,
  Proceeding to his duty.
I see thy dismal phiz and back,
  While Jock, his stroke to strengthen,
Brings down his brows at every swack,
  "I'll learn your frien' to lengthen,
      Your mills the day."

Poor wretch! in sic a dreadfu' hour
  O' blude and dirt and hurry,
What wad thy saftest luke or sour
  Avail to stap their fury?
Lang Mills, wad rise around thy lugs
  In mony a horrid volley;
And thou be kicket to the dugs,
  To think upo' thy folly
      Ilk after day.

Ye Senators! whase wisdom deep
  Keeps a' our matters even,
If sic a wretch ye dare to keep,
  How can ye hope for heaven?
Kick out the scoun'rel to his shift,
  We'll pay him for his sporting,
And sen' his mills and him adrift
  At ance to try their fortune
      Down Cart this day.

Think, thou unconscionable Shark!
  For heaven's sake bethink thee!
To what a depth of horrors dark
  Sic wark will surely sink thee—
Repent of sic enormous sins,
  And drap thy curst intention;
Or faith I fear, wi' brislt shins,
  Thou'lt mind this reprehension
      Some future day.

The following list of Scottish terms used in "The Shark" is taken from the glossary appended by Reverend Grosart to *The Poems and Literary Prose of Alexander Wilson.*

a'—all
abee—let alone
ae—one
aff—off

ance—once
auld—old
banes—bones
blades—fellows

bleeze—blaze
blude—blood
bodle—small coin
brislt—bruised
caft—bought
chiel—a young fellow
clippet—clipped
core—company
cork—a small manufacturer
cram—fill
cruk—crook, in *heuk and cruk*
dizens—dozens
draff—chaff
drap—drop
dugs—dogs
fiel—field
frae—from
gars—compels
girning—grinning
gowden—golden
granes—groans
groat—four-pence
harl—drag
harnishes—shawls of a particular pattern
haud—hold
heuk—as in *heuk and creuk*
ilka—every
ither—other
kicket—kicked
kist—chest
lugs—ears

luke—look
maist—most
mair—more
meikle—much
mony—many
neuk—corner
noddle—head
ony—any
owre—over
paper-spot—a kind of gauze of a spotted pattern
poortith—poverty
raiket—raked
rape—rope
rax—reach
reels—bobbins, or the quantity of work done
sae—so
saftest—softest
shift—adventure
sic—such
sicher—sure
stap—stop
swack—whack
syne—then, soon, immediately
toom—empty
trig—neat
vera—very
wad—would
wark—work
wha—who
whase—whose

Court Records of Wilson's Arrest

ANONYMOUS LETTER TO SHARP

Sir,

The enclosed poem, by particular circumstances, has fallen into my hands. The author, I can certainly assure you, is on the eve of concluding a bargain for the MMS. The offered price is five pounds.

If you know of any person who will advance *five guineas,* the manuscript from which I copied the enclosed, shall, with the most solemn regard to justice and secrecy, be immediately destroyed and buried in perpetual oblivion. If not, three days shall publish it to the world.

I give you *three hours* to deliberate on the offer, by which time I expect a final and determined answer, addressed to A. B., to lie in J. Nelson's, bookseller, Paisley, till called for. If the *price* or *copy* is not received by four o'clock this present afternoon, I can no longer prevent the author from proceeding with his production as he may think proper.——
I am, Sir, your wellwisher,

A. B.

Tuesday
Half-past 11 o'clock, A.M.

(Addressed to Mr. William Sharp, manufacturer, Paisley)

Paisley, 24 May, 1792

This is the letter referred to in my declaration of this date, emitted before the Sheriff Substitute of Renfrewshire.

ALEX. WILSON.

James Orr.

Unto his Majesty's Sheriff Depute of the County of Renfrew, or his Substitute

The petition of William Sharp, manufacturer in Paisley,

Humbly Sheweth,

That yesterday, the twenty-second current, the petitioner received an anonymous letter, signed A. B., inclosing verses entitled, "The Shark, or Lang Mills Detected," which, from their general strain, innuendos and circumstantial allusions, and likewise from the letter accompanying them—all which will hereafter be submitted to your lordship's consideration—are highly incendiary, tending in the grossest manner to traduce the petitioner's respectability; and, as the letter mentioned will obviously demonstrate, are composed with the view of extracting money from the petitioner, the letter declaring "that if five guineas are advanced, the manuscript from which the poem is copied, shall, with the most solemn regard to justice and secrecy, be immediately destroyed and buried in perpetual oblivion. If not, three days shall publish it to the world."

If publications of this nature shall be allowed to pass unregarded, and the conduct and character of people of business lampooned and satirised in the manner here attempted, it is difficult to discover to what degree of licentiousness such a spirit may proceed, or what characters, however respectable, may be held out and exposed to the ridicule and derision of the public. Impressed most seriously with such thoughts, both from considerations of personal and public safety, the petitioner does now most humbly request your lordship's assistance in the discovery and punishment of these highly libelous, incendiary, and dangerous publications.

That your petitioner, from various circumstances, has the best grounds to believe that these verses were penned and transmitted by Alexander Wilson, weaver in Paisley, a person well known for his productions in this way, some of which are at this moment the subject of enquiry, and prosecuted before your lordship.

May it therefore please your lordship to grant warrant for apprehending and bringing before you, the said Alexander Wilson, and any others whom the petitioner suspects may be useful in leading to a discovery of the author of the aforesaid poem; and in case the petitioner shall be able to convict the said Alexander Wilson thereof, or that he was aiding or assisting in framing the same, to grant warrant for imprisoning him within the tolbooth of Paisley, for such time as your lop. may seem proper, and to require him to produce and deliver up the manuscript, and prohibit him from ever publishing, printing, or in any way using the same,

and to fine and amerciate him in a proper sum in name of damages and expenses, and give the petitioner such remead in the premises as your lordship may seem proper.

According to Justice.

WILLIAM SHARP
Paisley, 23d May, 1792

Having considered the foregoing petition, grants warrants to   officers of the court, jointly and severally, to pass and apprehend the person of the before designed Alexander Wilson, and bring him before me for examination.

JAMES ORR

By Mr. James Orr, Sheriff Substitute of the shire of Renfrew, &c.

WHEREAS, information has been given me this day, that Alexander Wilson of Paisley, has written a poem, or been accessory, or art and part therein, entitled *"The Shark, or Lang Mills Detected,"*—tending to calumniate and traduce the character of William Sharp, silk manufacturer in Paisley, in the most unjustifiable manner, and apparently with a view of extracting money from Mr. Sharp, as appears from a letter under the signature of A. B., produced and shown to me alongst with the complaint exhibited against the said Alexander Wilson. That in consequence of the said application, I granted a warrant for apprehending the said Alexander Wilson, and bringing him before me in order to be examined thereanent, and the officers who went in quest of Wilson reported to me, that they had gone in search of him but could not find him at home, and that they had been informed he had gone off to Glasgow early this morning. That considering the poem to be a scandalous, false and injurious attack upon a person of established character, I consider it my duty in this stage of the business to prevent the publication of such an infamous production. And therefore I hereby prohibit and discharge the said Alexr. Wilson, and all printers and others, from writing, printing and publishing the said poem, entitled, "The Shark, or Lang Mills Detected," or under whatever title or denomination the said poem, entitled, "The Shark, or Lang Mills of Renfrew; certifying those who act in the contrary, that they will be deemed guilty, or art and part in writing and publishing an infamous libel against a man who has always held a fair reputation in the world. And in case the said Alexr. Wilson, or any other person, from a consciousness of the offence thereby committed, shall go to any other county in order to get the said poem printed and published, I do humbly recommend it to all sheriffs, magistrates, and justices of the peace, to use their endeavours in order to prevent the printing and publishing such a poem or libel, under the foregoing certification as to them shall seem proper; and that they will also grant warrant for apprehending the said Alexander Wilson, if found within their bounds, and bringing him before them, in order to be examined relative to the said poem, so as the malicious author and publisher may be detected and brought to condign punishment. Given at Paisley, the twenty-third day of May, one thousand seven hundred and ninety-two years.

JAMES ORR

ON THE COMPLAINT, WILLIAM SHARP agt. WILSON

Paisley, 24th May, 1792

Mr. James Orr, Sh. Sub.

Compeared the defender, Alexander Wilson, who being examined and interrogated, declares that the letter now exhibited to him, bearing date, Tuesday, half past eleven o'clock, under the signature of A. B. and addressed on the back thus, "Mr. William Sharp, manufacturer, Paisley," is of the declarant's hand-writing, and was written by him at the desire of the author of the poem, which was therewith sent to Mr. Sharp; and said poem now being shown to the declarant, declares and acknowledges that it is the same which he enclosed in the said letter, and both the said letter and poem are now docqueted and signed by the declarant and sheriff-substitute as relative thereto; and being interrogated, and desired to condescend upon the name of the author of the said poem, declares that the letter before alluded to contains his sentiments, or expresses his sentiments, upon the subject matter of the poem, and he declines giving any answer to the question. Being interrogated, if he is possessed of any other copies of the said poem? declares that he is not possessed of any other copy, nor does he know of any person possessed of any such copy, but acknowledges that he was possessed of the original manuscript from which he copied the poem sent to Mr. Sharp; and being interrogated, if he knows at whose instigation, or by whose desire, the said poem was written? he declines answering the interrogatory; and being interrogated, if he ever offered the original manuscript, or a copy of the said poem, to any printer in order to be printed? he declines giving any answer to the question; declares that he did not call at the shop of John Neilson, printer and stationer in Paisley, and enquire if there was any letter addressed to A. B., since he sent the said letter to Mr. Sharp, though he has had occasion to call daily at Mr. Neilson's shop about other matters; and being interro-

gated, if the five guineas, mentioned in the said letter, had been obtained from Mr. Sharp, whether the whole, or any part thereof, was intended to have been given to the author of the poem, or applied to the use and purposes of the letter writer? he declines giving any answer to the question. And this he declares to be truth.

ALEX. WILSON
JAMES ORR

Allan Maconochie, Esquire, his Majesty's Sheriff of the County of Renfrew.

To officers, executors hereof, jointly and severally, specially constituted; forasmuch as it is humbly meant and shown to me by William Sharp, manufacturer in Paisley, with the concurrence of Edward Jamieson, writer in Paisley, procurator of the Sheriff Court of Renfrew, and he, for himself and for the public interest, against Alexander Wilson, weaver in Seedhills of Paisley,

that where, by the laws of this and every well-governed realm, the writing, or causing to be wrote, scandalous and libellous papers in the stile of poems, or otherwise falsely attacking, traducing and scandalizing, and defaming the character of any person whatever, and throwing out reflections and insinuations against such person's honesty and integrity;

or the writing and composing, or causing to be wrote and composed, papers or libels of an incendiary nature, tending to create discord betwixt a manufacturer and his workers, and to stir up combination, opposition, and violence, among servants or workers against their masters or employers, more especially in a manufacturing town or neighborhood;

and the writing anonymous letter or letters, under fictitious or unknown signatures, and enclosing such poems, containing threatenings, in order to extort money from the person or persons to whom they were sent; are crimes of a heinous nature, and severely punishable.

Nevertheless, true it is and of a verity, that the said defender has presumed to commit, and is guilty, actor, or art and part of the said crimes, in so far as the said defender, having taken up a groundless malice and ill will at the private complainer, did, in the month of May last, at least within these twelve months past, maliciously write, or cause to be written, a very scandalous, ill-natured, and scurrilous paper, or libel, in the stile of a poem, intitled, "The Shark, or Lang Mills Detected," a poem containing this introduction or motto, *"Yes, while I live, no rich or sordid knave, shall walk in peace and credit to his grave";*

[269]

the whole of which paper or poem tends to hold out the person meant as the object thereof, in a detestable point of view, and a most injurious attack is wantonly made upon the private complainer's character, and reflections and insinuations are therein thrown out against his integrity, honesty and fair dealing, for the complainer's name is not there fully mentioned, yet such innuendos, allusions, and descriptions are therein thrown out, that the private complainer is the person against whom such insinuations are meant and intended to apply;

and the said paper or libel is of an incendiary nature, and has a tendency to create discord between the complainer and his workers, and to stir up combinations and excite violence and opposition among the complainer's servants against him in carrying on his business in the manufacturing town of Paisley and neighbourhood thereof, to his great hurt and prejudice;

and the defender, not satisfied with composing and writing, or causing to be composed and wrote, the above scandalous paper, entitled a poem, he sent a copy thereof, enclosed in a letter, both of his handwriting, to the private complainer, under the signature of A. B., threatening to publish the same to the world in three days, unless the private complainer sent him five guineas for the manuscript, in which he gives the complainer only three hours to deliberate whether to send the money or not; a copy of which poem, with the letter abovementioned, is herewith produced and referred to.

That the private complainer having preferred a complaint to my substitute against the said Alexander Wilson for his above conduct, he, in virtue of a warrant granted thereupon, was carried before Mr. James Orr, my substitute, and upon the twenty-fourth day of May last, did emit and sign a declaration, by which his guilt in the premises appears in the clearest manner, which complaint and declaration will be lodged in the hands of the sheriff-clerk of Renfrewshire in due time, that the defender and his doers may see the same, at least within the time aforesaid, such paper and libel has been maliciously composed and written;

and although the complainer's name is not therein fully published, yet it is only apparent, from the stile or strain in which it is wrote, and by its being enclosed in the foresaid letter addressed to the private complainer, is the person pointed out as the object of the satire; and the said defender, Alexander Wilson, ought and should be discerned and ordained to make a payment to the private complainer to the sum of fifty pounds sterling, in name of damages and assythment;

and he also ought and should be discerned and ordained to appear in open court, and beg pardon

of God and the complainer, and confess, acknowledge and declare, that the said insinuations thrown out against the complainer's character, in the foresaid libel, are scandalous and injurious; and the said defender ought to be fined and amerciated in the sum of ten pounds sterling, to the procurator-fiscal of court, to deter others from the commission of such crimes in times coming; and he ought to be imprisoned until payment of these sums;

and lastly, the said defender ought and should be discerned and ordained to make payment to the pursuers of the expenses of this process and extract decreet to follow hereupon.

Herefore it is my will &c.

Principal Lybell, dated 27th June, 1792

Paisley 10th July, 1792

In causa William Sharp and Fiscal against Alex Wilson

Mr. James Orr, Sh. Subt.

Act, N. Gibson instructs execution of citation of writs libelled on. Alt. absent. Craves that the Sheriff will hold the defender as confessed, and makes avizandum with the cause.

In respect to the defender's absence, holds him as confessed, and makes avizandum with the cause.

Paisley, 26th July, 1792

Mr. James Orr, Sh. Subt.

In respect to the defender's failure to appear, holds him contumacious—fines and amerciates him in the sum of Ten Pounds Scots to the Procurator-fiscal of Court for his contumacy; grants warrant for imprisonment till payment of that sum, and thereafter until he shall find sufficient caution acted in the books of this court, to attend the whole diets of probation, and for pronouncing sentence in this action, and authorizes the clerk of court immediately to issue precepts to that effect.

Paisley, 11th August, 1792

To the Honorable the Sheriff of Renfrewshire

The Petition of Alex Wilson weaver in Paisley and present prisoner in the Tolbooth of Paisley Humbly herewith

That I was this day imprisoned in the Tolbooth in virtue of a warrant of contumacy granted by your Lordship in an action brought against me at the instance of William Sharp manufacturer in Paisley with the concourse of the Procurator Fiscal of the Court, for having failed to appear and answer said Action.

That I having now satisfied the Procurator Fiscal for a Fine awarded against me by said Warrant and being unable to find Caution to the satisfaction of your Clerk I humbly hope your Lordship will allow me to be liberated upon [indecipherable: Iuratory?] Caution.

ALEX WILSON

BOND FOR ALEX WILSON
11 August 1792

I William Duncan weaver at Williamsburgh do hereby Bind and Oblige myself my heirs executors and successors as cautioner and surety acted in the Sheriff Court Books of Renfrewshire for Alexander Wilson weaver in Seedhills of Paisley

That he shall answer an action raised at the instance of William Sharp manufacturer of Paisley with concourse of Edward Jamieson writer in Paisley Procurator fiscal of said sheriff of Court and he for himself and the public interest before the sheriff depute of Renfrewshire and his substitute against him the said Alexander Wilson for the alleged crime of having in the month of May last or at least within twelve months preceding the seventh day of June last, maliciously written or caused to be written a very scandalous, ill-natured or scurrilous paper or libel in the stile of a poem, entitled "The Shark, or Lang Mills detected, a Poem," contains the introduction or motto, "Yes, while I live, no rich or sordid knave, shall walk in peace [sic] or credit to his grave." All the more particularly set forth in said action.

And that he the said Alexander Wilson shall attend the whole diets and Court of Probation and for pronouncing sentence in such action under the penalty of one hundred merks Scots to be paid by me and my foresaids in case of his failure and I consent to the registration hereof in the Books of Council and Session and Sheriff Court Books, and any others competent that letters of Horning on a charge of six days and all other necessary execution may pass here in common form and thereto constitute pross. for witness whereof I subscribe these present (written on this and the preceding page by James Craig apprentice to Robert Walkinshaw, Sheriff clerk of said shire) at Paisley the eleventh day of August one thousand seven hundred and ninety-two years before these witnesses James Mitchell weaver in Williams burgh and the said James Craig.

JA. MITCHELL WITNESS   WILLIAM DUNCAN
JAMES CRAIG WITNESS

Paisley, August 30, 1792
To the Honorable the Sheriff-Substitute of Renfrewshire,

The Petition of Alexander Wilson, Weaver in Paisley
Humbly Sheweth
That an action having been commenced at the instance of Mr. William Sharp, silk manufacturer in Paisley, against your petitioner, as the supposed author of a certain poem, enclosed and directed to the said William Sharp, your petitioner, in consequence of which, received a summons to compear before your Lordship in Court, upon an affixed day, in the hour of cause; but having failed to make his appearance at the time appointed, he was fined the sum of ten pounds Scots for contumacy.

That your petitioner having no design whatever of contemning the laws of his country, but by an unfortunate inadvertancy, in depending on a person of the law who had promised to speak for him, but who neglected, the above fine was exacted.

Your petitioner, therefore, humbly requests that your Lordship would see meet to remit part of the said fine of ten pounds Scots; and as the persons to whom he has applied have, for reasons best known to themselves, declined to appear for him, he solicits that your Lordship would think proper to nominate persons qualified for that purpose to answer for him in Court.

And your petitioner shall ever pray,

ALEX WILSON

Paisley, 30th August, 1792
Mr. James Orr, Sh. Subt.
The pursuer's pror. present. The defender gives in an incidental petition. Having considered the petition for the defender, nominates and appoints Messrs James Walkinshaw and John Snodgrass, procurators of court, to conduct the prisoner's defence, and allows them to see and answer the libel, to the 13th day of September next.

Paisley, 13th Sept. 1792
Answers by the defender, personally present. The pursuer's pror. to reply to 27th curt.
ANSWERS FOR ALEXANDER WILSON to the Libel brought against him by William Sharp, Silk Manufacturer in Paisley, with concourse of the Procurator-Fiscal.

The defender is, by the two most material points of the libel, accused of having made an attack upon the complainer's character, by writing a poem, entitled, "The Shark, or Lang Mills Detected," in which the complainer affirms that his character is there drawn and represented in a most detestable point of view; and that the defender did transmit the said poem to the complainer accompanied by a letter demanding money, and threatening to publish the said poem in case of a refusal. To the first of these accusations, the defender replies, that the aforesaid poem, which he acknowledges to have written, never in his eyes bore the least resemblance or contained one single feature expressive of the complainer's character. That he has known the complainer these many years, and has always, in conjunction with the world, esteemed and respected him as a very honest man, and the support of many industrious families. The gross acts of injustice, avarice and oppression, imputed to the hero of that poem, are so opposite to the known character of the complainer—so contradictory to the defender's own opinion of that gentleman, and so remote in every particular from his reputation with the public, that he is astonished that the complainer should for a moment have entertained the least idea of being the person meant in the above poem—an idea which the world would never have conceived, and which the complainer would not have had the most distant apprehension of, except from the single circumstance of receiving a copy from the writer.

This circumstance, innocent and undesigning as it was (from what motive the defender acknowledges himself unable to comprehend) is interpreted to the basest and most villainous of purposes. The letter is said to have demanded money, and to contain threatening in case of a refusal. It is a well known fact that the defender, for a considerable time before, had been employed in publishing and exposing his own composition to sale.

In these cases, it was his particular study to make application to persons most esteemed for their taste in literary matters—their liberality, and the encouragement they gave to works of genius. In this light stood the complainer, Mr. Sharp, and in this light the defender had ever viewed him. The defender, therefore, on completing the poem in question, transmitted it to the gentleman for inspection, intimating the value he set upon it, and expressing a wish to have it disposed of; and inquiring of the complainer, as of a friend, if he knew of any person to whom it might be disposed, and earnestly requesting that if he knew of none, to return it within three hours, as the author was on the eve of concluding a bargain with a bookseller for the MS.

But not one threatening expression, or one demand whatever, was made for money, but the price signified, and the author's property desired to be returned, which the complainer was polite enough to refuse. The same offers, at the same time, for any thing the complainer knows, were submitted to many others besides him, none of whom have thought proper to conclude themselves lampooned by the simple circumstance of a writer soliciting their advice and assistance in his pieces.

If it be asked why the defender, if these were his intentions, did not freely subscribe his name instead of the initials A. B., he replies: That he considers an author at free liberty to acknowledge, or not acknowledge, all or any of the productions on their first appearance to the public; and considers it prudent in some cases, as he did in the present, for an author to conceal his name until the world shall have decided on the merits of his piece.

The last resource of an author, when he cannot dispose of his copyright to advantage, is to become publisher, and that was what the defender, in the present case, declined, as a less safe and more troublesome method—a method where expense is certain and the gain uncertain. Can any man, therefore, be blamed for endeavouring to dispose of his property? And if I apply to the more intelligent and liberal for their assistance and advice, shall I, without the least shadow of reason or probability, be prosecuted as a libeler and incendiary. I say, without the least shadow of probability; for had the defender's intentions been such as he is accused of— had his design been, as the libel expresses it, to extort money from the complainer—had the complainer (as is affirmed) been the person meant as the subject of that poem, after thus exposing his character, demanding money, and threatening him by letter, what refuge could he have had, but in denying and refusing to know either poem or letter.

But the defender had no occasion for any such refuge. The complainer would have been the last person on earth he would ever have attributed such vicious conduct to. All he had, at heart, was a wish to dispose of his production; and the poem and letter being produced to him before your Lordship, he at once acknowledged to be the writer of both.

The defender, therefore, again declares his innocence of any such malicious intentions as he is accused of. He challenges the prosecutors to produce one single person who ever heard him mention the complainer as being the subject of that or any poem whatever, or ever witnessed him let fall one single expression derogatory of his probity or honour; so far were the defender's intentions from that, and so undeserving the treatment he has since received, that he no sooner was informed that the complainer imagined himself the subject of that poem, than he, the defender, from the sincerest motives of pity and humanity, refused the most liberal offers made to him for the MS. Kept the whole concealed from even his most intimate acquaintances, nor would ever have been prevailed upon to consent to its publication, had he not been driven to it by the foolish and determined severity of a rigorous prosecution, founded merely upon the complainer's chimerical suppositions. From the whole of what has been stated, the defender hopes that your Lordship will have no hesitation to assoilzie him from the charge, and allow him expense of process.

ALEX WILSON

Paisley, 11th October, 1792

Replies for the pursuer, with poem therein mentioned.

Avizandum, to the Sh. Sub.

Had the defender's intentions and friendship been as pure when he composed the poem produced and libelled as he affects in his defences, the Court would not have been troubled with this action, and the complainer would have saved a great deal of expense that he has incurred. The pretended friendship in these answers, however, is mere affectation, without any reality at bottom, and by no means will atone for the scurrility and abuse thrown out in the poem against the pursuer, and now published to the world.

That the poem produced is leveled at the complainer and no other, will appear at first sight. The very affinity between the title thereof and the defender's surname almost establishes the fact. But when your Lordship examines the third verse thereof, his name is expressly mentioned, and in the fourth verse the same is repeated; and as if that was not sufficient, the pursuer is figured out as one of the town-council, and treasurer thereof, all which applies to him and none else; and to all this, his sending the poem to the complainer, with the sole view to extort money from him, and not in the way of friendship, as he now says, or to take advice on its merits. The words are, "If you know any person who will advance five guineas, the manuscript from which I copied the inclosed shall, with the most solemn regard to justice and secrecy, be immediately destroyed and buried in perpetual oblivion. If not, three days will publish it to the world. I give you three hours to deliberate on this offer."

Can words be stronger, or the meaning more plain, to show the defender's design and intention to extort five guineas from the pursuer; and the threatening to publish it to the world, with a view to destroy his character, is held out as the motive to induce the pursuer to comply with his extraordinary demand. His threatening to publish it to the world shows that he considered the poem to be hurtful to the pursuer's character; and the same idea is conveyed in his offer to conceal the same for five guineas. Such conduct ought not to pass unpunished.

Was the defender allowed to go on in this manner, no character, however fair or respectable, would be safe at his hands. In the declaration libelled on, he tells your Lordship that he is not possessed of any such copy; yet it is now plain, that in this he was committing a gross falsehood, for since that period he has caused print and publish the same, a copy of which publication is herewith produced. It is submitted, then, how far such piece of conduct is not contempt of the authority of Court. For the pursuer maintains, that when the poem was the subject of legal discussion for the scurrility it contains, the defender was not at liberty, but at his peril, to print and publish it; and as he has done so, it is not doubted, first, that your Lordship will inflict such punishment on him as the fault deserves.

The defender has now fairly, in his defences, acknowledged his being the author of the poem, as well as the person who wrote and sent the same to the pursuer. The printed copy produced proves, and indeed in his defences he acknowledges, that he has printed and published the same; and his design, in so doing, was evidently to destroy the pursuer's character and reputation, and to raise division and discord betwixt him and his workers, as well as in an incendiary way to extort five guineas from the pursuer.

It is therefore not doubted, that your Lordship will immediately decern against the defender as libelled, with full expenses.

In respect whereof,

NATH. GIBSON

Paisley, 22nd January, 1792

Mr. James Orr, Sh. Sub.

Parties prors. present

Having advised the process, and received the opinion of the Sh-depute, finds that, upon a summary application from William Sharp against the defender, upon the twenty-fourth day of May last, he came before me for examination, when he acknowledged a letter, under the signature of A. B. and then authenticated by him, was of his handwriting, by which a poem was transmitted to complainer, which poem was also then authenticated by him:

Finds that, upon advising the said application, together with the said poem and letter produced, I, upon the twenty-third day of May last, prohibited and discharged the defender from writing, printing and publishing the said poem, entitled "The Shark, or Lang Mills Detected," or under whatever title or denomination the said poem or libel might appear, certifying him, that if he acted in the contrary, he would be deemed guilty, or art and part of publishing an infamous libel against the character of a man who has always held a fair reputation in the world;

Finds that afterwards the said William Sharp raised the present action against the defender for having sent to him the said poem, with the said letter signed A. B., to which action the concourse of the Procurator-Fiscal was given, and wherein it was concluded for a solatium and a fine;

Finds that, in the answers for the defender to the libel at the instance of Mr. Sharp and Fiscal, he admits his having consented to the publication of the poem, in consequence of what he is pleased to call the foolish and determined severity of a rigorous prosecution;

And finds that a printed copy of said poem, thus acknowledged to have been published with the defender's consent after the commencement of the prosecution, has been produced in process, coincides with the manuscript copy authenticated by the defender's signature;

Finds that, in the publication in the face of my interdict, the defender has been guilty of a very aggravated contempt of this court: Therefore grants warrants to   officers of this court, jointly to search for and apprehend the person of Alexander Wilson, defender, wherever he may be found within this shire, and to incarcerate him within the Tolbooth of Paisley, therein to remain for the space of fourteen days, and ay, and until he finds good and sufficient caution, to the extent of three hundred merks Scots, for his good behavior for two years to come; requiring, hereby, the magistrates of Paisley, and keepers of their prison, to receive and detain him accordingly;

Further ordains the defender instantly to deliver up to the clerk of court, every copy of the said poem in his possession, or to which he has access; and further, to answer upon oath, against next court day, such questions as I shall cause to put to him, in order to discover where any copies of said poem, printed and published contrary to my interdict, may be found;

And I further ordain, that before the said defender shall be let at liberty, he shall be conducted to the market-place at Paisley, and shall there, with his own hands, commit to the flames the whole copies of the said publication that shall have been delivered up to him, or otherwise collected, excepting always the copy libelled upon. And declares, that when this interdict has been fulfilled, the sheriff will then resume consideration of this process.

JAMES ORR.

Tolbooth of Paisley
February 4, 1793
To the Honorable, the Sheriff Substitute of the County of Renfrew

The Petition of Alex Wilson, present prisoner in the Tolbooth of Paisley,
Humbly Sheweth,

That in consequence of an interlocutor passed by your Lordship in causa William Sharp and Fiscal against your petitioner, he was adjudged to be imprisoned for the space of 14 days, to be then liberated, upon giving sufficient security of his good behavior for two years to come.

That your petitioner, well aware that the weight and influence of those whom he has the misfortune to be accused by, may prevent many persons of respectability in this place from befriending him in the manner he well knows they would cheerfully have done, and fearing lest his pursuers, availing themselves of these circumstances, may extend his imprisonment by insisting on better bail than your petitioner has in his power to give, your petitioner hereby informs your Lordship that John Bell, boiler to John King of Greenlaw, and brother-in-law to your petitioner, is the person your petitioner wishes to be taken as surety, and he is willing to engage himself as such.

May it therefore please your Lordship to cause inquiry to be made if necessary into the character and responsibility of the said John Bell, that he may be accepted of as bail for your petitioner, and that your petitioner may be liberated at the expiration of the time specified, which is tomorrow, February 5.

And your petitioner, as in duty bound, shall ever pray.

ALEXR. WILSON

Paisley, 5th February, 1793
Mr. James Orr, Sh. Sub.
Parties prors. present.

Compeared, Alexander Wilson, defender, who being examined and interrogated by whose desire and employment the poem libelled was printed, and who printed the same? the declarant begged leave to decline answering the questions. Acknowledges that the poem was printed at his expense; declares that the poem was sold by James Sclater, stationer; declares that he cannot say how many copies of the poem were thrown off by the printer; and being interrogated, if he knows how many copies were sold and disposed of? declines to answer the question; and being interrogated, if he knows that secret means were industriously used to disperse the said poem by throwing the same privately into houses and weaving shops in Paisley, and by whom such means were used? declares that he thinks it improper to answer such questions, and therefore declines answering the same; declares that he has not got any of the copies of the said poem collected, nor is he possessed of any copy thereof, and this he declares to be truth.

ALEX. WILSON

The defender lodges a petition, with a letter mentioning that he has got two copies of the poem libelled:

Paisley, 5th February, 1793

To the Honorable the Sheriff Substitute of the County of Renfrew

The Petition of Alexr. Wilson, present Prisoner in the Tolbooth of Paisley

Humbly Sheweth,

That your petitioner, having by your Lordship's interlocutor of date Jany 22nd, in the causa of William Sharp and Fiscal against your petitioner, being adjudged to be imprisoned for the space of fourteen days; to be taken before your Lordship, and there to deliver up the whole copies of a poem entitled, "The Shark, or Lang Mills Detected," to which he might have access or have in his possession; also, during his fourteen days imprisonment to collect all the said poems that were in his power, to give sufficient security of his good behavior for two years, and before his liberation to be conducted in custody to the market place, and there commit to the flames the whole of the poems so delivered up and collected.

That your petitioner, having now fulfilled every part of the interlocutor, except that of delivering up the poems, here declares; that he has no copies of said poem in his possession; that he has access to none; that willing to fulfill the interlocutor in every particular, he has done everything in his power to procure a copy or copies of said poem, and finds it absolutely impossible.

May it therefore please your Lordship, from the consideration of the above facts, to accept of the bail which your petitioner has in readiness, and to grant liberation to your petitioner according to the interlocutor, and your petitioner shall ever pray.

ALEX. WILSON

BOND OF CAUTION

Alexander Wilson

5 February 1793

to Keep the Peace

Thomas Witherspoon
for
Alexander Wilson

I, Thomas Witherspoon, weaver in the Seedhills of Paisley, do hereby bind and Oblige myself my heirs executors and successors and cautioners and

surety acted in the Sheriff's Court Books of Renfrewshire for Alexander Wilson weaver in the Seedhills of Paisley

That he shall keep the public peace for the space of two years from and after this date, and during that period shall not trouble nor molest any of his Majesties lieges during the said space of two years, or their good name, character or reputation by words or by printing of any kind under whatever title such writing or Printing may be and that under the penalty of three hundred merks Scots to be paid by me and my foresaids in case of his failure. All in terms of an interim sentence pronounced by the Sheriff substitute of said shire on the 22nd day of January last in the criminal action raised by the instance of William Sharp manufacturer in Paisley . . . [the remainder is the same as the previous bond of caution signed by William Duncan].

THOMAS WITHERSPOON

JA. PEACOCK   witness
JAMES CRAIG   witness

Paisley, Febry. 5, 1793

Mr. James Orr, Sh. Sub.

Having considered the petition for the defender, and letter therewith sent, ordains him to lodge the two copies of the poem libelled, mentioned in the said letter, in the hands of the clerk of court; and farther, ordains the defender to be carried in custody, on the sixth day of February current, at eleven o'clock forenoon, to the head of the outer stair of the Tolbooth of Paisley, and then and there, with his own hands, to commit to the flames the said two copies of the poem libelled on, in terms of the interlocutor, of date the twenty-second day of January last.

Eodem die.

The clerk of the court certifies that the defender has lodged in his hands two printed copies of the poem entitled "The Shark, or Lang Mills Detected," and that he has also lodged a bond, with sufficient caution, in terms of the interlocutor, date the twenty-second day of January last.

JOHN PEERS, dept.

Paisley, 6 February, 1793

Mr. James Orr, Sh. Subt.

The pursrs. pror. present.

The clerk of court reports, that this forenoon at 11 o'clock, he delivered up the two copies of the poem in his hands to the defender, who, with his own hands, committed the same to the flames, as ordained by the interlocutor of yesterday's date.

JOHN PEERS, dept.

Paisley, 23 April, 1793
Mr. James Orr, Sh. Subt. p.p.p.

Assigns the fourteenth day of May next for pronouncing sentence, and ordains the defender then to attend with certification.

JAMES ORR

Paisley, 14 May, 1793
Mr. James Orr, Sh. Subt. p.p.p. and def.p.

Having resumed the consideration of this process, and advised with the Sheriff-Depute: Finds that the defender has committed the wrongs charged, and that his conduct during the proceedings has tended to aggravate and not to alleviate the charge: Therefore fines and amerciates him in the sum of five pounds five shillings stg. to the private complainer, and in the sum of two pounds twelve shillings and sixpence, to the procurator-fiscal:

Finds the defender liable in expenses, modifies the same to three pounds, ten shillings sterling, and decerns against him therefore, and for the extract conform to the clerk's certificate: Grants warrant for imprisoning him in the Tolbooth of Paisley until payment of these sums, and authorizes the clerk of the court to alleviate or remit the fine to the procurator-fiscal in case the defender shall, within eight days from this date, give in a letter to the private complainer containing suitable acknowledgments for the wrong done him of which he is hereby convicted.

JAMES ORR.

CRIMINAL WARRANTS

Paisley, 4 January, 1794
The Petition of Alexnd Wilson present Prisoner in the Tolbooth, Paisley

Humbly Herewith

Incarcerated by virtue of a Warrant raised against him at the instance of the Procurator Fiscal and Suspicion of having circulated (six months past) certain Hand Bills calling a meeting by the Friends of Liberty and Reform to be held that night in Falconers Land Stories Street at five o'clock; Refer that however innocent I am of the crime laid to my charge I would wish to be admitted to bail which I am ready to produce.

Now may it please your Lordship to allow your Petitioner to be admitted to Bail and give order to the clerk of the Court to grant liberations to that purpose.

According to Justice.

ALEXANDER WILSON

Criminal Warrant
4th January 1794

I, William Wilson, weaver of Williamsburgh near Paisley, do hereby bind and Oblige myself my heirs executors and successors acted in the Sheriff's Court Books of Renfrewshire for Alexander Wilson, weaver in Williamsburgh

That he shall answer any criminal action before high and circuit courts of Justiciary or any other court Competent in the Instance of His Majesties Advocate Procurator for the alleged crime of being concerned in the framing and industriously circulating an advertisement addressed to "The Friends of Liberty and Reform" calling a general meeting of the Friends of Reform to be held that night in Falconer's Land Stories Street at five o'clock; and of having employed John Neilson, Printer in Paisley to print the said advertisement all in manner more particularly Presented to the Sheriff substitute of Renfrewshire in action of Edward Jamison, writer of Paisley, Procurator Fiscal for the said shire, on warrant of impressment was this day granted against the said Alexander Wilson. And that the said Alexander Wilson shall attend the whole diet of Probation and for Pronouncing Sentence and Action which may be raised against him for the foresaid crime and that under the Penalty of two hundred merks to be paid to the Procurator fiscal in case he fails. [The remainder is the same as the bond of caution by William Duncan and the peace bond signed by Thomas Witherspoon.]

WILLIAM WILSON

JOHN PEERS   witness
JA: PEACOCK   witness

Paisley 4 January, 1794

Having considered the foregoing petition, honors the offense bailable and admits the petitioner to bail; modifies the penalty to two hundred merks fine and upon caution being found sufficient authorizes the Clerk of Court to issue Letters of Liberation.

JAMES ORR.

II

Subscribers to the *American Ornithology*

In the last volume of the *American Ornithology,* published after Wilson's death, there was a list of 450 names, the original subscribers to the set of books. Wilson's letters and travel diaries show that he personally signed up the subscribers. He wrote to Bartram from Savannah (March 5, 1809) that he had gained 250 subscribers on his trip, and the list shows that number in the country he had covered. Wilson wrote to Alexander Lawson from Pittsburgh (February 22, 1810) that he had secured 19 subscribers there, and the list again shows that number from Pittsburgh. He wrote to William Dunbar from New Orleans (June 24, 1810), that he had signed up 63 subscribers in that city, the list showing 60 with addresses that can be found there.

Yet the list presented a number of problems. When George Ord published a supplement to the *Ornithology* in 1824 he ignored it altogether. It was never reprinted in the later editions of the work. In the expanded life of Wilson which he printed in the supplement, Ord wrote that Wilson's Southern trip to Savannah was a failure, few subscribers being secured. He also wrote that half the subscribers in the Philadelphia area were artisans and tradespeople, implying that collection of the $120 from each subscriber was consequently difficult, and commented bitterly that cultivated Americans had not supported Wilson's work, adding that it was the cost of securing subscribers which had absorbed the profits of the *Ornithology* and discouraged the publisher.

The list that follows is that which was originally printed, arranged in alphabetical order rather than by states, and with identification added. Standard reference works, including the *Dictionary of American Biography* and the *Biographical Directory of the American Congress,* have been used whenever possible. In the cases where no source is given, local directories have been used to provide as much identification as could be secured. In several cases—as that of George Armstrong of Pennsylvania—a number of individuals of the same name made a positive identification difficult; in such cases no data is given.

ALBANY LIBRARY. *New York.* Two of the original subscribers to the *Ornithology,* John Lansing and Stephen Van Rensselaer, were among the founders and trustees of the Albany Library, which was established in 1792.—Arthur James Weise, *History of the City of Albany,* Albany, N.Y., 1884, p. 409.

ALEXANDER, JAMES. *Louisiana.* He was one of the most prominent figures in the Burr conspiracy, an agent of Aaron Burr's in New Orleans, where he recruited men, and where he conferred with General Wilkinson on friendly terms. In December, 1806, he was arrested by Wilkinson, who wrote: "Oh God, would I hear from our Government! Alexander must be taken up—indeed he must—he said publicly at the Coffee House the other night that if Burr was a traitor I was one also." Alexander was sent to Washington to stand trial for treason, which precipitated the crisis. Released by the Circuit Court, he became an important witness against Wilkinson, returning to New Orleans to gather evidence against him.—*The Official Letter Books of W. C. C. Claiborne,* edited by Dunbar Rowland, Jackson, Mississippi, 1917, vol. I-VI. Thomas Perkins Abernathy, *The Burr Conspiracy,* New York: Oxford University Press, 1954.

ALEXANDER, ROBERT. *Louisiana.* A more shadowy figure in the Burr conspiracy, the brother of James Alexander, a resident of New Orleans.

ALSTON, JOHN ASHE. *South Carolina.* An obscure planter of great wealth, a brother-in-law of Aaron Burr's daughter Theodosia. William Alston built a great plantation called Afton near Georgetown in 1785. Joseph Alston, who married Theodosia Burr, was the older of his sons and John Ashe Alston the younger.—Alberta Morel Lochnicotte, *Georgetown Rice Plantations,* Charleston, S.C., 1955. *Rice Planter and Sportsman: the Recollections of J. Mott Alston,* edited by Avery R. Childs, Columbia, S.C., 1953.

AMERICAN PHILOSOPHICAL SOCIETY. *Pennsylvania.* "The Philosophical Society have done me the honor to elect me a member . . ." (Wilson to William Bartram, April 21, 1813). Founded in 1727 by Benjamin Franklin, the organization included the outstanding scientific figures in the United States. Thomas Jefferson was then serving as its president.

AMIES, THOMAS. *Pennsylvania.* Two copies. Amies was a celebrated paper maker, living at 185 Third Street in Philadelphia. He made the paper for the official copy of the Declaration of Independence authorized by Congress, the paper for the bank notes of the Bank of the United States, and prepared a special paper for the *Ornithology,* designed to preserve the color in the plates.—*Pennsylvania Magazine of History and Biography,* vol. L, pp. 10-11.

ARMSTEAD, THEODORICK (1777-1812). *Virginia.* Robert and Thomas Armstead, of the famous Virginia family, were born in Petersburg at about the same time and "one of the two was probably the father of Theodorick" (*William and Mary College Quarterly,* vol. VII, p. 183). At the time of Wilson's visit, Theodorick Armstead was newly married to Hannah Newton, also of an old and prominent family, and he had become one of the outstanding citizens of Norfolk. He subsequently became United States naval agent at Norfolk, and was renowned for "being foremost in every scheme of industry or charity."

ARMSTRONG, GEORGE. *Pennsylvania.*

ASTLEY, THOMAS. *Pennsylvania.* Two copies. Astley was prominent in civic affairs of all kinds, a philanthropist and a founder of the Horticultural Society.—Thomas Scharf and Thompson Westcott, *History of Philadelphia,* Philadelphia: Everts, 1884. *Pennsylvania Magazine of History and Biography,* vol. VIII, p. 313.

ATHENAEUM OF PHILADELPHIA. *Pennsylvania.* This famous private library, organized in 1813, apparently was one of the last institutions to subscribe to the *Ornithology* in Wilson's lifetime. It was founded by a group of young University of Pennsylvania graduates to be "a place of common resort, in which their leisure hours could be passed," but it was not until the next year, when 100 subscribers had been secured, that reading rooms were opened above Mathew Carey's book store on Fourth and Chestnut Streets.—*Encyclopedia of Philadelphia,* edited by Joseph Jackson, Harrisburg, Pa., 1931, vol. I, pp. 185-88.

BAILLIE, DAVID. *South Carolina.*

BAIRD, GENERAL THOMAS. *Pennsylvania.* A prominent lawyer in Pittsburgh, Baird was a leader in community enterprises, one of the original subscribers to the building of the first bridge over the Monongahela River in 1816.—*Pennsylvania Magazine of History and Biography,* vol. XXX, pp. 191-92.

BAKER, LOOE. *Mississippi.*

BALDWIN, HENRY (1780-1844). *Pennsylvania.* Associate Justice of the Supreme Court. Baldwin graduated from Yale in 1797, was admitted to the Pittsburgh bar in 1801, and in 1805 married Sally Ellicott, the daughter of Andrew Ellicott, the famous American intelligence officer. It was Ellicott who discovered proofs of the treasonable dealings of General Wilkinson with Spain. Baldwin was a pioneer in western Pennsylvania iron works, and an extremely successful lawyer, at the time of Wilson's visit in 1810.—Franklin Bowditch Dexter, *Biographical Studies of the Graduates of Yale College,* New York, 1911, vol. V, p. 243. *Dictionary of American Biography,* vol. I, pp. 533-34. Catherine van Cortlandt Mathews, *Andrew Ellicott, His Life and Letters,* New York, 1908.

BALTIMORE LIBRARY. *Maryland.*

BANARD, E. and R. *Virginia.*

BANCKER, CHARLES N. (1776-1869). *Pennsylvania.* He was a Philadelphia merchant, an agent for Stephen Girard, who gained immense profits from shipments and speculations in cargo during the Embargo. He later became president of the Franklin Insurance Company.—*Pennsylvania Magazine of History and Biography,* vol. LXVI, p. 31.

BARCLAY, WILLIAM S.B. *England.*

BARRON, ALEXANDER, M.D. *South Carolina.*

BARRY, WILLIAM TAYLOR (1758-1835). *Kentucky.* Born in Virginia, he grew up on the Kentucky frontier, graduated from Transylvania at Lexington, studied law at William and Mary, and was practicing law at Lexington at the time of Wilson's visit. Barry later became a member of Congress, governor of Kentucky, and Postmaster General, appointed by his close personal friend Andrew Jackson.—*Dictionary of American Biography,* vol. I, p. 657. *Biographical Directory of the American Congress, 1774-1949,* Washington: Government Printing Office, 1950, p. 820.

BARTLET, J. C. *Louisiana.* A Louisiana merchant, a partner in the firm of Bartlet and Cox.—*Official Letter Books of W. C. C. Claiborne,* vol. V, p. 186.

BARTO, J. J. *New York.*

BARTON, DR. BENJAMIN SMITH (1766-1815). *Pennsylvania.* He lived at 241 Chestnut Street in Philadelphia at the time he subscribed to the *Ornithology.* Dr. Barton was one of the foremost botanists of the nation, and the creator of the *materia medica* of the United States. Born in Lancaster, he was the son of an Episcopalian minister who remained a loyalist during the Revolution. Barton graduated from the University of Pennsylvania, studied at Edinburgh, and received his degree in medicine from the University of Göttingen.—William Allen, D.D., *An American Biographical and Historical Dictionary,* Boston, 1832. *Dictionary of American Biography,* vol. II, pp. 17-18. Howard A. Kelly, *A Cyclopedia of American Medical Biography,* Philadelphia, 1912, vol. I, pp. 54-55.

BARTRAM, WILLIAM (1739-1823). *Pennsylvania.* He was the son of John Bartram, the pioneer Quaker botanist and the founder of Bartram's Garden at Gray's Ferry near Philadelphia. In his youth William Bartram worked for a Philadelphia merchant, then as a merchant in Cape Fear, North Carolina. He explored the Catskills with his father in 1755, and later traveled through the Southern

wilderness with him. Some of his drawings of plants were shown by John Collinson (the Quaker merchant for whom his father was collector) to the Duchess of Portland, with the result that William Bartram was financed in explorations of the southeast portion of the United States (1773-1777) that gave him material for his *Travels.* He kept a diary in which he recorded the time of arrival of birds at Bartram's Garden, and his list of 219 American species was the most complete before Wilson's work. Both the *Ornithology* and Wilson's letters contain accounts of Bartram's contribution to the work.—William Darlington, *Memorial of John Bartram and Humphrey Marshall,* Philadelphia, 1849. *Dictionary of American Biography,* vol. II, pp. 28-29.

BEASLEY, REVEREND FREDERICK (1777-1845). *New York.* He was born in North Carolina, graduated with high honors from Princeton in 1797, and became rector of St. Peter's Episcopal Church in Albany, where he lived at the time of Wilson's visit. In 1809 he became provost of the University of Pennsylvania, and was later rector of a church in Trenton, New Jersey.—*Dictionary of American Biography,* vol. II, p. 98.

BEDFORD, DR. NATHANIEL. *Pennsylvania.* He was the first physician to practice in what became Allegheny county, where Pittsburgh was located. He was a vestryman in the Old Round Church (Episcopal) in Pittsburgh, where he settled in 1770.—*Pennsylvania Magazine of History and Biography,* vol. XIX, p. 351.

BEERS and HOWE. *Connecticut.*

BIDDLE, NICHOLAS (1786-1844). *Pennsylvania.* Biddle later became President of the Bank of the United States, involved in the historic feud with President Jackson. At the time of his association with Wilson, he was a young attorney and man of letters, living at 181 Chestnut Street in Philadelphia. His father was the vice-president of Pennsylvania, his mother the former Hannah Shepard of Beaufort, North Carolina. Biddle entered the University of Pennsylvania at ten, and was refused permission to graduate at thirteen because of his youth. At eighteen he was secretary to John Armstrong, the minister to France. Biddle was a close friend of Joseph Dennie, the editor of *The Port Folio,* and followed Dennie as editor in 1811. He published much of Wilson's work in the magazine, and was active in assisting him to secure United States citizenship.—*Pennsylvania Magazine of History and Biography,* vol. LXXV, pp. 36-46. Alexander Wilson papers, Pennsylvania Historical Society. *Dictionary of American Biography,* vol. II, pp. 243-45.

BIRCH, WILLIAM YOUNG (1760-1834). *Pennsylvania.* He arrived in Philadelphia from England in 1793, prospered as a publisher and bookseller, and left a fortune of $180,000 to the blind.—Henry Simpson, *The Lives of Eminent Philadelphians,* Philadelphia, 1859.

BIRCHETT, ROBERT. *Virginia.*

BLAKE, JOSEPH (1769-1865). *South Carolina.* He was born at Newington plantation near Charleston, the estate of his great-grandfather Governor Joseph Blake, where Mark Catesby lived and worked, 1722-1724 (Mark Catesby, *Natural History of Carolina, the Bahamas and Florida,* London, 1753). The Blake family lived in England and in South Carolina, and young Joseph Blake was educated at Eton and Cambridge, married the daughter of an English officer, and spent most of his time in London. Despite great losses in the Revolution, he nevertheless inherited large and valuable Carolina property. He sold Newington Plantation in 1830.—*South Carolina Historical and Genealogical Magazine,* vol. I, pp. 161-62.

BLANCHARD, THOMAS. *Virginia.* He lived in Norfolk, and was married to Amy Newton, the sister of Senator George Newton, who was also a subscriber to the *Ornithology.* Blanchard was a classical scholar and a poet, the author of a celebrated ode on the death of Washington.—Lyon Gardiner Tyler, *The Encyclopedia of Virginia Biography,* New York, 1915, vol. II, p. 356. *The Virginia Magazine of History and Biography,* vol. XXX, p. 87.

BLANQUES, JEAN. *Louisiana.* He was described by Governor Claiborne of Louisiana as a French agent. He lived at 24 rue St. Louis in New Orleans.—*Official Letter Books of W. C. C. Claiborne,* vol. II, p. 285. Charles L. Thompson, *New Orleans in 1805: A Directory and a Census,* Heartman's Historical Series, No. 48, New Orleans, 1936.

BLOCKLEY AND MERION SOCIETY FOR PROMOTING AGRICULTURE AND RURAL ECONOMY. *Pennsylvania.* Blockley was the district adjoining that of Kingsessing, where Wilson lived.

BLOOMFIELD, GENERAL JOSEPH (1753-1823). *Pennsylvania.* He was twice governor of New Jersey, and the town of Bloomfield, where Wilson lived at one time, was named for his family. A Revolutionary soldier of distinction, he married in 1778 Mary Mc-

Illvaine, the daughter of Dr. William McIllvaine, one of the most prominent of the emigrants from Scotland, whose home was in Burlington, near Wilson's school. Bloomfield took an active part in suppressing the Whisky Rebellion.—*Dictionary of American Biography,* vol. II, p. 385.

BLOUNT, JAMES GRAY. *North Carolina.* A descendant of the first settlers in North Carolina, he lived at New Bern, where his father established a plantation. The Blount family was an extensive one, including Senator Blount and Governor Blount of Tennessee.—Zella Armstrong, *Notable Southern Families,* Chattanooga, Tenn.: Lookout Publishing Co., 1918, pp. 32-34.

BLYTHE, JOSEPH. *South Carolina.*

BOAS, JOSEPH. *Pennsylvania.*

BOILEAU, NATHANIEL (1763-1850). *Pennsylvania.* He was a neighbor of Wilson's in his Milestown days, and the leading radical politician of Pennsylvania. Educated at Princeton, he acquired land in Bucks County after his marriage to Hester Leech in 1795. His first wife having died after bearing him a son, Boileau in 1804 married Ann Leech. His hold on the back-country radicals was almost absolute, and he was able to present Jefferson with the support of a state-wide Jeffersonian organization before Jefferson himself was sure of what his course was to be.—*Pennsylvania Magazine of History and Biography,* vol. LXII, pp. 213-24. Theodore Bean, *History of Montgomery County, Pennsylvania,* Philadelphia, 1884, pp. 508-9.

BOLLING, ROBERT. *Virginia.*

BOLTON, JOHN. *Georgia.* He was apparently connected with Bolton's Factory, the first textile mill in the South, built in 1811 near Mount Pleasant, Georgia.

BOSTON ATHENAEUM. *Massachusetts.* This celebrated private library was incorporated in 1807, growing out of the Anthology Club, publisher of New England's first literary magazine. It occupied the second floor of a building in Tremont Street, the third floor of which contained the private library of John Quincy Adams.—Samuel Adams Dale, *Old Landmarks and Historic Personages of Boston,* Boston, 1901, p. 37.

BOSWELL, WILLIAM. *Louisiana.*

BOURJEOY, M. *Louisiana.* No individual of this

name could be located; however, it may have been an Anglicized spelling of the name of Michael Bourgeois, who was a prominent Creole of New Orleans and one of the supporters of Governor Claiborne in upholding American rule of the city after the Louisiana Purchase.

BOWDOIN, JAMES. *Massachusetts*. Born in 1752, he was the son of the famous Revolutionary governor of Massachusetts. His sister married John Temple, who inherited a baronetcy, and James Bowdoin himself, after graduating from Harvard, studied at Oxford, toured Europe, and lived abroad. He served on the Governor's Council of Massachusetts during the Revolution. Jefferson appointed him minister to Spain, and he afterwards served in Paris, returning to the United States in 1808 after uncomfortable experiences with Napoleon. Married to his cousin, Sarah Bowdoin, he lived in retirement in his home on Beacon Street at the time of Wilson's visit. He was the last of his line, and left his fortune to found Bowdoin College.—*Dictionary of American Biography*, vol. II, p. 501.

BOYD, SAMUEL. *New York*. He was a counsellor, with his office at 21 Pine Street in New York, and his home adjoining.—*Longworth's New York Almanac*, 1808.

BRAND, WILLIAM. *Louisiana*. He lived on Gravier Street in New Orleans.—*New Orleans in 1805*.

BROKENBROUGH, GABRIEL. *Virginia*.

BRONSON, ENOS (1774-1823). *Pennsylvania*. Born in Connecticut, and a graduate of Yale in 1798, Bronson became the first principal of Deerfield Academy in Massachusetts. With Dr. Nathan Chapman, Horace Binney and others, he was trying to revive the Federalist Party in Pennsylvania at the time of his association with Wilson, editing the *Gazette of the United States*.—*Pennsylvania Magazine of History and Biography*, vol. LVII, pp. 355-58.

BROWN, BENJAMIN. *England*.

BROWN, JAMES. *Louisiana*. He was the brother of Senator John Brown of Kentucky, and brother-in-law of Henry Clay. Born in Virginia in 1766, he was an aide to General Isaac Selby in Kentucky, where he practiced law. Settling in New Orleans, he worked closely with Edward Livingston, was Secretary of State under Claiborne, and District Attorney, deeply involved in the events that led to the crisis of Burr's arrest. James Brown was Senator

from Louisiana in 1812, and later served as minister to France. After his retirement he made his home in Philadelphia.—Lewis Collins, *Historical Sketches of Kentucky*, Cincinnati, 1847. *Official Letter Books of W. C. C. Claiborne. Dictionary of American Biography*, vol. III, p. 122.

BROWN, JOSEPH. *Pennsylvania*.

BROWN, SAMUEL, M.D. *Mississippi*. A younger brother of James Brown, born in Virginia in 1769, the son of a Presbyterian minister, he was educated at Dickinson College, and studied medicine at Edinburgh. After following his brother James to Lexington, where he prospered, he moved to Mississippi, where he lived on a plantation at Fort Adams, not far from Natchez. He married Katherine Percy, the daughter of a plantation owner. He is credited with having improved methods of whisky distilling and with developing Kentucky caves as a source of niter for gunpowder, and with pioneering in inoculation against smallpox in Kentucky. After his wife's death he returned to the practice of medicine. —*Dictionary of American Biography*, vol. III, pp. 152-53. *Cyclopedia of American Medical Biography*, vol. I, pp. 118-19.

BRYANT, JOHN Y. *Pennsylvania*. He was a cabinetmaker, with a shop on the corner of Pine and Second Streets in Pennsylvania.—John A. Paxton, *Directory and Register*, Philadelphia, 1813.

BRYANT, MORDECAI Y. *Pennsylvania*. He owned a drug and paint store on North Second Street in Philadelphia.

BULLOCH, WILLIAM D. (1776-1852). *Georgia*. He was a wealthy Savannah attorney. United States Attorney for Georgia in 1807, a director of the Planters Bank, he became the mayor of the city in 1812. He bought the large estate outside Savannah formerly owned by General Anthony Wayne. Bulloch was later Senator from Georgia, and a founder and president of the Bank of Georgia.—*Savannah River Plantations*, Georgia Historical Society, 1943. *Biographical Directory of the American Congress*, p. 913.

BULLUS, JOHN. *New York*. He was United States naval agent for New York at the time of Wilson's visit, with offices on Pearl Street.—*Longworth's New York Almanac*, p. 92.

BURGWIN, G. H. B. *North Carolina*.

BURGWIN, JOHN F. *North Carolina*.

BURNSIDE, ROBERT. *Louisiana.*

BUTLER, PIERCE (1745-1822). *Pennsylvania.* Butler was born in Ireland, into the family of the Dukes of Ormond. He became a major in a British regiment stationed in Boston, and "attached himself to republican institutions." He married Mary Middleton, the daughter of a wealthy South Carolina family. A delegate to Congress in 1787, and to the Constitutional Convention in 1788, he signed the Constitution. He was a Senator from South Carolina until 1796, and again from 1802 until 1804. He made his home in Philadelphia.—*Dictionary of American Biography,* vol. III, pp. 364-65. *Biographical Directory of the American Congress,* p. 928. *Eminent Philadelphians,* p. 159.

BUTTLER, JAMES. *Kentucky.*

CALDWELL, CHARLES, M.D. (1772-1853). *Pennsylvania.* One of the leading physicians of Philadelphia, he was born in South Carolina, taught school, studied medicine at the University of Pennsylvania, and was a surgeon with the troops during the Whisky Rebellion. His reputation was established by his courage during the yellow fever plague of 1793. He was associated with Nicholas Biddle on *The Port Folio,* and became its editor in 1814. Tall and commanding, he was considered caustic and ill-natured as well. He was involved in a famous feud with Dr. Benjamin Rush, and his fierce attacks on the writings of Dr. Samuel Stanhope Smith (the son-in-law of Dr. Witherspoon, and the president of Princeton) were said to have caused Smith's death.—*Medical Journal of Dr. Charles Caldwell,* Pennsylvania Historical Society. *Autobiography,* edited by Harriet W. Warner, Philadelphia, 1855.

CALDWELL, JAMES. *Pennsylvania.*

CALVIT, MONFORT. *Mississippi.* He was a planter whose property was in the vicinity of Coles Creek. —*History of Natchez,* p. 134.

CAREY, MATHEW (1760-1839). *Pennsylvania.* Born in Dublin, Carey emigrated to Philadelphia in 1784. He was a newspaper editor before branching out to become a successful publisher of popular books, of which Parson Weems's life of Washington was the best known.—*Dictionary of American Biography,* vol. III, p. 489. *Eminent Philadelphians.*

CARR, THOMAS. *South Carolina.*

CARR, WILLIAM. *Pennsylvania.* Younger brother of Robert Carr, who printed the *American Orni-*

thology, he was a partner in the family printing firm.—*Pennsylvania Magazine of History and Biography,* vol. LIII, p. 382.

CARRIGAIN, PHILIP. *New Hampshire.* Son of a distinguished pioneer physician of Concord. A lawyer, and secretary of state for New Hampshire, he was also a celebrated mapmaker.—William Allen, D. D., *An American Biographical and Historical Dictionary,* p. 224.

CARRICK and DODGE. *New York.*

CARSTAIRS, THOMAS. *Pennsylvania.* At the time Wilson was securing subscriptions to the *Ornithology,* Carstairs was a carpenter and draftsman at 76 South Eighth Street in Philadelphia. Born in Largo, County Fife, Scotland, Carstairs subsequently became one of the leading builders of the city.—*The National Cyclopedia of Biography,* vol. XVI, p. 55. James Hardie, *The Philadelphia Directory and Register,* 1812.

CENAS, BLAZE. *Louisiana.* He was the postmaster of New Orleans, called "faithful and capable" by Governor Claiborne.—*Official Letter Books of W. C. C. Claiborne,* vol. III, pp. 83-84.

CHAUBAUDD, JOHN. *Louisiana.* He was the Recorder of Louisiana Territory, and Treasurer of Orleans County.—*Official Letter Books of W. C. C. Claiborne.*

CHAPMAN, DR. NATHANIEL (1780-1853). *Pennsylvania.* The acknowledged leader of Philadelphia medicine after Dr. Rush, he lived at 206 Chestnut Street at the time Wilson was securing subscriptions to the *Ornithology.* Born in Virginia, he was a private student with Dr. Rush, graduated with honors from the medical school of the University of Pennsylvania in 1801, and studied in London and in Edinburgh, where he became a social lion, the companion of Lord Buchan, Lord Dugald, Lord Stewart and others as fashionable. He was equally successful in social circles in Philadelphia when he began practicing there in 1804. His wife was Rebecca Biddle, a daughter of Colonel Clement Biddle. Dr. Chapman was the president of the American Philosophical Society for many years, and the first president of the American Medical Association. He was chosen by acclamation.—*Dictionary of American Biography,* vol. IV, p. 19. *Cyclopedia of American Medical Biography,* vol. I, pp. 171-72.

CHARLESTON LIBRARY. *South Carolina.* "At last I was obliged to walk the streets, and pick out those houses which, from their appearance, indicated wealth and taste of their occupants, and introduced myself. . . . I was going on in this way when the keeper of the library, a Scotsman, a good man, made me a list from the directory; and among these I spent ten days" (Wilson to Daniel Miller, March 9, 1809). The Charleston Library Society was established in 1743. Although the library was severely damaged by a fire in 1778, it had been rebuilt and was a notable collection, with several thousand volumes, and about 300 members.—Robert Mills, *Statistics of South Carolina,* Charleston, 1826, p. 437.

CHASE, THOMAS. *Maryland.* He was a licensed auctioneer, located at the corner of Federal and Second Streets in Baltimore.—James M'Henry, *Baltimore Directory and Citizens Register,* Baltimore, 1807.

CHATARD, DR. FERDINAND. *Maryland.* The son of a refugee planter from the revolution in Santo Domingo, Dr. Chatard studied medicine in Paris, London and Edinburgh. He married Eliza Moreau, the daughter of the U.S. consul at Martinique, from Brookline, Massachusetts. Dr. Chatard lived on Saratoga Street in Maryland at the time of Wilson's visit.—*Dictionary of American Biography,* vol. IV, p. 39. *Baltimore Directory and Citizens Register.*

CHEVES, LANGDON (1776-1857). *South Carolina.* He was born in Bull Town Fort, where his mother had taken refuge from the Indians during the Revolution. She was the daughter of an American officer with the Revolutionary forces; her husband was Alexander Chivas, born in Scotland, a trader to the Cherokees and a British officer. Cheves was raised by an aunt, worked in a Charleston supply house, studied law, and became a successful lawyer before entering Congress in 1810. He was considered one of the greatest orators of the time. Married to Mary Dulles, he fathered 14 children, and occupied his leisure with his hobby of building fine houses for them.—*Dictionary of American Biography,* vol. IV, p. 62. *Biographical Directory of the American Congress,* p. 917.

CHEW, BEVERLY. *Louisiana.* He was a justice of the court of common pleas in New Orleans at the time of Wilson's visit there. He lived in luxurious circumstances at 23 rue St. Louis in the French Quarter. He was later associated with Michael Fortier, one of the wealthiest of the French merchants, and Pierre Suave, a leading lawyer, in banking.—*Official Letter Books of W. C. C. Claiborne,* vol. I, p. 303. *New Orleans in 1805.*

CLAIBORNE, WILLIAM C. C. (1775-1817). *Louisiana.* Born in Virginia, William Claiborne attended Richmond Academy, and entered William and Mary, but left after a disagreement with one of the ushers. His father, a Revolutionary war veteran, failed, and at fifteen young Claiborne went to New York, where he worked in the office of John Beckley, the first Clerk of the House of Representatives and the first Librarian of Congress. When the Government moved to Philadelphia Claiborne moved also. He became known in literary societies as a debater, attracted the attention of Jefferson, and was asked by John Sevier to move to Tennessee. Sevier appointed him to the State Supreme Court of Tennessee, and Claiborne was in Congress as a supporter of Jefferson in 1797. Jefferson appointed him governor of Mississippi territory when he was only twenty-five, and then governor of Louisiana after the Louisiana Purchase. Claiborne refused to act at the time of Wilkinson's dictatorial conduct during the Burr crisis. He was wounded in a duel with Daniel Clark that grew out of his charges that Clark was a party to Burr's schemes. His first wife having died in 1804, he married the daughter of a French family of New Orleans, carefully nurtured good relations with the French citizens, and resisted Wilkinson's attempt to create panic, while inclining to view the Burr expedition with the utmost gravity. When Louisiana became a state he was elected governor, and had been elected Senator at the time of his death.—*Official Letter Books of W. C. C. Claiborne,* Introduction by Dunbar Rowland. *Dictionary of American Biography,* vol. IV, p. 115.

CLARK, DANIEL (1766-1810). *Louisiana.* He was born in Sligo, Ireland, studied at Eton, and worked in New Orleans for an uncle, with whom he purchased land near Baton Rouge. At one time a business and social associate of General Wilkinson, he was an intermediary between Wilkinson and Andrew Ellicott, and in 1801 carried to Jefferson reports of Wilkinson's dealings with Spain. A territorial representative to Congress, he provided material for an inquiry into Wilkinson's conduct, publishing his *Proofs of the Corruption of General Wilkinson* in 1809. At the time of Wilson's visit, Clark was living at 4 rue d'Chartres in the French Quarter. He had formed "an irregular union" with Zuline des Granges; he listed his household as consisting of one free female and two female slaves. After Clark's death one of the most famous lawsuits in American history developed over his large estate, the bequest to two girls who were said to be his daughters by Zuline des Granges being challenged, the case repeatedly reaching the Supreme Court before the Civil War.—*Dictionary of American Biography,* vol. IV, p. 125. *New Orleans in 1805.*

CLINTON, DE WITT (1769-1828). *New York.* Governor of New York on many occasions, and the builder of the Erie Canal, Clinton was mayor of New York City at the time of his association with Wilson. He graduated from Columbia in 1786, practiced law, was elected to the Senate in 1801, and was active in encouraging science and literature in all ways—he personally wrote newspaper notices of the *American Ornithology.* Clinton was defeated for the Presidency in 1812.—*Dictionary of American Biography,* vol. IV, p. 221.

COALE, EDWARD J. *Maryland.* He was the City Register of Baltimore, lived on Saratoga Street, and became a prominent bookseller. At one time he was associated with George Simpson, the cashier of the Bank of the United States in Philadelphia (and also a subscriber to the *Ornithology*) in publishing a short-lived literary magazine.

COCHRAN, ROBERT. *North Carolina.*

COCHRAN, THOMAS. *South Carolina.*

COFFER, JOSHUA. *Virginia.* "Mr. Coffer, of Fairfax county, Virginia, a gentleman who has paid great attention to the manners and peculiarities of our native birds, told me that he raised and kept two humming birds for some months in a cage, supplying them with honey dissolved in water, on which they readily fed" (*American Ornithology,* vol. I [Jardine edition], pp. 180-81).

COLEMAN, JAMES. *Kentucky.* He was one of the clerks in the merchant house of James Morrison in Lexington, Kentucky, at the time of Wilson's visit there, and when he subscribed to the *Ornithology.* He later started his own firm, Coleman and Megowan.—William A. Leavy, "A Memoir of Lexington and Its Vicinity," edited by Nina Visscher, *Register of the Kentucky State Historical Society,* vol. 40, p. 124.

COLEMAN, ROBERT. *Pennsylvania.* Born in Ireland in 1748, Coleman reached Philadelphia when he was sixteen, worked for a prothonotary in Reading, and at eighteen was employed by Peter Grubb, the pioneer Pennsylvania ironmaker, at Hopewell Forge. After only a few months Coleman was employed by James Old at Quittopenhill Furnace. He married Old's daughter, and in 1773 rented Speedwell Furnace near Norristown, then buying Elizabeth Furnace near Lancaster in 1776 and soon emerging as

the foremost ironmaster in the state. He died in 1825.—*Pennsylvania Magazine of History and Biography,* vol. XI, pp. 71-72.

COLLINS, THOMAS. *Pennsylvania.* He was a Pittsburgh lawyer who was born in Ireland and educated at Trinity College in Dublin. His father, a leading Dublin merchant, became a governor in the West Indies. Collins was admitted to the Pittsburgh bar in 1794, practiced for twenty years, and in 1814 was buried in the Catholic cemetery in the nearby town of Butler.

COLUMBIA COLLEGE LIBRARY. *New York.* At Wilson's visit in 1808, the college was located in downtown New York, in a block formed by College Place, Barclay, Church and Murray Streets. The nucleus of one of the greatest libraries in the world was formed with gifts from England soon after 1754, including books from the Earl of Bute and from Oxford University. During the Revolution much of the original library was lost, but it was rebuilt, aided with a legislative grant in 1792. The first substantial assistance which Wilson received (outside personal friends in Philadelphia) came from the support of the Columbia faculty, encouraged by the enthusiasm of Dr. Peter Wilson, the professor of languages, for the *Ornithology,* who was undoubtedly responsible for the Columbia Library subscription. Until 1849 the books seem to have been available to the students on loan, the last borrowing apparently having been made when the Library was on Madison Avenue in mid-town Manhattan, near the present location of Rockefeller Center. The Wilson books were subsequently stored with works of natural history in the stacks of the Geology Library, and then placed with other rare books in Special Collections.—James Grant Wilson, *Memorial History of the City of New York,* New York, 1893, vol. III, p. 519; vol. IV, pp. 85-87.

CONGRESS, LIBRARY OF. When the Library of Congress was organized in 1802, President Jefferson appointed John Beckley, the first Clerk of the House, to hold the post of Librarian as well. Beckley "if not born in England, was educated at Eton, and I have heard Governor Tazewell say that he was a classmate of Fox" (Hugh Blair Grigsby, "The History of the Virginia Federal Convention of 1788," *Virginia Historical Society Collections,* IX, pp. 63-64). Beckley was also said (by the unidentified editor of the *Collections,* presumably the secretary of the Virginia Historical Society) to have been the son of Sir William Bickley, Baronet, who died in Virginia in 1771. Beckley studied at William and Mary, and was a member of Phi Beta Kappa, apparently being one of the founders of that society, since it was organized in William and Mary in 1776. Beckley made available to James Thompson Callender the confidential material in the files of Congress on the relationship of Alexander Hamilton and Myra Reynolds, which led to Callender's attempted blackmail and his exposure of Hamilton, and prompted Hamilton's public confession and his retirement from public life. (Philip March, "John Buckley, Mystery Man of the Early Jeffersonians," *Pennsylvania Magazine of History and Biography,* vol. LXXII, 1948.) Beckley did little with the Library of Congress in the five years that he served as Librarian. It was housed in a committee room off the House, and consisted of a thousand or two thousand volumes.

Beckley died in the fall of 1807. Dr. Samuel Latham Mitchill, who had aided Wilson in New York, was now a Congressman, and head of the Joint Committee on the Library. The Committee refused Jefferson's request to separate the posts of Clerk and Librarian, turned down his candidate, and appointed Patrick Magruder to succeed Beckley. Book purchases began on a considerable scale, $2,282 being spent in a few months. A new fiscal period had begun when Wilson arrived in Washington, and the *Ornithology* was purchased with the new funds recently authorized.—William Dawson Johnston, *History of the Library of Congress,* Washington: Government Printing Office, 1904.

CONNER, WILLIAM. *Kentucky.*

COOK, JAMES. *Kentucky.*

COOPER, THOMAS APTHORP. *New York.* The first great American tragic actor, Cooper was born in England, and was adopted by William Godwin, the author of *Caleb Williams* and the father-in-law of Shelley. Godwin, a distant relative of Cooper's mother, educated Cooper according to his radical theories. At nineteen Cooper made his professional debut in Edinburgh (1792) with Mrs. Siddons. He was hissed from the stage. The demonstration, however, was attributed to conservative political members of the audience indicating their dislike of the views young Cooper was known to possess. Immediately after, Cooper was sensationally successful as Hamlet and then as Macbeth in Covent Garden in London, reportedly the youngest actor to triumph in those roles. He was hired to appear in the United States for a payment of $750 and a guarantee of $25 a week. Popular from the start, he remained for a long period as manager of the Park Theatre in New York, sometimes dividing each week into appearances in Philadelphia and New York. He

married Mary Fairlie, the most spectacularly beautiful New York belle of the time, and spent his later years in a mansion which he built in Bristol, Pennsylvania. Their daughter married a son of President Tyler, and became the White House hostess.—Arthur Clapp, *A Record of the Boston Stage,* Boston, 1853. Arthur Hornblow, *A History of the Theatre in America,* Philadelphia, 1919.

COX, JOHN C. *Louisiana.* Unidentified; however, Governor Claiborne referred to a man of this name during the Burr crisis, as refusing to cooperate with Wilkinson's plan to form a naval force by impressing citizens to serve as sailors.

CRAIG, WILLIAM. *Pennsylvania.* Apparently the merchant, born in 1741, died in 1818, who inherited considerable land in Bucks County from his Scottish-born father.—William Montgomery Clement, *The Craig Family in Pennsylvania,* 1921.

CRAMER, ZADOCK. *Pennsylvania.* He was an author, publisher and bookseller in Pittsburgh, born in New Jersey, and an authority on the rivers of the West. In 1801 he published *The Navigator,* a detailed guide to the river system from Pittsburgh to New Orleans. Eight editions were published in the next ten years. At the time of Wilson's visit, in 1810, Cramer was preparing a new edition, the first with maps.—*The Navigator, Containing Directions for Navigating the Monongahela, Allegheny, Ohio and Mississippi Rivers,* Pittsburgh, 1814. Donald Jackson, "The Race to Publish Lewis and Clark," *Pennsylvania Magazine of History and Biography,* vol. LXXXV, pp. 163-77.

CRIPPS, JOHN SPLATT. *South Carolina.* Cripps was born in England, and taken to South Carolina by his widowed mother in 1766. She married soon after landing Alexander Gillon, of Rotterdam and London, a member of a family of wealthy Dutch merchants, who was a passenger on the ship. Gillon established an American trading company, and took Cripps into partnership. During the Revolution, Gillon was an American agent in Europe, securing arms and loans in Amsterdam. He later became a phenomenally successful privateer, operating with Spanish forces in the West Indies, while Cripps ran the mercantile firm.—*National Cyclopedia of American Biography,* vol. II, p. 659.

CROMWELL, THOMAS. *Pennsylvania.* He maintained warehouses along the river front in Pittsburgh at the time Wilson set out by rowboat down the Ohio. Cromwell was a vestryman on the Old Round Church in Pittsburgh, and a subscriber to the Monongahela Bridge.—*The Navigator,* p. 21. *Pennsylvania Magazine of History and Biography,* vol. XXX, p. 191.

CROSBY, MOSES G. *South Carolina.*

CUMMINGS, DR. JOHN. *Georgia.* He was a physician, the first president of the Hibernian Society of Savannah, one of the leading financiers of the city, and captain of the Savannah Volunteer Guards.— Lucian Lamar Knight, *Georgia's Landmarks, Memorials and Legends,* Atlanta, 1913, vol. I, p. 400.

DARTMOUTH COLLEGE LIBRARY. *New Hampshire.* The college in 1808, at the time of Wilson's first visit, consisted only of the original building, Dartmouth Hall, built in 1784. Wilson was cordially received there: "Dr. Wheelock, the President, made me eat at his table," he wrote, "and the professors vied with each other to oblige me" (Wilson to Daniel Miller, October 26, 1808).

DAVIS, JOHN P. (1761-1847). *Massachusetts.* The son of a Plymouth merchant, graduated from Harvard in 1777, Davis was the youngest delegate to the state convention that ratified the Constitution. After serving in the legislature, he was asked by Washington to become Comptroller of the Currency. He later served as United States attorney, and was appointed a Federal judge by John Adams, interpreting maritime law for 40 years. He was president of the Massachusetts Historical Society.— *Dictionary of American Biography,* vol. V, p. 132.

DEARBORN, HENRY ALEXANDER SCAMMEL (1783-1851). *New Hampshire.* Born in Exeter, and educated at Williams College, Dearborn accompanied his father, the Secretary of War under Jefferson, to Washington, to assist in his office. He studied law under Joseph Story, and practiced in Salem. An officer of the Boston Custom House in later years, he was dismissed by President Jackson because he loaned cannon to Rhode Island to suppress Dorr's Rebellion. He wrote a maritime geography of Egypt and Turkey, and a study of commerce and navigation of the Black Sea.—*Dictionary of American Biography,* vol. V, p. 176.

DEBLOIS, GILBERT. *Louisiana.*

DE CHAUMONT, LE ROY. *New York.* His father was a friend of Benjamin Franklin, and owned the house in Passy which was Franklin's headquarters in France during the Revolution. The older De Chaumont spent a fortune in the American cause,

and claims for reimbursement were settled by the United States government in 1790, Le Roy de Chaumont acquiring immense tracts of land along the St. Lawrence River. He built sawmills, grist mills, blast furnaces and powder mills, attracting French émigrés to settle there. After the fall of Napoleon, several of the leaders of Napoleon's secret police made their homes there.

DERBIGNY, PIERRE. *Louisiana.* He was an active supporter of the cause of the United States in French New Orleans, a tireless, enthusiastic and attractive figure. In 1820 he was a candidate for governor, and while his opponent, Thomas Bolling Robertson, received a plurality, the election was thrown to the legislature, which favored Derbigny. He refused the governorship in advance on the grounds that the vote for Robertson clearly showed the will of the people. A few years later Derbigny was elected governor, but was killed before taking office when his carriage overturned.—*Official Letter Books of W. C. C. Claiborne. Dictionary of American Biography,* vol. V, p. 248. *Lamb's Biographical Dictionary of the United States,* edited by John Howard Brown, Boston, 1900.

DERBY, ELIAS HASKET. *Massachusetts.* The oldest son of the great Salem merchant who pioneered in the China trade, young Derby at twenty-one captained the *Grand Turk* and a crew of boys on an amazing three-year voyage that cleared $100,000. Wilson referred to him as General Derby, from his rank as brigadier general of the state militia.—*Dictionary of American Biography,* vol. V, pp. 250-51.

DESILVER, ROBERT. *Pennsylvania.* He was a prominent bookseller in Philadelphia, famous for a fine edition of Birch's *Views of Philadelphia.* At one time he published *The Port Folio.*

DESILVER, THOMAS. *Pennsylvania.* He was a bookbinder, usually in conjunction with the books published by his brother, operating his bindery at 2 Walnut Street in Philadelphia.

DEVEREAUX, JOHN. *North Carolina.*

DE WITT, SIMEON. *New York.* A celebrated cartographer, he was a student at Rutgers at the start of the Revolution, was recommended to Washington by his cousin De Witt Clinton, and remained to serve as mapmaker for the army and head of the map department of the government. He was Surveyor General of New York State for 50 years, and owned the land which was occupied by Cornell University and the city of Ithaca. His wife's sister married Charles Brockden Brown, the pioneer American novelist.—William Allen, D. D., *An American Biographical and Historical Dictionary. Dictionary of American Biography,* vol. V, p. 274.

DICK, WILLIAM. *North Carolina.*

DICKINSON COLLEGE. *Pennsylvania.* At the time Wilson visited this Presbyterian institution in 1810 it had passed through a crisis which nearly destroyed it. After the death of the first president, Charles Nisbet, in 1804, Reverend Robert Davidson (1750-1812), minister of the Presbyterian church at Carlisle, acted as president, but did not maintain discipline, gambling, drunkenness, lewd behavior, duels and two suicides in one semester leading to demands for its closing. Jeremiah Atwater, the first president of Middlebury, took over the presidency and between October, 1809, and November, 1810, rebuilt the college. It had about 90 students at the time of Wilson's visit. The state legislature had appropriated $3,500 for books for the college library.

DINSMORE, SILAS. *Mississippi.* He was United States agent to the Choctaw Indians, and was hired by Wilkinson to arrest Burr, promised $500 if he succeeded.—Thomas Perkins Abernathy, *The Burr Conspiracy,* p. 175. Dunbar Rowland, *Encyclopedia of Mississippi History,* Madison, Wis., 1907, vol. I, p. 649.

DOUGHTY, JOHN. *New York.* Referred to as General Doughty, he was aide-de-camp to General Schuyler in the Revolution, later an outstanding artillery officer.—Francis B. Heitman, *Historical Register and Dictionary of the United States Army,* Washington: Government Printing Office, 1903, vol. I, p. 380.

DOW, ROBERT, M.D. *Louisiana.* He was an American physician who practiced in New Orleans before the Louisiana Purchase. Claiborne appointed him to the first Board of Health in the city in 1804, and he was also a member of the legislative council, but asked to be excused because of professional and family obligations.—*Official Letter Books of W. C. C. Claiborne,* vol. II, p. 194.

DRAYTON, WILLIAM. *South Carolina.* Born in St. Augustine in 1776, Drayton's early years were divided between the United States and England, his mother having died in England while visiting her parents there. He became a celebrated Charleston

lawyer, a Federalist, a strong opponent of the War of 1812 who supported the government after war was declared. Andrew Jackson urged his appointment as Secretary of War. A judge, he settled in Philadelphia when he retired, and as its last president formally closed the Bank of the United States. —*Dictionary of American Biography,* vol. V, p. 448.

DUCATEL, EDMUND GERMAINE. *Maryland.* Ducatel was a druggist at 20 Baltimore Street in Baltimore at the time of Wilson's visit.—*Baltimore Directory and Citizens Register. National Cyclopedia of American Biography,* vol. IV, p. 544.

DUER, WILLIAM ALEXANDER (1780-1858). *New York.* Duer's father was a member of the Continental Congress. His mother was the daughter of General William Alexander, of the Scottish earldom of Stirling. After boyhood in New York and England, Duer attended Erasmus Hall in Brooklyn, studied law, sailed with Decatur as a midshipman, and joined Edward Livingston in the early days of the American occupation of New Orleans. He later opened a law office in Rhinebeck, New York, and was president of Columbia College from 1829 until 1842.—*Dictionary of American Biography,* vol. V, p. 488. James Grant Wilson, *Memorial History of the City of New York,* vol. III.

DUNBAR, WILLIAM. *Mississippi.* The younger son of Sir Archibald Dunbar of Scotland, he was born in 1749, studied mathematics and astronomy, and set out for the United States in 1771 when his health failed. An Indian trader, he became a partner of John Ross of Philadelphia, a fellow Scot who had become one of the wealthiest colonial merchants. Their plantation near Baton Rouge was lost by slave uprisings and raids during the Revolution, in which Ross served as an American agent in Europe. Dunbar next built the Forest, a model plantation near Natchez. He worked with Andrew Ellicott in surveys of the Spanish-American boundary, and explored the Red River for Jefferson, whose close friend he was. He died in 1810, leaving a large fortune to his children.—Mrs. Dunbar Rowland, *Life, Letters and Papers of William Dunbar,* Mississippi Historical Society, 1930. *Dictionary of American Biography,* vol. V, p. 507.

DUNCAN, ABNER L. *Louisiana.* He was a prominent New Orleans lawyer, a volunteer aide to Jackson during the battle of New Orleans—Marquis James, *Andrew Jackson, The Border Captain,* Indianapolis: Bobbs-Merrill, 1933.

DUNLAP, JOHN. *Virginia.*

DUPLESSIS, FRANCIS. *Louisiana*. He lived with his family of eight persons and eight slaves on the rue de Conti in New Orleans. Francis Duplessis, Jr., was a quartermaster of the militia in 1811.—*Official Letter Books of W. C. C. Claiborne. New Orleans in 1805.*

DUPLESSIS, P. L. B. *Louisiana*. Born in Philadelphia of French parents, he settled in New Orleans in 1803, married a Creole lady, raised a family of four sons, and was of value to Claiborne as an interpreter and supporter of the Americans to the French.—*Official Letter Books of W. C. C. Claiborne.*

EAGLES, RICHARD. *North Carolina*.

EDDOWS, RALPH. *Pennsylvania*. He was a merchant, living at 324 High Street in Philadelphia.—William H. Furness, *Sermon on the Death of Ralph Eddows,* March 31, 1833, First Society of Unitarian Christians of Philadelphia.

EDDY, THOMAS. *New York*. Born in Philadelphia in 1758 of a Quaker family, Eddy was an early abolitionist, a founder of Bloomingdale Asylum for the care of the insane, a founder of the House of Refuge, the New York Bible Society, and the New York Savings Bank. He also aided Governor Clinton in putting over the Erie Canal, and amassed a fortune as an insurance broker.—*Dictionary of American Biography,* vol. VI, p. 15.

ELLERY, ABRAHAM R. *Louisiana*. He was a lawyer, living on Levee Street in New Orleans.—*Official Letter Books of W. C. C. Claiborne. New Orleans in 1805.*

ELLIOT, STEPHEN. *South Carolina*. "Mr. Elliot, of Beaufort, a judicious naturalist . . ." (*American Ornithology,* vol. I, p. 187; vol. III, p. 60). In addition to his home in Beaufort, South Carolina, Elliot also owned property in Georgia which Wilson used as his base for explorations into the countryside. He wrote *Botany of South Carolina and Georgia.*—Robert Molloy, *Charleston,* New York, 1947, p. 99.

ELLIS, SARAH. *Mississippi*. She was the former Sarah Percy, sister of Mrs. Samuel Brown, above.—May Wilson McBee, *Natchez Court Records, 1767-1805,* Ann Arbor, Mich., 1953.

EMPIE, REVEREND ADAM. *New York*. He followed Dr. Beasley, another subscriber to the *Ornithology,* at St. Peter's Episcopal Church in Albany.—Rev. Joseph Hooper, *A History of St. Peter's Church,* Albany, 1900.

ENOCKS, THOMAS. *Pennsylvania*. He was a Pittsburgh capitalist, one of the builders of the Monongahela Bridge.

ENSLEN, A. *Pennsylvania*. "The white-winged crossbill represented on this plate was shot in the neighborhood of Great Pine Swamp by my friend Mr. Ainsley, a German naturalist, collector for the emperor of Austria" (*American Ornithology,* vol. II, p. 43). Enslen was also collector for the Prince of Lichtenstein, and was associated with Frederick Pursh in the botanical garden of William Hamilton outside Philadelphia.—Frederick Pursh, *Flora Americae Septentrionalis,* London, 1814.

EPPES, JOHN. *District of Columbia*. The nephew of Thomas Jefferson, he studied science and law in Philadelphia in 1791 under Jefferson's direction. Marrying his cousin, Mary Jefferson, he became a successful planter in Virginia, was a scholar, and served two terms in the House of Representatives and one in the Senate.—*Dictionary of American Biography,* vol. VI, p. 170.

EVANS, LEWIS. *Mississippi*.

FARRAND, BENJAMIN. *New York*.

FARRAR, BENJAMIN. *Mississippi*. A neighbor of William Dunbar's near Natchez, he was one of the founders of the Mississippi Society.—*Encyclopedia of Mississippi History,* vol. I, pp. 698-99.

FARRELL, JOHN B. *Louisiana*.

FISHER, MIERS. *Pennsylvania*. The son of Joshua Fisher, whose merchant firm was one of the largest in the Colonies, Miers Fisher was born in 1748. He studied law with Benjamin Chew in Philadelphia, and at eighteen formed a partnership, Gilpin and Fisher, dealing in flour shipments on the eastern shore of Maryland. A Quaker, he was exiled to Virginia with his father and brothers during the Revolution, suspected of sympathy with the British. He won Washington's confidence after the Revolution, and his generosity and courage during the plague restored him to popular esteem. Marrying Sarah Redwood, an heiress of Newport, he devoted his wealth to encouraging industry throughout the area, usually with his brother-in-law Joshua Gilpin. In 1795 he purchased a farm, Urie, at Fox Chase outside Philadelphia, adjoining the property of Joshua Sullivan where Wilson worked when he first reached the United States. Miers Fisher was the American agent for the father of John James Audubon, who owned property near Philadelphia, and Audubon lived at Urie under Fisher's care. —*Colonial Families of Philadelphia,* edited by John Jorner, Philadelphia, 1911, vol. II, pp. 664-68. James Leander Bishop, *History of American Manufactures, 1608-1806,* Philadelphia, 1863-1867, vol. II, pp. 63, 207. Francis Herrick, *Audubon the Naturalist,* New York, 1917, vol. I, pp. 99-122.

FISHER, REDWOOD (1782-1856). *Pennsylvania.* The fifth of the seventeen children of Miers Fisher, he was a supercargo on merchant voyages (once concealing $300,000 in gold when his ship was boarded by pirates in China), subsequently a woolen manufacturer, newspaper publisher, and author. He was a close friend of Henry Clay.— *Eminent Philadelphians,* p. 362.

FISHER, WILLIAM W. *Pennsylvania.* He was a merchant with offices at 99 South Front Street in Philadelphia.

FITZHUGHES, GILES. *District of Columbia.*

FLOOD, WILLIAM, M.D. *Louisiana.* A prominent New Orleans physician, he was a member of the legislative council, a firm supporter of Claiborne, and a major in the militia, commanding 300 rifles during the Burr crisis. During the War of 1812 he carried out intelligence assignments for Claiborne in Florida.—*Official Letter Books of W. C. C. Claiborne,* vol. IV, pp. 113, 132-34.

FOERING, MAJOR FREDERICK. *Pennsylvania.* He was a justice of the peace in Philadelphia, a merchant, and active in municipal politics. He was commissioned a major during the War of 1812. —*Pennsylvania Magazine of History and Biography,* vol. VI, p. 278. Letters of Alexander Wilson, Houghton Library, Harvard: Wilson to Daniel Miller, February 22, 1809.

FORMAN, J. *Mississippi.* He was associated with the financial operations of William Dunbar in Natchez.—Mrs. Dunbar Rowland, *Life, Letters and Papers of William Dunbar.*

FORTIER, MICHAEL. *Louisiana.* He was one of the wealthiest merchants of New Orleans, and a supporter of Governor Claiborne. He also volunteered to aid Jackson at the Battle of New Orleans, in which he commanded Negro troops.—*Official Letter Books of W. C. C. Claiborne.*

FREEMAN, THOMAS. *Mississippi.* He was William

Dunbar's associate in the explorations of the Red River and Ouachita Valley, and was surveyor for Andrew Ellicott on the Spanish-American boundary survey. "Freeman is one of the greatest rascals and liars in existence."—Ellicott, in Catherine Van Cortlandt Mathews, *Andrew Ellicott, His Life and Letters.*

FULTON, ROBERT (1755-1815). *New York.* The inventor of the steamboat was born in Pennsylvania, growing up in Lancaster among expert gunsmiths and mechanics after the death of his father. At seventeen he was sufficiently successful as a Philadelphia portrait painter to purchase a farm for his mother and sisters. At thirty-one he traveled to London to study with Benjamin West, remaining twenty years. He devoted most of his time to mechanics, especially his submarine, returning to New York in 1806, and in the summer of 1807 (at which time Wilson asked him to subscribe to the *Ornithology*) he blew up a brig in New York harbor with his invention. He signed up for the set of Wilson's books immediately after returning from Albany on the successful voyage of the first steamship, the *Clermont,* August 17, 1807.—*Dictionary of American Biography,* vol. VII, p. 68.

GALLATIN, ABRAHAM ALFONSE ALBERT (1761-1849). *District of Columbia.* Secretary of the Treasury. Born in Geneva of an aristocratic family, he was an orphan at nine, and at nineteen became a trader in the West Indies and New England. He took part in two expeditions during the Revolution, taught French at Harvard, speculated in land, and acquired social and family connections by his second marriage in 1793. After three terms in Congress, he was treasurer from 1801 until 1814, subsequently serving ten years on diplomatic missions in Europe.—*Dictionary of American Biography,* vol. VII, p. 103.

GAPPER, MRS. *Pennsylvania.* She was listed in the directory of Philadelphia as a gentlewoman living at 218 Chestnut Street.

GARDINER, JOHN L. *New York.* The owner of Gardiner's Island of 3,000 acres east of Long Island, he was "an intelligent and obliging friend" to Alexander Wilson (*American Ornithology,* vol. II, p. 96). His hobby was the study of eagles.

GASTON, WILL. *North Carolina.* Born in New Bern in 1778, he graduated from Princeton in 1796, with highest honors. Gaston was elected to Congress in 1803. He was a successful lawyer, and was retained by the Earl of Granville to bring suit for lands granted his ancestors, covering two-thirds of North Carolina. Gaston engaged in the case because he did not want it said counsel could not be secured in the United States. He was a Roman Catholic, and while the state constitution then prohibited members of that Church from holding public office, the provision was disregarded in his case.—Ex-Governor Benjamin Perry of North Carolina, *Reminiscences of Public Men*, Greenville, N.C., 1891.

GEORGETOWN LIBRARY. *District of Columbia.* The town of Georgetown was at the head of navigation on the Potomac, and was retained as an independent community within the District of Columbia.

GIBBONS, J. *Virginia.*

GIBBS, COLONEL G. *New York.* Three copies. Gibbs was the son of a Newport merchant, the founder of the *American Journal of Science,* and a collector of minerals.—*Dictionary of American Biography,* vol. VII, p. 244.

GIBSON, JAMES. *Pennsylvania.* He was a lawyer and landowner, whose family property adjoined Gray's Ferry. Secretary of the Asylum Company, which bought land where French émigrés were settled, Gibson was credited with saving the lake ports of Pennsylvania against New York claims by his far-sighted purchases.—*Pennsylvania Magazine of History and Biography,* vol. LXX, pp. 206-7.

GILES, WILLIAM BRANCH (1762-1830). *Virginia.* He studied at Hampden College, at Princeton and at William and Mary, was elected to Congress in 1790, and became the most ruthless and destructive demagogue in the House, resigning in 1798 because he favored the destruction of the Union. Again in Congress during Jefferson's administration, he tried to impeach Justice Marshall, injuring Jefferson's cause by his violence in professed support of the President. He retired to his estate, Wigwam, in 1817, but emerged again to become governor of Virginia, 1827-1830.—*Dictionary of American Biography,* vol. VII, p. 283.

GILLIAM, DR. JAMES SKELTON. *Virginia.* He was related to Thomas Jefferson in one of the involved ramifications of Virginia family history. His mother was Lucy Skelton, who inherited large properties from her brothers Reuben, Bathurst and Meriwether. Lucy Skelton's mother was Jane Meriwether. By her second marriage, Jane Meriwether became Mrs. John Wayles. Wayles's daughter

Martha Wayles married first, Bathurst Skelton, and second, Thomas Jefferson.—*William and Mary College Quarterly,* vol. XII, pp. 60-63.

GILPIN, JOSHUA. *Pennsylvania.* Joshua and Thomas Gilpin established the first paper mill on the Brandywine in 1787, and it became a famous tourist attraction. Joshua Gilpin personally shredded new colored silk handkerchiefs to add to bank note paper, in demonstrations to visiting schoolchildren. Lemonade, crackers, cheese and fruit were given free to visitors. "His gardens were filled with fruit and with choice lemon trees in full bearing. There was a greenhouse adjoining, and an ice-house, in which the work people were allowed to keep their provisions" (Elizabeth Montgomery, *Reminiscences of Wilmington,* Philadelphia, 1851, pp. 32-41). The Gilpin and Fisher families were intermarried, and partnerships between them were innumerable. Joshua Gilpin was interested in botany, traveled widely, and was on terms of close friendship with Lord Stanley, Charles Grenville, Baron de Montesquieu and other European statesmen.—*Eminent Philadelphians,* p. 400.

GILPIN, THOMAS. *Pennsylvania.* He also carried on his own business as a merchant at 14 Dock Street in Philadelphia.

GLASGOW UNIVERSITY LIBRARY. *Scotland.*

GOLDSBOROUGH, CHARLES WASHINGTON. *District of Columbia.* He was Chief Clerk of the Navy Department.—*Dictionary of American Biography,* vol. VII, p. 365.

GRANGER, GIDEON. *District of Columbia.* The Postmaster General, he was a native of Connecticut, a Yale graduate of 1787, and served in the state legislature before Jefferson appointed him to the Post Office Department. He was suspected of being involved with Burr's conspiracy, and it was when he relayed to Jefferson accounts of Burr's actions which Congressmen had given him that Jefferson determined to act. Granger's resignation was forced by Madison in 1817 over a disagreement about the Philadelphia postmaster.—*Dictionary of American Biography,* vol. VII, p. 483. Thomas Perkins Abernathy, *The Burr Conspiracy,* p. 86.

GREEN, CHARLES B. *Mississippi.*

GREENHOW, DR. JAMES. *Virginia.* The son of an English-born merchant of Williamsburg, he attended William and Mary and studied medicine in Edinburgh. His stepmother was the sister of Virginia's Governor Tyler.—*William and Mary College Quarterly,* vol. VII, p. 17.

GRIFFIN, THOMAS. *Virginia.* He was an obscure member of a famous family, since his father, Samuel Stuart Griffin, who was born in Philadelphia, was the son of Lady Christian Griffin of the family of the Scottish earldom of Taquair. At the time of Wilson's visit to Virginia, Thomas Griffin lived in Yorktown, where he died in 1836.—*William and Mary College Quarterly,* vol. XX, pp. 204-7, 301-2.

GRIMES, JOHN. *Georgia.*

GRINNEL, SLOSS HOBART. *New York.* This name was printed by Ord as "Hobartgrinnel, Sloss." A list of Federal employees in the Baltimore directory, however, printed it as given above. He was a lieutenant in the Navy when he subscribed to the *Ornithology.*

GRYMES, P. *Louisiana.* He followed James Brown as United States Attorney in New Orleans.—*Official Letter Books of W. C. C. Claiborne.*

GUERIN, F. M. *Louisiana.*

HALL, CHARLES. *New York.*

HALL, JUDGE DOMINICK. *Louisiana.* Born in South Carolina in 1765, a lawyer in Charleston, this intrepid jurist was appointed a Federal judge by President Adams, and by Jefferson judge of the District Court of Louisiana. There he astounded Wilkinson by firmly resisting the latter's arbitrary actions during the Burr crisis, insisting on the rights of citizens before the court, and displaying an integrity in the cause of justice that made him the only person in the city Wilkinson feared. Judge Hall became nationally famous because of his dispute with Andrew Jackson after the Battle of New Orleans. When Jackson retained martial law, and refused to act on a writ of habeas corpus, on the technicality that he had not received official word of peace, Judge Hall ordered his arrest for contempt of court, and Jackson ordered Judge Hall out of the city. On his return he held Jackson for trial, and fined him $1,000 when he was found guilty. At the time of Wilson's visit to secure a subscription to the *Ornithology* Judge Hall was perhaps as greatly esteemed as a public servant as any man in the South.—*Dictionary of American Biography,* vol. VIII, p. 123. Marquis James, *Andrew Jackson, The Border Captain,* pp. 282-87.

HAMBLETON, S. *Louisiana.*

HAMILTON, WILLIAM. *Pennsylvania.* The best-known botanical garden of the time was not Bartram's Garden, but Woodlands, the great estate of William Hamilton, a short distance away on the banks of the Schuylkill River. An aristocrat who never sympathized with the Revolution, Hamilton owned the land on which Lancaster was built. He collected rare plants and flowers, first introducing into America the Lombardy poplar and the ginkgo tree. Dr. Barton conducted his botany classes of the University of Pennsylvania on the grounds of Woodlands, and Enslen, the botanist for the Emperor of Austria, and Pursh, who catalogued the discoveries of Meriwether Lewis, were employed as gardeners.—Frederick Pursh, *Flora Americae Septentrionalis. Eminent Philadelphians,* p. 483.

HAMMOND, ABIJAH. *New York.* One of the largest taxpayers in New York City, he was a philanthropist, active in the drilling of free wells to provide fresh water. He gave the city equipment especially designed for the purpose, which was tested by drilling a well in City Hall Park. Hammond was a pallbearer at Hamilton's funeral.—James Grant Wilson, *Memorial History of the City of New York,* vol. III, pp. 80, 102.

HANSFERD, LEWIS, M.D. *Virginia.* He was a descendant of Thomas Hansford, one of the rebels hanged by Sir William Berkley in 1676.—*William and Mary College Quarterly,* vol. XXII, p. 219.

HARDING, LYMAN. *Mississippi.* He was a close friend of William Dunbar at Natchez. He acted as Aaron Burr's counsel at his trial in Mississippi, before Burr was sent east to stand trial.—Thomas Perkins Abernathy, *The Burr Conspiracy,* p. 217.

HARMAN, THOMAS. *Louisiana.* He lived on the rue de Camp in New Orleans.—*New Orleans in 1805.*

HARRISON, GEORGE. *Pennsylvania.* He was the United States naval agent in Philadelphia, ordinarily a lucrative post, as naval agents received two per cent of all the money they paid on public accounts, one per cent of all the money they received for the sale of public property, and one-half of one per cent of the money they dispensed on payrolls. Harrison lived in the former Clymer mansion on Chestnut Street at Seventh Street.—Scharf and Westcott, *History of Philadelphia,* vol. I, p. 704.

HARTFORD LIBRARY. *Connecticut.* It was started in 1774 as the Hartford Library Company. "Few facts of its history are now obtainable. It appears that the library soon grew to far more proportion. . . ."—J. Hammond Trumbull, *Memorial History of Hartford County,* 1881.

HARTWELL, CYRUS. *New Hampshire.*

HASSELL, CHRISTIAN G. *South Carolina.*

HASSELL, WILLIAM. *North Carolina.*

HAYDOCK, SAMUEL. *Pennsylvania.* He was a Philadelphia merchant, living at 38 South Second Street.—John A. Paxton, *Directory and Register.*

HAYWOOD, JOHN. *South Carolina.*

HEADLY, JAMES. *District of Columbia.* He was from Lexington, Kentucky, and had recently been in Virginia, where he married, when he subscribed to the *Ornithology.—William and Mary College Quarterly,* vol. VI, p. 313. William Leavy, *A Memoir of Lexington and Its Vicinity,* p. 315.

HEAP, DR. SAMUEL (1781-1853). *Louisiana.* He was born in Carlisle, Pennsylvania, graduated from medical school in 1803, became a surgeon in the Navy, and served in New Orleans under Commander David Porter. In 1810, at the time of Wilson's visit to New Orleans, Dr. Heap married Margaret Porter, the sister of David.—*Dictionary of American Biography,* vol. VIII, p. 123. Edward Callahan, *List of Officers of the Navy of the United States and the Marine Corps from 1775 to 1900,* New York, 1901.

HENDERSON, STEPHEN (1776-1838). *Louisiana.* One of the wealthiest merchants of New Orleans, Henderson was born in Scotland. He married Zelia d'Estrehan, of a prominent Creole family, building a famous plantation house up the Mississippi from New Orleans. His wife dying young, he left his fortune to provide for the freeing of slaves, and the purchase of land for them.—Harnett Kane, *Plantation Parade,* New York, 1948, pp. 135-38.

HENRY, WILLIAM. *Pennsylvania.*

HERMEN, ALFRED. *Louisiana.*

HERRIT, JOHN W. *North Carolina.*

HEYWARD, THOMAS (1746-1809). *South Carolina.* A signer of the Declaration of Independence, edu-

cated in England, he served in Congress during the Revolution, was wounded at Port Royal and captured at the fall of Charleston. He lived in venerated old age at his plantation, White Hall, at the time of Wilson's visit.—*Dictionary of American Biography,* vol. VIII, p. 609.

HIGGINSON, GEORGE. *Massachusetts.* He lived on Mount Vernon Street in Boston.

HOBSON, JONATHAN. *Liverpool, England.*

HORRY, PETER. *South Carolina.* Although this name was listed by Ord as "Peter Harry," there can be no question but that the subscriber was General Peter Horry, the celebrated Revolutionary hero and close associate of Francis Marion, who was living on his plantation near Charleston at the time of Wilson's visit.—*National Cyclopedia of American Biography,* vol. VI, p. 101. *South Carolina Historical and Genealogical Magazine,* vol. II, pp. 280-84.

HOSACK, DAVID, M.D. *New York.* The son of a British artillery officer, born in 1769, Hosack graduated from Princeton, studied medicine with Dr. Rush, practiced briefly, and then left his wife and child for three years of medical training in Scotland and England. Professor of Botany at Columbia, and the attending physician at the Burr-Hamilton duel, Hosack was a founder of Bellevue Hospital, the Humane Society, and other organizations. He built his celebrated botanical garden on land later occupied by Rockefeller Center.—*A Cyclopedia of American Medical Biography,* vol. II, pp. 12-13. *Dictionary of American Biography,* vol. IX, p. 239.

HOUNSFIELD, EZRA. *New York.*

HOWARD, JOHN E. *Pennsylvania.*

HOWELL, COLONEL. *Pennsylvania.*

HUNTERIAN MUSEUM. *Glasgow, Scotland.*

INGERSOLL, C. J. *Pennsylvania.* He was an attorney at 154 Walnut Street in Philadelphia, the son of Jared Ingersoll.—Scharf and Westcott, *History of Philadelphia,* vol. I, pp. 151-57.

IRONSIDE, GEORGE. *New York.*

IRVINE, D. M. *South Carolina.* "Dr. M. Irvine was a skilful physician and a brave soldier."—Robert Mills, *Statistics of South Carolina,* p. 456.

IZARD, RALPH STEAD (1783-1818). *South Carolina.* He was the oldest of the seven children of Ralph Izard, the famous American agent in France during the Revolution. He married Esther Middleton, and inherited valuable rice plantations on the Peedee River.—*South Carolina Historical and Genealogical Magazine,* vol. II, p. 328.

JACKSON, FRANCIS JAMES (1770-1814). *London, England.* He was Great Britain's minister plenipotentiary at Washington from 1809 until 1811.

JACKSON, JAMES MADISON. *Georgia.* The son of Senator James Jackson, who was a Revolutionary hero and the principal opponent to backers of the Yazoo land speculation, he was a leading citizen of Savannah, a judge of the state court.—Rev. William Bacon Stevens, *A History of Georgia,* Philadelphia, 1859.

JAMES, WILLIAM. *South Carolina.* The son of a major in the Revolutionary army, he accompanied his father into action with Marion when he was only fifteen. The author of a life of Francis Marion, he was a judge at the time of Wilson's visit.

JANUARY, THOMAS. *Kentucky.* One of the earliest settlers in Lexington, he operated his store at the corner of Main and Broadway, was a Founder of Transylvania University, and a leader in civic enterprises of all kinds.—William A. Leavy. "A Memoir of Lexington and Its Vicinity," *Register of the Kentucky State Historical Society,* vol. 40, pp. 119, 129.

JARVIS, REVEREND SAMUEL. *New York.* He was a founder and one of the first professors of the General Seminary of New York, and rector of St. John's Episcopal Church.—James Grant Wilson, *Memorial History of the City of New York,* vol. IV, p. 596.

JEFFERSON, THOMAS (1743-1826). *Virginia.* The third President of the United States. Jefferson subscribed to the *Ornithology* by mail on October 9, 1807, after receiving the printed prospectus describing the set of books, adding to his order: "He salutes mr. Wilson with great respect." Wilson called at the White House at noon on Saturday, December 17, 1808, to show the President the first volume. Jefferson, who was then preparing to return to Monticello after Madison's inauguration in March, spent considerable time with Wilson discussing possible subscribers. A week later, Wilson wrote to Jefferson that he had "tolerable success" in securing subscriptions in Washington, where he signed up several Cabinet members. Undoubtedly many of the subscribers in Virginia were gained as a result of Jefferson's recommendation, for Wilson wrote that he was seeing Joshua Coffer (who subscribed), at Jefferson's suggestion, and that the President had put him in touch with other naturalists. —James Southall Wilson, *Alexander Wilson, Poet-Naturalist,* New York, 1906.

JOHNSTON, ALEXANDER. *Pennsylvania.*

JOHNSTON, ROBERT. *Maryland.*

JONES, JOSEPH. *Pennsylvania.* He first appeared in the Philadelphia directory for 1814 as a gentleman, 7 York Building.

JONES, WILLIAM. *Pennsylvania.* "That gigantic man," as he was described by Townsend Ward, was six feet, four inches tall. He owned the farmhouse where Wilson boarded while he taught school at Gray's Ferry, and which Wilson described in his poem, "The Solitary Tutor," and in the essay on hummingbirds in the *Ornithology.* Wilson was living in Jones's home in Philadelphia when he died, and he was buried in the Jones family plot in Old Swedes churchyard. Jones's son Nicholas Jones was the husband of Susannah Miller, the sister of Sarah Miller, to whom Wilson left all his possessions in his will.—*Pennsylvania Magazine of History and Biography,* vol. IV. Wilson Monument Scrapbook, Free Public Library, Paisley, Scotland. Will of Jacob Miller, Pennsylvania Historical Society. Alexander Grosart, *Poems and Literary Prose of Alexander Wilson,* vol. II, facsimile of invitation to Wilson's funeral.

KEITH, JAMES. *South Carolina.*

KENNEDY, JAMES. *District of Columbia.*

KENNER, WILLIAM. *Louisiana.* A pioneer American merchant in New Orleans, he settled there during the Spanish occupation, prospered, and became one of the leading figures in developing the sugar industry of Louisiana.—Harnett Kane, *Plantation Parade,* p. 188.

KIMBALL, HAZEN. *Georgia.*

KIMBALL, LEON. *Massachusetts.*

KING, CHARLES. *New York.* The son of the statesman Rufus King, he was educated in England while his father was minister at St. James's, married the daughter of the merchant Archibald Gracie and worked in Gracie's firm in New York, subsequently becoming editor of the New York *American* and president of Columbia.—*Dictionary of American Biography,* vol. X, p. 382.

KING, RUFUS (1755-1827). *New York.* Twice minister to England in critical periods, and twice the Federalist candidate for Vice-President, King was unsurpassed as a statesman and as an orator. It was his resolution outlawing slavery in the Northwest Territory that arrested its spread, and he was far-sighted in his attempt to abolish slavery, with the sale of public lands to pay for the emancipation of the slaves.—*Memoir and Correspondence of Jeremiah Mason,* edited by G. S. Hillard, Boston, 1873. *Dictionary of American Biography,* vol. X, p. 399.

KINLOCK, CLELAND (1746-1825). *South Carolina.* The descendant of a younger son of a Scottish noble family, he was born in Charleston, inherited large estates at seven, and was educated at Eton and in Holland before settling in Charleston after the Revolution.—*Dictionary of American Biography,* vol. X, p. 414.

LABUZAN, CHARLES. *Georgia.*

LANG, JOHN. *Pennsylvania.* He was a baker in Philadelphia, located at 26 Pewterplate Alley.

LANSING, JOHN (1754-1829). *New York.* A secretary to General Schuyler in the Revolution, he became mayor of Albany, chancellor, and chief justice of the State Supreme Court. He disappeared from his home in New York City in 1829, and no trace of him was ever found.—*Dictionary of American Biography,* vol. X, p. 608.

LARDNER, JOHN. *Pennsylvania.* He first appeared in the Philadelphia directory in 1814 as a gentleman living at 108 Walnut Street.

LATROBE, BENJAMIN. *District of Columbia.* Born in England and educated in Germany, where he served in the Prussian army, Latrobe became a London architect and was appointed engineer of the city before he settled in Norfolk, Virginia, in 1796. After designing the Capitol, he lived in Washington as surveyor of public buildings at the time of Wilson's visit. He was involved in Burr's conspiracy, and died on a visit to New Orleans in 1820.—*Dictionary of American Biography,* vol. XI, p. 20. *Eminent Philadelphians,* p. 638. Thomas Perkins Abernathy, *The Burr Conspiracy,* p. 76.

LAWRENCE, NATHANIEL. *Liverpool, England.*

LAWRENCE, WILLIAM. *New York.*

LAWSON, ALEXANDER. *Pennsylvania.* The engraver who made most of the plates for the *Ornithology,* Lawson was born in Lanark, Scotland, in 1773, moved with his parents to Manchester in 1789, and in 1794 emigrated to the United States. After working for Thackera and Vallance for two years he started his own firm, and quickly became the foremost engraver of the city. He married Elizabeth Scaife, an Englishwoman.—*Dictionary of American Biography,* vol. XI, p. 56. William Dunlap, *History of the Arts of Design in the United States. Eminent Philadelphians.*

LEE, J. LEMAN. *Massachusetts.*

LE GRAND, ABNER. *Kentucky.* He is listed as "H. Legrand" by Ord, but was undoubtedly Abner Le Grand, the son-in-law of William Morton, or Lord Morton, the expatriate English leader of Lexington. Having married Sarah Morton against his father's wishes, and receiving no assistance from his father-in-law, Le Grand nevertheless formed his own firm in Lexington, managing to keep going for some time, and gaining in public esteem by his failure. He subsequently operated an auction and commission house.—William A. Leavy, "A Memoir of Lexington and Its Vicinity," *Register of the Kentucky State Historical Society,* vol. 40, p. 362.

LEWIS, JOSEPH. *Pennsylvania.* A merchant, living on South Second Street in Philadelphia, he owned warehouses on Dock Street.

LEWIS, JOSHUA. *Louisiana.*

LEWIS, REEVE. *Pennsylvania.* He also was a Philadelphia merchant, located on South Fourth Street.

LEWIS, SAMUEL N. (1785-1840). *Pennsylvania.* He was one of the most prominent Philadelphia manufacturers, operating the largest white lead factory in the country. He was the founder of the Society for Supplying the Poor with Soup, and treasurer of the fishing club, the State in Schuylkill. —Scharf and Westcott, *History of Philadelphia,* vol. III, pp. 2275-76.

LEXINGTON LIBRARY. *Kentucky.* James Brown, Thomas January and Samuel Postlewaite, among Wilson's subscribers, were among the first 13 shareholders when the Library was organized in 1795.

By 1804 there were 780 volumes. A lottery in 1810, the year of Wilson's visit, raised money for the purchase of books.—William Leavy, *A Memoir of Lexington and Its Vicinity,* pp. 129-31. W. H. Perrin, *Kentucky: A History of a State,* Chicago, 1807, p. 289.

LINCOLN, DANIEL W. *New Hampshire.*

LIVINGSTON, BROCKHOLST (1757-1823). *New York.* Justice of the Supreme Court. The son of the governor of New Jersey, he was a student at Princeton under Dr. Witherspoon, fought in the Revolution, and was private secretary to John Jay, his brother-in-law. He lived at 37 Broadway at the time of Wilson's visit.—*Dictionary of American Biography,* vol. XI, p. 312. *Longworth's New York Almanac.*

LIVINGSTON, ROBERT B. (1745-1813). *New York.* A graduate of Columbia, and John Jay's law partner, he was minister to France, where with James Monroe he negotiated the Louisiana Purchase. At the time of Wilson's visit, he was largely concerned with Fulton's steamboat, which he had backed.—*Dictionary of American Biography,* vol. XI, p. 320.

LLOYD, JAMES. *Massachusetts.* He was a merchant, living on Kilby Street in Boston.

LORMAN, WILLIAM. *Maryland.* A partner in the firm of Lorman and Fulford, merchants, he lived in St. Paul's Lane in Baltimore.

LOUDON, ARCHIBALD. *Pennsylvania.*

LOYALL, GEORGE. *Virginia.* Born in Norfolk in 1789, he was a twenty-year-old graduate of William and Mary when he subscribed to the *Ornithology.* He later served in Congress, and became naval agent in Norfolk.—William Allen. D. D., *An American Biographical and Historical Dictionary.*

LUCAS, FIELDING. *Maryland.*

MACNAIR, EBENEZER. *Virginia.* A resident of Richmond, he died in 1821.—*Virginia Magazine of History and Genealogy,* vol. XX, p. 369.

MACNEIL, ARCHIBALD. *North Carolina.* A member of the state legislature at the time of Wilson's Southern trip, he was later a Congressman (1825-27). He settled in Texas in 1836, and during the gold rush led a group of 100 men to California. He died in a sandstorm in Arizona, in which most of the party perished.—*Biographical Directory of the American Congress,* p. 1549.

MADISON, JAMES. *Virginia.* The fourth President of the United States, Madison was awaiting his inauguration in March, 1809, when Wilson visited him to secure his subscription to the *Ornithology.*

MAGRUDER, PATRICK. *District of Columbia.* The second Librarian of Congress, he served until shortly before the burning of Washington during the War of 1812.—William Dawson Johnson, *History of the Library of Congress.*

MANIGAULT, GABRIEL. *South Carolina.* Born in 1758, a member of a prominent and wealthy South Carolina family, Manigault was a rice planter, but he was also an extremely gifted amateur architect whose buildings gave Charleston much of its distinctive charm. He had completed Society Hall shortly before Wilson's visit. He died in that same year, 1809.— Robert Molloy, *Charleston,* pp. 142, 193.

MARIS, RICHARD (1772-1817). *Pennsylvania.* A merchant, living at 88 Mulberry Street in Pennsylvania, Maris was married to Rachel Ross, and had accumulated considerable property.

MARTIN, JAMES. *Pennsylvania.* He was a bookbinder, at 369 High Street in Philadelphia.

MASON, GEORGE. *District of Columbia.* He was the son of John Mason, the builder of a magnificent mansion on Analostan Island in the Potomac, and the grandson of the celebrated George Mason of Gunston Hall, the author of the Bill of Rights.— Hugh Taggart, *Old Georgetown,* Columbia Historical Society, Washington, vol. II, pp. 120-24.

MASON, JOHN, D.D. (1770-1829). *New York.* Educated at Columbia and at the University of Edinburgh (1791), he traveled extensively through Britain to raise funds for the General Theological Seminary, which he established in New York in 1804, becoming professor of theology. He was later president of Dickinson College.—*Dictionary of American Biography,* vol. XII, p. 368.

MATHER, JAMES. *Louisiana.* A member of the legislative council in Claiborne's time as governor, he later became mayor of New Orleans.—*Official Letter Books of W. C. C. Claiborne.*

MATHER, JAMES, JR. *Louisiana.*

McALPIN, JAMES. *Pennsylvania.* He was a merchant tailor, at 122 Chestnut Street in Philadelphia.

McINSEY, JOSEPH. *Pennsylvania.*

McIntyre, Archibald. *New York.* An able and far-sighted industrialist, he developed the iron ore deposits in the Adirondacks, their location near the headwaters of the Hudson revealed by an Indian named Sabelle. He built steel mills in New Jersey, and shipped high-grade ore to Pennsylvania works. He was building the Elba Works on the Au Sable River at the time of Wilson's visit.—James Leander Bishop, *History of American Manufactures,* vol. I, p. 537.

McKesson, John. *New York.*

McKinnie, Joseph P. *Georgia.* A Savannah capitalist, he was one of the organizers of the Savannah Steamship Company. Their vessel, built in the New York yards of Potts and McKinnie, was the *Savannah,* the first steamship to cross the Atlantic.

Medical Society of South Carolina. "The first medical society in South Carolina was formed in 1789 and incorporated in 1794."—Robert Mills, *Statistics of South Carolina.*

Messonier, Henry. *Maryland.* He was a merchant, living on South Street in Baltimore.—*Baltimore Directory and Citizens Register.*

Miller, Daniel H. (1783-1831). *Pennsylvania.* Congressman from 1823 until 1831, a Jacksonian Democrat, he was one of Wilson's closest friends. In his early years he was an ironmonger, living on Second Street near Arch in Philadelphia, with his brother-in-law Nicholas Jones his neighbor. Miller was an Episcopalian, a vestryman of St. John's Church from its founding. He established a large and profitable glass works in New Jersey, and in politics was an intimate adviser of Governor George Wolf of Pennsylvania.—Correspondence in the Pennsylvania Historical Society. Obituary, *National Gazette and Literary Register,* April 24, 1831.

Miller, Joseph M. *Pennsylvania.* An innkeeper in Philadelphia, he was an uncle of Daniel Miller, who was named in his will (1829) as executor of his estate.

Miller, M. *Georgia.* He was the Attorney General of the state at the time of Wilson's visit in 1809.

Miller, William. *Louisiana.* At the time Wilson was in New Orleans (May, 1810) a William Miller had recently arrived there from Virginia, searching for a permanent location, Governor Claiborne sending letters of introduction to prominent citizens to aid him in his purchase of property.—

Official Letter Books of W. C. C. Claiborne, vol. IV, p. 373.

Milligan, Joseph. *District of Columbia.* He was a printer and book publisher, located in Georgetown, then an independent town in the District.

Mitchell, David B. *Georgia.* He was one of the allies of Senator Jackson in opposing the Yazoo land speculation, and subsequently became governor of Georgia.—Rev. William Bacon Stevens, *A History of Georgia,* vol. II, p. 202.

Monroe, James. *Virginia.* Fifth President of the United States. Monroe was a fifty-one-year-old Virginian in a temporary state of suspended political activity at the time he subscribed to the *Ornithology.* After four years abroad as minister in Paris and London, he returned to his plantation, Oak Hill, in December, 1807. Shortly after Wilson's visit Monroe's career began again when he was elected to the Virginia House of Delegates, after which he was elected governor, and returned to the national scene as Madison's Secretary of State.

Montgomery, William W. *Louisiana.* His home was on Levee Street in New Orleans.

Moore, Rt. Reverend Bishop Benjamin (1748-1816). *New York.* The president of Columbia College, Bishop Moore was graduated from Columbia in 1768, ordained in England, and became rector of Trinity Church in New York in 1800, Bishop of New York the following year.—*Dictionary of American Biography,* vol. XIII, p. 115.

Moreau Lislet. *Louisiana.* The confusions about this man's name were baffling. He appeared among Wilson's subscribers as Listet, Moreau. Claiborne called him variously Moreau de Listery, Moreau Lislel, Mr. Moreau Lislet, and was relieved to be able to call him simply Judge Moreau after elevating him to the bench.—*Official Letter Books of W. C. C. Claiborne.*

Morgan, Benjamin. *Louisiana.* He was originally from Philadelphia, a merchant who became a surveyor and was employed by the Spanish authorities in New Orleans.

Morgan, George W. *Louisiana.* He was a captain of the militia at the time of Wilson's visit to New Orleans in 1810.—*Official Letter Books of W. C. C. Claiborne.*

Morris, Gouverneur. *New York.* The celebrated

Revolutionary figure, he graduated from Columbia in 1768, served in the Continental Congress, was a delegate to the Constitutional Convention, and later minister to France, and Senator from New York.—*Dictionary of American Biography,* vol. XIII, p. 209.

MORRISON, JAMES. *Kentucky.* At the time of Wilson's visit to Lexington in 1810, Morrison was devoting his immense wealth "to elegant hospitality and the judicious patronage of deserving young men." Commonly called Colonel Morrison, he was one of the first merchants in Lexington, moving there from Pittsburgh after an heroic Revolutionary career. He was a land commissioner, Supervisor of Revenue, Navy agent, Quartermaster General during the War of 1812, and chairman of the board of trustees of Transylvania, to which he left $50,000. —Lewis Collins, *Historical Sketches of Kentucky,* vol. II, p. 180, 277. William Leavy, *A Memoir of Lexington and Its Vicinity,* p. 313.

MORSE, JEDEDIAH, D. D. (1761-1826). *Massachusetts.* One of the most famous of New England ministers, he graduated from Yale in 1783 and for more than 30 years was pastor at Charlestown, Massachusetts. He was also celebrated as a geographer.

MORTON and WALLACE. *Pennsylvania.*

MORTON, WILLIAM. *Kentucky.* The younger son of a titled English family, he was known as Lord Morton in Lexington. He used the family crest on his plate, lived lavishly, and at the time of Wilson's visit in 1810 was building Thorn Hill, a mansion in five acres of park in the town. Morton was the organizer of an insurance company, the first in the state, at a time when the legislature was hostile to banking and would not charter banks. As is well known, Aaron Burr, meeting the same situation in New York, organized a company to supply New York City with fresh water, one clause in the charter permitting the water company to invest surplus funds, which made it a bank—it became the Bank of Manhattan. Using the same device, Lord Morton established a prosperous insurance company which issued notes and loaned money. The bank thus established loaned $25,000 to further Burr's conspiracy.—Lewis Collins, *Historical Sketches of Kentucky,* pp. 438-516. William Leavy, *A Memoir of Lexington and Its Vicinity.* Thomas Perkins Abernathy, *The Burr Conspiracy,* p. 23. *Encyclopedia Americana,* 1904, vol. II. "Banks and Banking," *Lexington and the Blue Grass Country,* Federal Writers Project, Lexington, Ky., 1938.

MOUNTAIN, JAMES. *Pennsylvania.* He was a resident of Pittsburgh at the time he subscribed to the *Ornithology.*

MURRAY, GEORGE. *Pennsylvania.* An engraver who cut many of the plates for the *Ornithology,* Murray lived at 230 Pine Street.

MURRAY, JOHN R. *New York.* A prominent Presbyterian layman, he was a founder and for eight years president of the New York Chamber of Commerce and a founder of the New York Academy of Fine Arts.—Martha Lamb, *History of the City of New York.* John W. Francis, *Old New York,* New York, 1866.

NEILL, LEWIS. *Pennsylvania.* He was a merchant in Philadelphia, in the firm of Lewis and Hurley Neill.

NEUFVILLE, ISAAC. *South Carolina.*

NEVILLE, PRESLEY. *Pennsylvania.* He was a Pittsburgh resident when he subscribed to the *Ornithology,* a prominent member of the Old Round Church (Episcopal).—*Pennsylvania Magazine of History and Biography,* vol. XIX, p. 350.

NEW HAMPSHIRE MEDICAL SOCIETY. *New Hampshire.*

NEW ORLEANS LIBRARY. *Louisiana.* This was originally a privately owned circulating library, purchased and converted into a free public library in 1842.—John Smith Kendell, *History of New Orleans,* New York, 1922, vol. II, p. 662.

NEW YORK SOCIETY LIBRARY. *New York.* Started in 1700, with gifts of books from England, it was chartered by George III in 1772, but was largely destroyed during the Revolution. It was the official Library of Congress when the government was located in New York. In 1795 a magnificent building was erected in the garden of Joseph Winters on the corner of Nassau and Cedar Streets, where this famous institution was located at the time Wilson secured it as a subscriber. John Forbes, who served from 1794 to 1824, was librarian at the time.— James Grant Wilson, *Memorial History of the City of New York,* vol. IV, pp. 106-9. Martha Lamb, *History of the City of New York,* p. 418.

NEWTON, GEORGE (1768-1847). *Virginia.* He was born in Norfolk of a prominent family, married a widow from the Barbadoes, and prospered. A

United States Senator from 1798 to 1805, he later served in the House.—*Virginia Magazine of History and Biography,* vol. III, p. 306. *Biographical Directory of the American Congress,* p. 1614.

NOTT, ELIPHALET, D. D. (1773-1866). *New York.* A celebrated Presbyterian clergyman at Albany, he became president of Union College, and amassed a fortune from a patented stove and other heating devices.—*Dictionary of American Biography,* vol. XIII, p. 580.

NOTT, WILLIAM. *Louisiana.* "Livingston, Workman, Major Nott, the brothers Alexander and some of the first characters in the United States were involved in a scheme to seize Baton Rouge, erect the ancient Mexican standard, and collect forces there . . ." (From the first official report of the Burr conspiracy in the spring of 1806).—*Official Letter Books of W. C. C. Claiborne.* Thomas Perkins Abernathy, *The Burr Conspiracy,* p. 26.

OGDEN, DAVIS B. *New York.* A capitalist and a prominent Whig, he was a founder of the New-York Historical Society.

O'HARA, GENERAL JAMES (1754-1819). *Pennsylvania.* The founder of Pittsburgh, he served heroically with General Anthony Wayne after reaching Pennsylvania from Ireland, built a glass works and brewery, accumulated wealth, and was hospitable, liberal, beneficent and exceedingly popular.—*Dictionary of American Biography,* vol. XIV, p. 3.

ORD, GEORGE (1781-1863). *Pennsylvania.* Little can be definitely stated about this remarkable man, the least known of familiar people. His biographer was unable to learn whether he was born in Philadelphia or in England, and while he was well educated it was not known where he went to school. His father, born in Britain, was a sea captain, and is said to have smuggled munitions to the colonists during the Revolution. He married the daughter of a wealthy Swedish family, and formed the firm of George Ord, ship chandler and rope maker. Nothing is known of the early years of his son, except that he was acquiring a collection of obsolete words, which led to a quarrel with the author of the dictionary, Noah Webster, and Ord reportedly gave his collection to the English editor of a revision of Dr. Johnson's dictionary. After his father's death, Ord was nominal head of the firm, in which his mother was a partner, but he was known only as a sportsman and hunter. In 1812 Ord "associated himself with a coterie of more advanced naturalists" who organized the Academy of Natural Science in

Philadelphia. As a result of his work with Wilson, he was elected to the Philosophical Society, was secretary for nine years, and president for seven years. He married in 1815. A daughter died in infancy, and a son became an accomplished portrait painter. Ord gave a fortune to the Pennsylvania Hospital, where his wife was confined with a mental illness. Beginning about 1824 (so far as is known), his conflict with Audubon, springing from his charge that Audubon plagiarized Wilson's work, lasted until his death. He found an ally in Charles Waterton, the eccentric English naturalist, with whom he spent much time touring Europe. After his death the Philosophical Society commissioned Henry Lea, the historian, to write Ord's biography, but no trace of any such work has been found. The family worshipped at Old Swedes Church, where both Ord and his father are buried.—*Proceedings of the Delaware Ornithological Club,* vol. XII, Philadelphia, 1908. Records, Old Swedes Church, Philadelphia. Pennsylvania Historical Society.

OVERACKER, GEORGE. *Mississippi.* He was an associate of William Dunbar, and a member of the jury which tried Aaron Burr.

OVERTON, JAMES, M.D. *Kentucky.* He was one of the founders of the Kentucky Society for Promoting Useful Knowledge. William Barry was his brother-in-law.—William Leavy, *A Memoir of Lexington and Its Vicinity,* p. 315. Lewis Collins, *Historical Sketches of Kentucky,* p. 274.

PAHLEN, COUNT J. *Russia.*

PATTERSON, REVEREND ROBERT. *Pennsylvania.*

PATTON, CHARLES. *Louisiana.* He was a slave auctioneer in New Orleans.

PEALE, RUBENS (1784-1865). *Pennsylvania.* A son of Charles Willson Peale, he managed the Philadelphia Museum his father founded, later creating similar institutions in Baltimore and New York.—*New-York Historical Society Dictionary of Artists in America, 1564-1860.*

PELL, ALFRED S. *New York.*

PENDELL, THOMAS H. *Kentucky.*

PENNSYLVANIA HOSPITAL. *Pennsylvania.* Two copies. Founded in Philadelphia in 1750, and occupying the area from Spruce to Pine Streets, and from Eighth to Ninth, the Pennsylvania Hospital buildings were "the largest and most conveniently calculated in the United States for the humane and charitable purpose for which they were erected" (*The Traveler's Directory*, 1802). The Library of the hospital was established in 1762.

PENNSYLVANIA LEGISLATURE. *Pennsylvania*. Three copies. Wilson attended the session of the legislature in February, 1810, disgusted with "a pitiful, squabbling, political mob," but adding, "I must exempt from this censure a few intelligent individuals, friends of science and possessed of taste . . ." (Letter to Alexander Lawson, February 22, 1810).

PENTLAND, E. *Pennsylvania*.

PHILADELPHIA LIBRARY. *Pennsylvania*. Three copies. The Library Company, the outgrowth of Benjamin Franklin's Club for Mutual Improvement, was the oldest public library in the United States, opening in 1731. "It was incorporated in 1742, since which time the collection of books has greatly increased (to) upward of 12,000 volumes . . ." (*Traveler's Directory*, 1802).

PIKE, JOHN C. *Virginia*.

PINCKNEY, GENERAL CHARLES COTESWORTH (1746-1825). *South Carolina*. He was born in South Carolina, educated at Oxford, studied law in London, and military arts at the Royal Academy in France. He was in command at Fort Moultrie in the Revolution, a minister to France (ordered out of the country by the Directory) and a candidate of the Federalists for the Presidency in 1804 and 1808.—*Dictionary of American Biography*, vol. XIV, p. 614.

PINCKNEY, MAJOR THOMAS (1750-1828). *South Carolina*. Brother of the above, he was educated at Oxford and the Middle Temple, an aide to General Lincoln in the Revolution, governor of South Carolina, and minister to England. His plantation, Fairfield, adjoined that of General Peter Horry.—*Dictionary of American Biography*, vol. XIV, p. 617. *South Carolina*, Federal Writers Project, New York, 1941, p. 280.

PITOT, J. *Louisiana*.

POLLOCK, GEORGE. *Pennsylvania*. He was listed in the Philadelphia directory as a gentleman who lived at 172 Chestnut Street.

PORTER, COMMODORE DAVID (1780-1843). *Louisiana*. Born in Boston, a midshipman on the *Constitution*, he fought in Tripoli, and was an outstanding naval figure when ordered to New Orleans at the time of the Terre aux Boeufs crisis. During the War of 1812 his exploits on the *Essex* made him a national hero. He entered the Mexican navy in 1826. Still later he was American consul-general to the Barbary States, and chargé d'affaires at Constantinople.—*Dictionary of American Biography*, vol. XV, p. 83.

POSTLEWAITE, SAMUEL. *Mississippi*. With his brother John Postlewaite (cashier of the Kentucky Insurance Bank) he created a famous inn at Lexington, renowned for its civilized standards on the frontier. Moving to Natchez, Samuel Postlewaite was successful as a merchant, "and married a young lady of beauty and wealth." This was Ann Dunbar, the oldest daughter of William Dunbar. Postlewaite was one of Burr's agents. He was the executor of William Dunbar's estate.—Thomas Perkins Abernathy, *The Burr Conspiracy*, p. 101. Mrs. Dunbar Rowland, *Life, Letters and Papers of William Dunbar*. William A. Leavy, "A Memoir of Lexington and Its Vicinity," *Register of the Kentucky State Historical Society*, vol. 40, p. 125.

POTTS, WILLIAM. *Virginia*.

PRENTICE, JOSEPH (1745-1809). *Virginia*. He was a graduate of William and Mary, a member of Patrick Henry's privy council during the Revolution, and a judge of the general court until his death. It was his resolution in the Virginia house of delegates that led ultimately to the calling of the Constitutional Convention.

PRINCE, REVEREND DR. JOHN (1751-1813). *Massachusetts*. The most prominent of the Unitarian ministers of New England, he graduated from Harvard in 1776, and was called to the First Church in Salem, where he remained until his death. He left his large and valuable library to the church.

PURDIE, THOMAS. *Virginia*. He was a resident of Norfolk, a graduate of William and Mary.

PURVIANCE, HENRY. *Kentucky*. A wealthy planter who lived near Lexington, he built up a large and valuable library, which was purchased by the Lexington Library in 1812-1813.—William Leavy, *A Memoir of Lexington and Its Vicinity*, p. 131.

QUINCY, JOSIAH (1772-1864). *Massachusetts*. At the time of Wilson's visit to Boston in 1808, he was a lawyer, with offices on Half Court Square in Boston. He had been elected to Congress as a Federalist. From 1829 until 1849 he was president of Harvard. —*Dictionary of American Biography*, vol. XV, p.

308. *Biographical Directory of the American Congress,* p. 1711.

RADCLIFFE, L. C. *South Carolina.*

RALPH, JOHN R. *England.*

RALSTON, G. *Virginia.* He was a partner in the firm of A. and G. Ralston in Richmond.

RAPHAEL, STEPHEN. *Maryland.* He was a merchant, with offices on South Street in Baltimore.

REA, ALEXANDER. *New York.*

REED, JOSEPH. *Pennsylvania.* He was a lawyer, and the recorder of the city of Philadelphia.

REIGART, ADAM. *Pennsylvania.* A native of Lancaster, Pennsylvania, he founded the firm of Adam Reigart and Son, wine and spirit merchants.—S. W. Carruthers, M. D., *Ancestry of the Family of John Haldman and Anna Reigart.*

RICHARDSON, CHARLES. *South Carolina.*

RICHARDSON, NATHANIEL. *Pennsylvania.* Born in Ireland in 1779, he came to Pittsburgh with his father in 1798, operating a store there while his father traded down the Ohio and Mississippi. He built the first greenhouse in Pittsburgh, prospered as a drygoods merchant, and failed when he started a music store. "He was well educated and very fond of music. He was also fond of hunting, always kept good dogs, and used to send to England for them." —Lawrence Eton Richardson, *Nathaniel Richardson, 1779-1851,* Concord, N. H., 1960.

RICHMOND LIBRARY. *Virginia.* It was launched in 1788, and books were purchased from funds raised by lottery. Thomas Nicholson was librarian.—Samuel Mordecai, *Richmond in By-Gone Days,* Richmond, 1856.

RITTENHOUSE, JOHN B. *District of Columbia.*

ROBERTSON, THOMAS BOLLING. *Louisiana.* The third governor of Louisiana, he was a graduate of William and Mary.—*Dictionary of American Biography,* vol. XVI, p. 28.

ROBERTSON, WILLIAM. *New York.* A merchant, dealing in chinaware, Robertson's store was at 226 Greenwich Street in New York.—*Longworth's New York Almanac.*

RODGERS, DR. JOHN K. B. *New York.* He was a distinguished physician, one of the founders of the American Museum, from which the New-York Historical Society developed.—James Grant Wilson, *Memorial History of the City of New York,* vol. III, pp. 16, 60.

ROGERS, JOHN. *New York.* A grocer, he operated a store in Oak Street in New York City.

ROGERS, DR. WILLIAM. *Louisiana.* He practiced medicine in New Orleans, was connected with the Charity Hospital there, and lived at 80 rue de Chartres.—*Letter Books of W. C. C. Claiborne. New Orleans in 1805.*

ROSCOE, WILLIAM (1753-1831). *England.* A celebrated lawyer, representing Liverpool in Parliament, he was also a well-known historian and biographer, and an amateur botanist of ability. Roscoe was a pioneer in the movement to emancipate the slaves. —*Dictionary of National Biography.*

ROSE, WILLIAM STEUART. *London, England.*

RUSSELL, ABRAHAM. *New York.* He was a mason and builder.—*Longworth's New York Almanac.*

RUSSELL, HAMILTON. *Louisiana.*

SARGEANT, WINTHROP. *Mississippi.* The first territorial governor of Mississippi, replaced by Claiborne when his term expired, Sargeant lived in retirement on his plantation near Natchez when he subscribed to the *Ornithology.*—*Dictionary of American Biography,* vol. XVI, p. 368.

SAUL, JESSUP. *Louisiana.* "Jessup Saul" may have been a misreading of Joseph Saul, who was a prominent citizen of New Orleans at the time of Wilson's visit there.

SAUVE, PIERRE. *Louisiana.* He was a member of the legislative council in the territorial government, one of the most prominent of the French citizens to support the American government, resigning, however, when Claiborne vetoed the civil code that had been drawn up by James Brown and Moreau Listlet.—*Official Letter Books of W. C. C. Claiborne.* Thomas Perkins Abernathy, *The Burr Conspiracy,* p. 169.

SAVANNAH LIBRARY. *Georgia.* While the library was started as a circulating library on a commercial basis in 1798, it had only recently been organized as a public library at the time of Wilson's visit in 1809.

SAY, WILLIAM LEVI. *Virginia.*

SCHENK, PETER. *New York.* He was the surveyor of the customs in New York at the time of Wilson's visit in 1808. He was active in encouraging science, one of the founders of the American Institute.

SCHNEIDER, JOHN. *New York.*

SCHOOLBRED, JAMES. *Virginia.*

SCHRODER, HENRY. *Maryland.* A merchant, his firm (Henry Schroder & Son) was located at No. 1 Schroder Row in Baltimore.—*Baltimore Directory and Citizens Register.*

SEIP, DR. FREDERICK. *Mississippi.* He was William Dunbar's physician, and an enthusiastic and perceptive amateur ornithologist.—Mrs. Dunbar Rowland, *Life, Letters and Papers of William Dunbar.*

SELKELD, GEORGE. *London, England.*

SHAEFF, GEORGE. *Pennsylvania.* A carpenter, he had his shop in Rose Alley in Philadelphia.

SHAW, WILLIAM A. *Pennsylvania.* He was a merchant in Philadelphia.

SHELDON, DANIEL. *District of Columbia.*

SHORT, WILLIAM (1759-1849). *Pennsylvania.* Born in Virginia and educated at William and Mary, he received from Washington the first appointment to public office under the Constitution, with the unanimous consent of the Senate. He followed Jefferson as chargé d'affaires in Paris, and after long diplomatic service in Europe made his home in Philadelphia. He was one of Jefferson's close personal friends.—*Eminent Philadelphians,* p. 888.

SIMPSON, GEORGE, JR. *Pennsylvania.* He was the cashier of the Bank of the United States.

SIMPSON, WILLIAM. *Louisiana.*

SINGLETON, WILLIAM, M.D. *Virginia.*

SITGREAVES, SAMUEL. *Pennsylvania.*

SMEDES, ABRAHAM K. *New York.* He was a New York merchant, located on Pearl Street.

SMITH, CHARLES. *Pennsylvania.*

SMITH, D. A. *Maryland.* He was the cashier of the Mechanics Bank in Baltimore.

SMITH, J. KILTY. *Louisiana.* He was one of the most prominent merchants of New Orleans.—Marquis James, *Andrew Jackson, the Border Captain,* pp. 215-16.

SMITH, JACOB G. *Maryland.* He was a stage-coach operator with headquarters in Baltimore.

SMITH, NATHAN, M.D. (1762-1828). *New Hampshire.* He started the medical school at Dartmouth and later at Bowdoin. Born in Massachusetts, he taught in rural schools, saw service on the Canadian border during the Revolution, and studied medicine after assisting at an amputation.—William Allen, D.D., *An American Biographical and Historical Dictionary,* p. 699.

SMITH, R. S. *District of Columbia.*

SMITH, SAVAGE. *South Carolina.*

SMITH, WILLIAM LAUGHTON (1758-1812). *South Carolina.* At the time of Wilson's visit he had retired, and was serving as an official of the Charleston Library Society. Born in Charleston and educated in England and Switzerland, he married Charlotte Izard, the daughter of Ralph Izard. Smith served in Congress, where he was instrumental in getting James Thompson Callender discharged as reporter of debates. He was chargé d'affaires for Portugal and Spain.—*Dictionary of American Biography,* vol. XVII, p. 365.

SNYDER, SIMON. *Pennsylvania.* This name is listed as Smith Snyder, but is plainly an error, as Wilson wrote (February 22, 1810) that the newly elected Governor Snyder had subscribed to his books: "He seems an active man, of plain good sense, and little ceremony. . . ."—*Dictionary of American Biography,* vol. XVII, p. 389.

SPENCER, ELIZA. *Pennsylvania.*

SPENCER, ROBERT. *Pennsylvania.*

STEELE, JOHN. *Mississippi.* The Secretary of State of Mississippi, and Winthrop Sargent's personal secretary, he was a director of the Bank of Mississippi at Natchez.—*Official Letter Books of W. C. C. Claiborne.*

STEPHENS, W. *Georgia.*

STERRETT, JAMES. *Maryland.* General James Sterrett was a partner in the firm of Sweeting and Sterrett. He lived on Holliday Street in Baltimore.

STILES, JOSEPH. *Georgia.* He owned Vale Royal, a 1,000-acre plantation that became the dock area of Savannah. It had formerly belonged to the Scottish adventurer and Indian trader Lachlan McGillivray, and was worth about $275,000 at the time of Wilson's visit.—*Savannah River Plantations.*

ST. MARY'S COLLEGE. *Maryland.* This was a famous Jesuit institution, located on Pennsylvania Avenue in Baltimore.

STOTT, WATSON. *Pennsylvania.*

SULLIVAN, JOSHUA. *Pennsylvania.* A weaver, land-owner and innkeeper, he lived on property adjoining that of Miers Fisher in Fox Chase near Philadelphia, where Wilson worked on a loom. He was a Worshipful Grand Master of St. John's Lodge of the Masonic order. He owned a number of inns (in addition to property in New York State), the most famous of which were the Cross Keys and the Spread Eagle in Philadelphia.—Alexander Grosart, *Poems and Literary Prose of Alexander Wilson,* vol. I, p. 95. Townsend Ward, "A Walk to Darby," *Pennsylvania Magazine of History and Biography,* vol. III. James Hardie, *The Philadelphia Directory and Register.*

SUTTON, GEORGE. *Pennsylvania.*

SWAN, BENJAMIN L. *New York.* He was a director of the Bank of America, and one of the leading capitalists of New York City.

TANNER, BENJAMIN (1775-1848). *Pennsylvania.* Born in New York, he became an engraver in Philadelphia, launching an engraving business with his brother in 1811 to produce maps, and in 1818 starting another firm to manufacture bank notes. John Vallance, another of the engravers who worked on the *Ornithology,* was at one time his partner.

TAYLOR, JOHN. *South Carolina.* A Senator from South Carolina, and later governor of the state, Taylor was a member of Congress at the time of Wilson's visit.

TAYLOR, ROBERT H. *Virginia.*

TELFAIR, THOMAS. *Georgia.* The son of Governor Edward Telfair, he was one of the wealthiest men in the state. He was representing Georgia in the House of Representatives at the time Wilson visited Georgia.—*Dictionary of American Biography,* vol. XVIII, p. 361. *Biographical Directory of the American Congress,* p. 1903. Lucian Lamar Knight, *Georgia's Landmarks, Memorials and Legends,* vol. II, p. 545.

THOMAS, MOSES. *Pennsylvania.* His bookstore was located at 52 Chestnut in Philadelphia.—John A. Paxton, *Directory and Register.*

THORNDIKE, ISRAEL. *Massachusetts.* One of the outstanding New England merchants, who pioneered in trade with Russia, he was the brother-in-law of Moses Brown, the first American textile manufacturer. At the time of Wilson's visit he had recently left Salem to establish his home and warehouses in Boston. He was a discriminating collector, and returned to the United States a 3,000-volume collection of historical material assembled in Germany.—William Allen, D.D., *An American Biographical and Historical Dictionary. Dictionary of American Biography,* vol. XVIII, p. 498.

TRAPIER, W. W. *South Carolina.*

TRICOU, JOSEPH. *Louisiana.* He was one of the largest taxpayers of New Orleans, maintaining ten household slaves in his Royal Street home.—*New Orleans in 1805.*

TRIMBLE, JACOB. *Louisiana.*

TURNBULL, ALEXANDER. *Pennsylvania.*

TYLER, JOHN (1747-1813). *Virginia.* He was the governor of Virginia from 1808 until 1811 (being succeeded by James Monroe), then serving as a United States district judge. His son John became the tenth President of the United States.—*Dictionary of American Biography,* vol. XIX, p. 97.

URQUHART, DAVID. *Louisiana.* He lived on the rue de Chartres, and kept six household slaves there. He was a member of the territorial convention, where he argued for immediate statehood for Louisiana.—*New Orleans in 1805. Official Letter Books of W. C. C. Claiborne.*

URQUHART, THOMAS. *Louisiana.*

VALLANCE, JOHN. *Pennsylvania.* He was the veteran engraver of Philadelphia, an extremely talented craftsman, but unsteady and temperamental. He was located at the Academy of Fine Arts on Chestnut Street.

VANDER HORST, GENERAL ARNOLDUS. *South Carolina.* One of a noteworthy group of soldiers who fought with Marion, he became governor of South Carolina after the Revolution.—David Duncan Wallace, *South Carolina*, Chapel Hill, N. Car., 1951.

VAN RENSSELAER, STEPHEN. *New York.* He was a native of Albany, married to the daughter of Supreme Court Justice William Paterson. He became an outstanding officer in the War of 1812.—*Dictionary of American Biography*, vol. XIX, p. 211.

VAUGHAN, WILLIAM. *London, England.* An extremely prominent and powerful London merchant, an author and a fellow of the Royal Society, Vaughan was the son of a famous engineer and canal builder. His mother was Sarah Hallowell of Boston.—*Dictionary of National Biography.*

VERPLANCK, DANIEL CROMMELIN. *New York.* Born in 1762 of an old Dutch family in New York, he was sent to Holland to be educated. Elected to Congress (1802-1809) he was subsequently a judge, and a leader in philanthropic enterprises in New York. He maintained his office at 8 Pine Street at the time of Wilson's visit.—Martha Lamb, *History of the City of New York*, p. 418.

VICK, BURWELL. *Mississippi.* He was the son of Newitt Vick, the founder of Vicksburg.

VON PHUL, HENRY. *Kentucky.* He was a clerk or a salesman in the mercantile house of Thomas Hart in Lexington, Kentucky, at the time of Wilson's visit there in 1810. The following year he moved to St. Louis, becoming a partner in the hat firm of William Smith, and became wealthy. He died in 1874, the oldest merchant in the city. —William Leavy, *A Memoir of Lexington and Its Vicinity*, p. 256.

WADDINGTON, JOSHUA. *New York.* A director of the Bank of New York, and one of the leading capitalists of the city, Waddington was a Tory, a target for retaliatory legislation after the Revolution. Alexander Hamilton defended him as a matter of principle in a famous case based on the laws of trespass, by which patriots who had been driven from their homes during the Revolution claimed damages from Tories as responsible. Hamilton won the case.—James Grant Wilson, *Memorial History of the City of New York*, vol. III, p. 29.

WADSWORTH, DANIEL. *Connecticut.* He was the son of Colonel Jeremiah Wadsworth, a great merchant who fought in the Revolution and also carried out confidential missions in France. Wadsworth organized the Hartford Fire Insurance Company.—J. Hammond Trumbull, *Memorial History of Hartford County.*

WALKER, ROBERT. *Virginia.*

WARDER, JOHN. *Pennsylvania.* He was a merchant in Philadelphia. —John A. Paxton, *Directory and Register.*

WARREN, JOHN, M.D. (1753-1815). *Massachusetts.* He entered Harvard at fourteen, and graduated at eighteen. After studying medicine with his older brother Joseph, he practiced in Salem, took part in the Boston Tea Party, and when Joseph was killed at Bunker Hill, volunteered for service. Washington put him in charge of the military hospital at Cambridge, though he was only twenty-two. He saw service in New York, Long Island, at Trenton and Princeton. He organized the medical school at Harvard after the Revolution, serving as professor of anatomy and surgery.—*Dictionary of American Biography*, vol. XIX, p. 479.

WARREN, JOHN COLLINS (1778-1856). *Massachusetts.* The oldest son of the above, he practiced with his father. He was an amateur naturalist, president of the Boston Society of Natural History.—*Dictionary of American Biography*, vol. XIX, p. 480.

WASHINGTON, GENERAL WILLIAM (1752-1810). *South Carolina.* After his heroic exploits in the Revolution, this great soldier settled in Charleston, the home of his wife's family.—*National Cyclopedia of American Biography*, vol. II, pp. 492-93.

WATKINS, JOHN, M.D. *Louisiana.* The mayor of New Orleans at the time of the Burr crisis, he denounced General Wilkinson for his arbitrary rule of the city, demanding an investigation. Watkins in turn was denounced by Governor Claiborne for his association with Burr.—Thomas Perkins Abernathy, *The Burr Conspiracy*, pp. 30, 227.

WAY, A. and J. *District of Columbia.* This firm printed government documents. However, Andrew Way was the creator of a famous glass works on the Potomac.—Robert Harkness, "The Old Glass

House," *Records of the Columbia Historical Society,* Washington, vol. XVIII, pp. 209-38.

WAYNE, JAMES M. *Georgia.* Born in Savannah, the son of a British officer, Wayne graduated from Princeton in 1808, and was studying law in Savannah at the time of Wilson's visit in 1809. He served in the Georgia Hussars in the War of 1812, was mayor of Savannah, a judge, and served three terms in Congress. Jackson appointed him to the Supreme Court.—Rev. George White, *Historical Collections of Georgia,* New York, 1855, pp. 379-85.

WEEKS, EZRA. *New York.* He was an architect in New York, his offices located on Harrison Street. —*Longworth's New York Almanac.*

WELLS, LEMUEL. *New York.*

WEST, BENJAMIN (1738-1820). *England.* He was born in the town of Springfield near Philadelphia. Success as a portrait painter enabled him to go to Rome in 1760, and in 1763 his success in London led to his decision to remain there. He was a court painter to George III, and president of the Royal Academy. "I lately received from the celebrated Mr. West a proof impression of his grand historical picture of the death of Admiral Nelson— a present which I highly value" (Alexander Wilson to William Bartram, April 21, 1813).—*Dictionary of American Biography,* vol. XX, p. 6.

WEST, JOHN B. *Kentucky.* He was the first watchmaker in Kentucky, settling in Lexington in 1788. He was the son of the rector of St. Paul's Church in Baltimore; his brother was an artist who studied with Benjamin West. John West the watchmaker was an inventor as well, and built a steam engine in which springs, rather than a flywheel, prevented the connecting rods from getting on dead center. A steamboat was built with his engine for a trip to New Orleans, but evidently was not a success.— Lewis Collins, *Historical Sketches of Kentucky,* vol. I, p. 273.

WHEELAN, ISRAEL. *Pennsylvania.* He was the treasurer of the Schuylkill Bridge Company.

WHITE, DR. *Georgia.* A Dr. James White was a prominent Georgia citizen, appearing historically a short time earlier as United States Indian Commissioner. He dealt with McGillivray at one time.— Rev. William Bacon Stevens, *A History of Georgia,* vol. II, p. 432.

WILDER, J. and J. *Virginia.*

WILKINS, CHARLES. *Kentucky.* He was born in Pennsylvania and became one of the first merchants in Lexington. He was city clerk for many years, and a stockholder in the Kentucky Insurance Company. —William Leavy, *A Memoir of Lexington and Its Vicinity,* pp. 56, 312.

WILKINS, COLONEL JAMES. *Mississippi.* He was a young merchant of Natchez at the time of Wilson's visit. During the financial crisis of 1814, he personally carried thousands of dollars from Pittsburgh to keep the bank in Natchez open.—Joseph Dunbar Shields, *Natchez, Its Early History,* Louisville, Ky., 1930, p. 156.

WILKINS, WILLIAM. *Pennsylvania.* "William Wilkins, a merchant in Pittsburgh, and General Wilkins, . . . were brought into the conspiracy . . ." (Thomas Perkins Abernathy, *The Burr Conspiracy,* p. 76).

WILKINS, GENERAL WILLIAM. *Pennsylvania.* Secretary of War in the cabinet of General Tyler, Wilkins was born in Carlisle, graduated from Dickinson in 1802, and settled in Pittsburgh, where he became president of the Monongahela Bridge Company. Elected to Congress in 1828, he was a Senator in 1831, and subsequently minister to Russia. He was a major-general in the Pennsylvania Home Guards.—*Biographical Directory of the American Congress,* p. 2014.

WILKINSON, GENERAL JAMES (1757-1825). *District of Columbia.* He was the ranking general in command of the Army of the United States at the time Wilson met him in Charleston. Born in Maryland, he was a physician at the outbreak of the Revolution, was commissioned a captain, served under Benedict Arnold, and became aide-de-camp to General Gates and a brigadier general. He married a sister of Colonel Clement Biddle of Philadelphia. Settling in Kentucky after the Revolution, he was given a monopoly of trade down the Mississippi—all goods destined for New Orleans had to pass through his firm—in return for acting as a Spanish agent. In command of the troops at New Orleans he acted with Burr, then denounced him to Spain, and in the Burr trial was the government's chief witness against Burr. However, the trial turned into an inquiry into him, and the Terre aux Boeufs tragedy that came shortly after— Wilkinson insisted on quartering his troops in pestilential grounds below New Orleans, 795 of 2,000 dying of fever—ended his influence. He was cleared in an inquiry by Congress on the eve of

APPENDICES

the War of 1812, led troops unsuccessfully into Canada, and reached Washington in time to witness the burning of the capital. He was an agent of the American Bible Society in Mexico City when he died.—*Dictionary of American Biography,* vol. XX, p. 221. Daniel Clark, *Proofs of the Corruption of General James Wilkinson. Encyclopedia of Mississippi History.*

WILLIAMS, THOMAS. *Louisiana.* He was the collector of the Port of New Orleans, the closest friend of William Dunbar.—Mrs. Dunbar Rowland, *Life, Letters and Papers of William Dunbar.*

WILLIAMSBURG COLLEGE LIBRARY. *Virginia.* This evidently referred to the library of William and Mary, Wilson having spent some time at the college, where he was cordially received by the president, Bishop Madison.

WILLIAMSON, JOHN POSTELL. *Georgia.* The mayor of Savannah at the time of Wilson's visit, he inherited vast plantations, and owned several hundred slaves, buying Clifton, with 150 slaves, for $63,000. He lost heavily in the great Savannah fire of 1820.—*Savannah River Plantations,* p. 207.

WILLIAMSON, THOMAS. *Virginia.*

WILSON, JOHN LYDE. *South Carolina.* He lived at Columbia, South Carolina, and at the time of Wilson's visit in 1809 was a young lawyer who had recently been elected to the legislature. He subsequently became governor of South Carolina, favoring nullification, and a vehement opponent of Andrew Jackson.

WILSON, DR. PETER. *New York.* Born in Scotland and educated at the University of Aberdeen, he reached New York in 1763. He served six terms in the New Jersey legislature while acting as principal of an academy in Hackensack. From 1789 until 1820 he was professor of Greek and Latin at Columbia.—James Grant Wilson, *Memorial History of the City of New York,* vol. III, p. 519.

WINN, JOHN W. *Mississippi.*

WOODRUFF, G. *Georgia.*

WOODRUFF, GEORGE. *Pennsylvania.*

WORSELEY, W. W. *Kentucky.* He was the founder of the Lexington *Reporter,* the second newspaper to be started in Kentucky. About the time of Wilson's arrival in Lexington, he opened "a very handsome bookstore."—William Leavy, *A Memoir of Lexington and Its Vicinity,* p. 320.

WYNAN, JOHN. *New York.* He was a lawyer, with offices on Partition Street at the time of Wilson's visit.—*Longworth's New York Almanac.*

YEATES, JASPER. *Pennsylvania.* He was an eminent judge, the central figure of an attempted impeachment by Nathaniel Boileau.—William Allen, D.D., *An American Biographical and Historical Dictionary,* p. 745.

YOUNG, THOMAS. *Georgia.* He was a capitalist living in Savannah, one of the delegates to a convention to promote internal improvements, roads, canals and industry, in the state.—Lucian Lamar Knight, *Georgia's Landmarks, Memorials and Legends,* vol. II, pp. 863-64.

SOURCES

Alexander Wilson, *The American Ornithology,* Philadelphia: Bradford and Inskeep, 1808-1814, 9 vols.

Alexander Wilson, *American Ornithology: or The Natural History of the Birds of the United States,* with a continuation by Charles Lucian Bonaparte. The illustrative notes and life of Wilson by Sir William Jardine, bart., London: Whittaker, Treacher and Arnot, 1832, 3 vols.

The Poems and Literary Prose of Alexander Wilson, edited by Reverend Alexander B. Grosart, Paisley: Alexander Gardner, 1876, 2 vols.

WORKS ABOUT WILSON

Allen, Dr. Elsa Guerdrum, "The History of American Ornithology Before Audubon," *Transactions of the American Philosophical Society,* New Series, XLI, No. 3, 1951, pp. 387-591.

Allen, Dr. Elsa Guerdrum, "The American Career of Alexander Wilson," *Atlantic Naturalists,* VIII, No. 2, Nov.-Dec. 1952, pp. 61-76.

Anonymous, "Memoir of Wilson," *Poetical Works of Alexander Wilson,* Paisley, 1859.

Anonymous, *Men Who Have Risen,* London: J. Hagy & Co., n.d.

Anonymous, *Memoir of Alexander Wilson of Paisley,* Philadelphia: Carey and Lea, 1831.

Brightwell, C. Lucy, *Difficulties Overcome: Scenes in the Life of Alexander Wilson the Ornithologist,* London, 1861. A book for young people.

Crawfurd, Andrew, "Some Incidents in the Life of Alexander Wilson, collected in the Parish of Lochwinnoch," *The Paisley Magazine,* I, No. 11, November, 1828.

Crichton, Thomas, "Biographical Sketch of the late Alexander Wilson," by Senex. Reprinted from *The Weavers' Magazine,* vol. II, 1819.

Dickson, Reverend J. Bathurst, *The Life, Labors and Genius of Alexander Wilson,* Paisley: James Cooke, 1856. A pamphlet.

Hetherington, W. M., *Memoir of Alexander Wilson,* Edinburgh: Constable, 1831.

Paton, Allan Park, *Wilson the Ornithologist. A new chapter in his life,* London: Longmans Green, 1863. Wilson's letters to Charles Orr.

Peabody, William B. O., "Life of Alexander Wilson," *Library of American Biography,* edited by Jared Sparks, vol. II, Boston: Hilliard and Gray, 1839.

Seymour, Charles C. B., *Self-Made Men,* London, 1858.

Welker, Robert Henry, *Birds and Men: American Birds in Science, Art, Literature and Conservation, 1800-1900,* Cambridge, Mass.: Harvard University Press, 1955.

Wilson, James Southall, *Alexander Wilson, Poet-Naturalist,* New York: Neale, 1906.

UNPUBLISHED SOURCES

Parochial Registers, County of Renfrew, Paisley, in the Register General's Office, Edinburgh.

Cairn of Lochwinnoch Matters. Collected betwixt 1827 and 1837 by Andrew Crawfurd. 46 manuscript volumes, in the Paisley Free Public Library and Museum, presented by Miss Young of Freemount Terrace, Dowanhill, Glasgow. This extraordinary work was compiled by Dr. Crawfurd after he was stricken with fever and left an invalid as he began to practice medicine in Lochwinnoch. Each day he entered some local item of history, gossip, folklore, accounts of births and marriages, causes of deaths, suicides, fires, the number of windows in local factories, illegitimate births and accounts of curling matches, or bonspiels, wages, prices, sicknesses and weather conditions. The townspeople, in particular the elderly people, learning of his interest, made it a practice to call and give him their recollections. Often almost unbearably tedious, the *Cairn of Lochwinnoch* nevertheless builds up to one of the most remarkable and detailed accounts of the life of a community. It has been quarried by generations of Scottish historians for its social history. The smuggling of Wilson's father, the Wilson family, and Wilson's experiences in the region are detailed in the *Cairn,* which has been drawn on extensively. It has not been used in previous accounts of Wilson's life, except for a fragment published in the *Paisley Magazine* in 1828.

Church of Scotland Archives, Tolbooth St. Johns, Edinburgh.

Monument Scrapbook. This is a collection of material accumulated during the movement to raise a statue to Wilson in Paisley. It includes accounts of meetings, speeches by local historians, details on place of birth and the location of incidents in Wilson's life, several letters of Wilson not otherwise noted, and some items of information about people with whom Wilson associated in the United States that are not found in the American records of his life.

Treasonable Practices in Scotland. This is a collection of reports from British intelligence agents in Scotland to the Home Office in London, 1792-1793-1794, entitled *Correspondence—Home Office.*

The Library of the Museum of Comparative Zoology, Harvard University, contains a large collection of Wilson's letters, drawings, and some unpublished verse, the gifts of John E. Thayer. Most of the letters are published in Reverend Grosart's two-volume edition of Wilson's poetry and prose, which is remarkably complete. However, Grosart used no names in the letters, substituting dashes, and the individuals concerned are identified in this collection.

The Historical Society of Pennsylvania collection includes Wilson's certificate of naturalization, letters to the parents of his students, and a few notes on personal matters. The letters of Daniel Miller are in the autograph collection of Simon Gratz, and Wilson's illness is in the manuscript Journal and Ledger of Dr. Charles Caldwell, May 1, 1811, to February, 1815.

SUPPLEMENTARY MATERIAL

SCOTLAND

Anderson, William, *The Scottish Nation,* Edinburgh, 1880.

Archeological and Historical Collections County of Renfrew, Parish of Lochwinnoch, Paisley: Alex. Gardner, 1890, 2 vols.

Brodie, David, accountant, of Paisley, *A Short Set of Book-keeping by Double Entry,* Paisley, 1831.

Contemporaries of Burns and the More Recent Poets of Ayrshire, Edinburgh: Paton, Carber and Gilder, 1840.

Crichton, Thomas, "Memoir of the Life and Writings of John Witherspoon D D, late president of the College of New Jersey," *Edinburgh Christian Register.*

Crichton, Thomas, "Memoir of Wilson," in *The Weavers Magazine and Literary Companion,* Paisley: John Neilson, 1819, vol. I, May, 1819, pp. 97-107; June, 1819, pp. 145-60; July, 1819, pp. 193-218; August, 1819, pp. 241-72.

Cumming, Robert, *Essay Delivered at the Pantheon on Thursday, April 14, 1791, on the question, "Whether the exertions of Allan Ramsay or Robert Fergusson have done most to honor Scottish poetry";* with *Willie and Jaime,* an eclogue, Edinburgh, 1791.

Cumming, Robert, *Poems on Several Occasions,* with *The History of Mr. Wallace,* a novel, Edinburgh, 1791.

Cunningham, John, *The Church History of Scotland,* Edinburgh, 1882, 2 vols.

Foster, Joseph, *Members of Parliament—Scotland, 1357-1882,* London: Privately printed, 1882.

Fullerton, Colonel, *General View of the Agriculture of the County of Ayr*, Edinburgh, 1793.

Gilmour, David, *Paisley Weavers of Other Days*, Edinburgh, 1898.

Graham, H. C., *Social Life in Scotland in the 18th Century*, London, 1899.

Groome, Francis, ed., *Ordnance Survey*, London: Mackenzie, 1902.

Kay, John, *A Series of Original Portraits and Caricature Etchings by the late John Kay, with biographical sketches and illustrative anecdotes*, Edinburgh: Hugh Paton, 1837.

Lees, J. Cameron, *The Abbey of Paisley*, Paisley, 1878.

MacKeen, Norman, *An Eighteenth Century Lodge in Paisley*, Paisley: Alexander Gardner, 1909.

Mann, J. T., and Traill, H. D., *Social England*, London: Cassell, 1909.

Meek, Robert, *A Biographical Sketch of the Life of James Tytler*, Edinburgh, 1805.

Meikle, Henry, *Scotland*, New York: Neilson, 1947.

Meikle, Henry, *Scotland and the French Revolution*, Glasgow, 1912.

Metcalfe, William, *A History of Paisley, Scotland, 600-1908*, Paisley: Gardner, 1909.

Motherwell, William, *The Harp of Renfrewshire*, Paisley: Gardner, 1819.

Paisley Directory, Paisley: Neilson, 1812.

Parkhill, John, *The History of Paisley*, Paisley: Stewart, 1857.

Ramsay, Philip A., *Views of Renfrewshire*, Edinburgh: Lizars, 1834.

Ross, J., ed., *The Book of Scottish Poems: Ancient and Modern*, with memoirs of the authors by J. Ross, Paisley: Alexander Gardner, 1882.

Sharp, Elizabeth A., *William Sharp, a Memoir*, London: Heinemann, 1910.

Sinclair, Sir John, *The Statistical Record of Scotland*, Edinburgh: William Creech, 1793, 20 vols. This invaluable work was made up of reports from the ministers in every parish in Scotland, including census figures, births, deaths, farm conditions, weather, housing, industry, education. The *Statistical Record* naturally varied in quality from parish to parish, but is still a testimony to the high degree of literacy and the intellectual interests of the Scottish clergy of the time.
Beith, vol. VIII, 1793.
Cambeltown, vol. X.
Lochwinnoch, vol. XV, 1795.
Paisley, vol. VI.
Row, vol. IV.
Stranaer.

Tannahill, Robert, *Poems and Songs* edited by David Semple, Paisley: Alex. Gardner, 1900.

Topographical, Statistical and Historical Gazetteer of Scotland, Edinburgh: Fullerton, 1854, 2 vols.

Wilson, James Grant, *The Poets and Poetry of Scotland*, New York: Harpers, 1876, 2 vols.

Witherspoon, Rev. John, *Seasonable Advice to Young Persons*. Preached at the Laigh Church in Paisley, February 21st, 1762, Glasgow: Printed by Robert Urie, 1762.

UNITED STATES

Abbot, John, *The Natural History of the Rarer Lepidopterous Insects of Georgia*, Collected from the observations of Mr. John Abbot, by James Edward Smith, London: Printed by T. Bensley, 1797, 2 vols.

Allen, Dr. Elsa Guerdrum, "John Abbot, Pioneer Naturalist of Georgia," *Georgia Historical Quarterly*, vol. 41, No. 2, June, 1957.

Anderson, Sarah Travers Lewis, *Lewises, Meriwethers and Their Kin*, Richmond: Dietz Press, 1938.

Audubon, J. J., *The Life and Adventures of J. J.*

Audubon, the Naturalist, edited by his Widow, New York, 1868.

Bakeless, John, *Lewis and Clark*, New York, 1947.

Bennett, Whitman, *A Practical Guide to American Nineteenth Century Color Plate Books*, New York, 1943.

Bishop, James Leander, *History of American Manufactures, 1608-1806*, Philadelphia, 1863-1867, 2 vols.

Caldwell, Dr. Charles, *Autobiography*, with a

preface, notes and appendix by Harriet W. Warner, Philadelphia: Lippincott, Grambo and Co., 1855.

Callender, James Thomson, *History of the United States in the Year 1796,* Philadelphia: Snowden and McCorkle, 1797.

Callender, James Thomson, *The Political Progress of Britain,* Edinburgh, 1792.

Callender, James Thomson, *The Trial of James Thomson Callender for Sedition,* Richmond, 1800.

Carman, Albert Pruden, *Thomas Carman and Phoebe Pruden Carman,* Urbana-Champaign, Ill., 1935.

Cassell, Daniel K., *History of the Rittenhouse Family,* Germantown, Pa.: Privately printed, 1849.

Catesby, Mark, *The Natural History of Carolina, Florida and the Bahama Islands,* London, 1753.

Clark, Daniel, *Proofs of the Corruption of General James Wilkinson,* Philadelphia, 1809.

Collins, Varnum Lansing, *President Witherspoon, a Biography,* Princeton, N. J., 1925, 2 vols.

Cotterell, R. S., "The Natchez Trace," *Tennessee Historical Magazine,* April, 1921.

Darlington, William, *Memorial of John Bartram and Humphrey Marshall,* Philadelphia: Lindsay and Blakiston, 1849.

Dunlap, William, *History of the Arts of Design in the United States.* Boston: Goodspeed, 1918.

Ellicott, Andrew, *Journal,* Philadelphia, 1797.

Elliot, Major Charles Winslow, *Winfield Scott,* New York: Macmillan, 1937.

Folsom, Joseph Fulford, *Bloomfield Old and New,* Bloomfield, N. J., 1912.

Ford, Worthington Chauncey, *Thomas Jefferson and James Thomson Callender,* Brooklyn: Historical Printing Club, 1912.

Hamilton, Alexander, *Observation on Certain Documents written by Himself,* Philadelphia, 1796-1800.

Herrick, Francis, *Audubon the Naturalist,* New York: Appleton, 1917.

Hyslander, Clarence J., *American Scientists,* New York: Macmillan, 1935.

Jacobs, James Ripley, *Tarnished Warrior: Major General James Wilkinson,* New York: Macmillan, 1938.

Jorner, John W. ed., *Colonial Families of Philadelphia,* Philadelphia, 1911.

Leslie, Charles Robert, *Autobiographical Recollections,* edited by Tom Taylor, London, 1860.

Marshall, Park, "The True Route of the Natchez Trace," *Tennessee Historical Magazine,* September, 1915.

Mathews, Catherine van Cortlandt, *Andrew Ellicott, His Life and Letters,* New York, 1908.

McClellan, William Smith, *Smuggling in the American Colonies,* 1912.

Montgomery, Elizabeth, *Reminiscences of Wilmington,* Philadelphia, 1851.

Oberholtzer, Ellis Paxson, *Philadelphia, a History of the City and its People,* Philadelphia, n.d.

Pierce, Charles, *A Meteorological Account of the Weather in Philadelphia from January 1, 1790, to January 1, 1847,* Philadelphia: Lindsay and Blakiston, 1847.

Prescott, William H., *Charles Brockden Brown,* Boston, 1832.

Pursh, Frederick, *Flora Americae Septentrionalis. A Systematic Arrangement and Description of the Plants of North America,* London: White, Cockrane & Co., 1814, 2 vols.

Ramsay, G. D., *The Smugglers' Trade,* London: Royal Historical Society, 1952.

Rhoads, Samuel, "George Ord," *Cassina, the Proceedings of the Delaware Valley Ornithological Club,* Philadelphia, 1908.

Rowland, Dunbar, *Encyclopedia of Mississippi History,* Madison, Wis., 1909.

Rowland, Mrs. Dunbar, *Marking the Natchez Trace,* Mississippi Historical Society, 1910.

St. Andrews Society of Philadelphia, *Historical Catalogue 1749-1907,* Philadelphia, 1907.

Scharf, J. Thomas, and Westcott, Thompson, *History of Philadelphia,* Philadelphia, 1884.

Stone, Witmer, "Bird Migration Records of William Bartram," *The Auk, A Quarterly Journal of Ornithology,* July, 1913.

Stone, Witmer, "Some Unpublished Letters of Alexander Wilson and John Abbot," *The Auk, A Quarterly Journal of Ornithology,* October, 1906.

Stringham, Emerson, *Alexander Wilson, a*

Founder of Scientific Ornithology, Kerrville, Texas, 1958.

Ward, Townsend, "Second Street and Its Associations," *Pennsylvania Magazine of History and Biography,* vol. IV, 1880.

Ward, Townsend, "A Walk to Darby," *Pennsylvania Magazine of History and Biography,* vol. III, 1879.

Wharton, Francis, *Revolutionary Diplomatic Correspondence of the United States.* Published by the authority of Congress, Government Printing Office, 1889.

Wharton, Francis, *State Trials in the United States During the Administrations of Washington and Adams,* Philadelphia: Carey and Hart, 1849.

Wilkinson, James, *Memoirs of My Own Time,* Philadelphia, 1816.

Williams, Samuel Cole, *Early Travels in the Tennessee Country,* Johnson City, Tenn., 1928.

Index

INDEX

Brodie, David, 43-45, 47, 49, 52, 55-56, 60, 61, 75-76, 154, 259
Broom, Jacob, 84
Brown, Catherine (*see* Wilson, Mrs. Catherine Brown Urie)
Brown, Charles Brockden, 90, 114, 156, 163, 210
Brown, James, 231-32
Brown, Peggy, 63
Brown, Dr. Samuel, 230-31
Brown, Mrs. Samuel (*see* Percy, Katherine)
Bruce, James, 114
Bryan and Schatter, 191
Buccleuch, Duchess of, 63
Bulloch, William, 185
Bunting, cow, 155
Bunting, indigo, 115, 138, 153, 245
Bunting, painted, 181, 184, 228, 231
Bunting, rice, 99
Bunting, snow, 130, 132
Bunting, towhee (bullfinch, chewink, swamp sparrow), 181
Burns, John, 50
Burns, Robert, 33, 42, 47-48, 60, 62-65
Burr, Aaron, 93, 179

Caldwell, Dr. Charles, 187, 240, 258
Callender, James Thompson, 63, 73, 89-93, 121, 158, 178-79, 236
Cameron, Lady Margaret, 63
Campbell, Sir Alexander, 63
Captain Tom (slave of Reuben Lewis), 212, 216
Carman, Caleb, 96-97
Carman, John, 96-97
Carman, Joseph, 235
Carman, Mrs. Joseph (*see* Oliver, Elizabeth)
Carman, Joshua, 96-98
Carman, Margaret, 97, 108-9, 199, 235, 243-44, 260-61
Carman, Mary, 97
Carr, Robert, 155, 186, 192, 249, 256
Carr, Mrs. Robert (*see* Bartram, Ann)
Carrigain, Philip, 163
Catbird, 99, 116, 245
Catesby, Mark, 135, 170, 173, 177-78, 183, 186, 240-41
Cedarbird, 134, 138, 150
Chase, Thomas, 167

Chat, yellow-breasted, 115, 138, 245
Chatard, Dr. Ferdinand, 167
Chuck-will's-widow, 170, 219
Clark, Andrew, 60
Clark, Daniel, 188, 227, 229, 231
Clark, William, 187
Clay, Rev. Mr., 258
Clinton, De Witt, 162
Coale, Edward, 167
Cobbett, William, 137
Cochran, Robert, 172
Coffer, Joshua, 169
Colbert, George, 219
Colbert, Levi, 219
Collins, Thomas, 193
Collinson, Peter, 119, 186
Cooper, Thomas, 162, 169
Cooper, Mrs. Thomas (*see* Fairley, Mary)
Coryell, Henry, 258
Coues, Dr. Elliot, 238
Craig, Andrew, 39
Craig, John, 36, 38, 39, 52, 60
Craig, Mrs. John (*see* Duncan, Meg)
Cramer, Zadock, 193
Crane, blue, 231, 244
Crane, whooping, 175-76, 202, 244, 252
Creeper, pine, 115
Crichton, Thomas, 39, 54, 55, 56, 58-59, 66, 70-71, 74, 77, 79, 85, 89, 93, 98, 247, 259-60
Cripps, John Splatt, 179
Cromwell, Thomas, 193
Crossbill, 128
Crow, Clark's (Clark's nutcracker), 141
Crow, fish, 181-82, 231
Cuckoo, black-billed, 184-85
Cuckoo, yellow-billed (cowbird, rain crow), 151, 184
Cumming, Robert, 63
Cuvier, Baron Georges, 238

Da Costa, Francis, 148-49
Dalhousie, Countess of, 63
Dashwood, Sir Francis, 18
David, Jacques Louis, 149
Davidson, Archibald, 105-7
Davis, John, 162
Dennie, Joseph, 186-87
Derbigny, Charles, 232
Derby, Elias Hasket, 162
De Witt, Simeon, 163
Dickinson, Emily, 112, 157

Dill, Ann (second wife of Dr. John Witherspoon), 86
Dinsmore, Silas, 230
Dobie, James, 60
Dodington, Bubb, 18
Dove, mourning, 172
Dove, turtle, 172, 176
Drury, Dru, 183
Ducatel, Edmund, 167
Duck, black, 96
Duck, buffle-headed (butterball), 95
Duck, canvasback, 94-95, 128, 173
Duck, gadwall, 197
Duck, long-tailed (south-southerly, oldwife), 96
Duck, mallard, 96, 173
Duck, pintail (sprigtail) 95, 202
Duck, scaup (bluebill), 96, 157
Duck, summer, 96, 170
Dunbar, Sir Alexander, 226
Dunbar, Archibald, 228
Dunbar, Sir Archibald, 226
Dunbar, Eliza, 228, 234
Dunbar, Margaret, 228
Dunbar, Robert, 228
Dunbar, Thomas, 228
Dunbar, William, 225-33, 256
Duncan, Alexander, 118-19, 134
Duncan, George, 118, 170-71
Duncan, Isabel, 89, 106-7, 118
Duncan, James, 134
Duncan, Meg (Mrs. John Craig), 36, 37, 38, 39, 52, 59, 60, 154
Duncan, William, marries Mary Wilson, 28; characteristics, 36; Wilson becomes his apprentice, 28; starts business, 44; Wilson's distrust of, 45; provides Wilson with pack, 61; agrees to go to America with Wilson, backs out at the last moment, 78; leaves for America, 116; deserts family, drinks up passage money, 117; Wilson's comment on, 118
Duncan, William, son of William Duncan and Mary Wilson Duncan, 28; turns to Wilson in childhood, 35; taught by Wilson, 35; leaves with Wilson for America in place of his father, 78; arrival in the United States, 83-88; weaves, looks for farm land, 88-89; buys farm with Wilson in western New York, 101; urges Wilson to

INDEX

INDEX

volumes published, 254; quarrels with Bradford over money, 254; trip through New England to collect for books already sold, 255-56; arrested as a spy, released, 255; forced to color his own plates as his colorists leave, 256; elected the Philosophical Society, 256; last illness, 258; makes his will, leaving property to Sarah Miller, 258; his death, 259

Wilson, Allan, 39

Wilson, Mrs. Catherine Brown Urie, second wife of Alexander Wilson, stepmother of the ornithologist, 27, 38-39

Wilson, David, 246

Wilson, Janey, 24

Wilson, Jean (Mrs. John Bell) 15, 27, 87

Wilson, Margaret (sister of Alexander Wilson, died in infancy), 15, 28

Wilson, Margaret, half-sister of Alexander Wilson, 24, 28

Wilson, Mary (sister of Alexander Wilson, *see* Duncan, Mrs. William)

Wilson, William, 77

Wistar, Caspar, 239

Witherspoon, David, 172

Witherspoon, David and Agnes, twin children of Tom Witherspoon and Jean M'Lean his wife, 77

Witherspoon, Frances (Mrs. David Ramsay), 86, 177

Witherspoon, James, 172

Witherspoon, Dr. John, American revolutionary leader, baptizes Wilson, 15; place in history, 18; involved in scandal in Paisley, 19; rebukes blasphemous Medmenham Monks ritual, 19; names participants, 20; sued for libel, fined, 21; denounces John Snodgrass, 20; asked to head Princeton College, 20, 23; departure for America, 23; accused of disloyalty to the Throne, 23; phenomenal success at Princeton, 23; declares British intelligence officers responsible for ill will between colonies and England, 23; signs Declaration of Independence, 23; becomes director of American intelligence abroad, 23-24; his success, 24; returns to Paisley after the Revolution, 37; Thomas Crichton's memoir of Witherspoon, 55; baptizes William Sharp, 66; friend of Captain Oswald, reported American spy in Scotland, 72; marries Ann Dill, 86; recognition of his colossal achievement at his death, 86; his anonymous works first published under his own name by Bradford, 137; his home in Princeton after his death, 159; students, 23, 163; marriage of his daughter Frances, 177; subsequent career of one of his agents, 226

Witherspoon, Mrs. John (*see* Montgomery, Elizabeth)

Witherspoon, Thomas, 17, 24, 35, 75-77, 79, 86, 186

Witherspoon, Mrs. Thomas (*see* M'Lean, Jean)

Witherspoon, William, boyhood friendship with Wilson, 17, 21, 24, 35; Wilson's letters to, 45; part of Paisley literary circle, 47; contracts tuberculosis, 53; death, 53; Wilson's poems in memory of, 53, 60; closest friendship of Wilson's life, 86, 154

Woodcock, 157

Woodpecker, downy, 138

Woodpecker, golden-winged, 99, 116, 138, 145, 156

Woodpecker, hairy, 138

Woodpecker, ivory-billed, 173-76

Woodpecker, Lewis', 142

Woodpecker, red-banded, 138

Woodpecker, red-cockaded, 175

Woodpecker, red-headed, 84, 150, 156

Woodpecker, yellow-bellied, 138

Woods, Mrs. William, 141

Wren, Carolina, 169

Wren, golden-crested, 134, 138

Wren, house, 116, 245

Wren, marsh, 188

Wren, ruby-crowned, 116, 138, 155

Wren, winter, 138

Yeats, William Butler, 261

Young, William, 84